Mathematics
Today

Curriculum and Instruction

Janet S. Abbott
Coordinator of Mathematics
Chula Vista City School District
Chula Vista, California

David W. Wells
Formerly Director of Instruction
    and Mathematics Education
Oakland Schools
Pontiac, Michigan

Consulting Educators

Elizabeth H. Abbott
Formerly Teacher of Title I
Computer Assisted Instruction
Greenville Public Schools
Greenville, Mississippi

Wilma B. Blossman
LaSalle Elementary School
Baton Rouge, Louisiana

Dr. Barbara Branch
Principal
White Station Junior High School
Memphis, Tennessee

Barbara Brunjes
Fourth Grade Teacher
St. James Elementary School
St. James, New York

Dr. Phillip E. Duren
Mathematics Consultant, K-12
Stark County Department of
    Education
Louisville, Ohio

Dr. E. Alma Flagg
Educational Consultant
Newark, New Jersey

Betty Jean Gould
Learning Development Specialist
Sachem Central School District
Holbrook, New York

William Ezra Hansen
Supervisor of Math and Science
    Kindergarten through 12
Davis County School District
Farmington, Utah

Ann Helms
Elementary Principal
Clubview Elementary School
    of Muscogee County
Columbus, Georgia

Terri Katsulis
Administrator
Chicago Public School
Chicago, Illinois

Alice D. Lombardi
Formerly Mathematics Specialist
Division of Curriculum & Instruction
New York City Board of Education
New York, New York

Wallace Manning
Director of Federal Programs
    District 91
Idaho Falls, Idaho

Leonard E. Thomas
Parent
Flint Community Schools
Flint, Michigan

Yvonne Tomlinson
Classroom Teacher
Riverdale High School
Jefferson, Louisiana

Mathematics
Today

HBJ Harcourt Brace Jovanovich, Publishers

Orlando   New York   Chicago   San Diego   Atlanta   Dallas

PHOTO CREDITS

Ken Karp: Cover

Archibald, Roger/Woodfin Camp & Associates 121; Aurness, Craig/Woodfin Camp & Associates 226 (right), 311; Frost, Helena/Frost Publishing Group 226 (left), 243 (center), 316; Ganges, Halley 122, 123, 124, 125, 126, 127, 130, 132, 184, 226 (top), 278, 313; Grant Heilman Photography 221, 243 (left, right), 258, 259, 274, 275; Heron, Michal 1, 31, 57, 85, 112, 137, 173, 209, 249, 269, 287, 319; New York Convention and Visitors Bureau 93; Nichols, Michael K./Woodfin Camp & Associates 152; Reininger, Alan-Contact Press Images/ Woodfin Camp & Associates 22.

ART CREDITS

Bryan, Charles 153, 180, 181, 194, 204, 279, 281, 306, 308, 332, 333; Burd, Michael 163, 178, 179, 288, 289, 300; Butz, Susan 166, 174, 175, 186, 187, 210, 211, 214, 235, 238, 239, 254, 256, 257, 270, 276, 282, 292, 293, 311; Cole, Olivia 13, 14, 16, 17, 27, 42, 47, 64, 65, 76; Collier, Roberta 90, 100, 104, 120, 121; Cooley, Rick 128, 148, 149; Del Rossi, Ric 18; Galkin, Simon 44, 49 (left), 51, 54, 92, 94, 126, 129, 131, 170, 192, 200, 201, 217, 221, 265, 281, 282; Grant, Leigh 60, 61, 62, 70, 75, 79, 87; Henderson, Meryl 10, 11, 48, 49 (right), 72, 73, 86; Lipstein, Morissa 124, 125, 138, 140, 142, 144, 146, 154, 156, 158, 160, 189; Major, Anthony 169, 203, 212, 330; Mulkey, Kim 4, 8, 9, 58, 66, 67, 74; Parnell, Sue 36, 103, 130, 133, 167, 168, 182, 183, 188, 189, 190, 191, 196, 198, 199, 226, 227, 240, 241, 250, 251, 252, 260, 261, 272, 273, 280, 298, 299, 309; Perleberg, Patricia 107, 109, 127, 164, 165, 230, 231, 310; Roccia, Gail 176, 177, 184, 185; Schaedler, Sally 2, 12, 25, 68; Schofield, Dennis 88, 96, 97, 98, 101; Shein, Bob 53, 205, 263, 335; Snyder, Joel 23, 46.

PRODUCTION AND LAYOUT
Dimensions and Directions, Ltd.

PICTURE RESEARCH
Helena Frost/Rory Maxwell

Printed in the United States of America
ISBN: 0-15-350704-7

CONTENTS

chapter **6** Multiplication Facts

chapter **7** Division Facts

chapter **8** Measurement

chapter **9** Multiplying by One-Digit Numbers

Addition and Subtraction Facts

Sums to 10

Sharon picks 3 green pears. Adam picks 5 yellow pears. How many pears do they pick in all?

You add to find how many in all.

They pick 8 pears in all. $3 + 5 = 8$

Here are two ways to show addition.

addend $\longrightarrow$ 3   The **addends** are the numbers to be
addend $\longrightarrow$ $+5$ added.

$3 + 5 = 8 \longleftarrow$ sum $\longrightarrow$ 8   The **sum** is the answer.

When one of the two addends is 0, the sum equals the other addend.

$4 + 0 = 4$ $0 + 6 = 6$

Practice • Find the sums.

1. $4 + 1 =$ ___?___   2. $3 + 1 =$ ___?___   3. $2 + 1 =$ ___?___

4. $2 + 3 =$ ___?___   5. $1 + 5 =$ ___?___   6. $3 + 4 =$ ___?___

7. $0 + 2 =$ ___?___   8. $9 + 0 =$ ___?___   9. $6 + 2 =$ ___?___

Mixed Practice • Find the sums.

10. $2 + 4 =$ _____   11. $3 + 1 =$ _____   12. $2 + 5 =$ _____

13. $5 + 2 =$ _____   14. $1 + 3 =$ _____   15. $1 + 1 =$ _____

16. $3 + 2 =$ _____   17. $2 + 6 =$ _____   18. $5 + 0 =$ _____

19. $8 + 1 =$ _____   20. $3 + 3 =$ _____   21. $2 + 8 =$ _____

22. $\begin{array}{r} 2 \\ +2 \\ \hline \end{array}$
23. $\begin{array}{r} 4 \\ +2 \\ \hline \end{array}$
24. $\begin{array}{r} 8 \\ +2 \\ \hline \end{array}$
25. $\begin{array}{r} 3 \\ +5 \\ \hline \end{array}$
26. $\begin{array}{r} 3 \\ +3 \\ \hline \end{array}$
27. $\begin{array}{r} 5 \\ +5 \\ \hline \end{array}$
28. $\begin{array}{r} 3 \\ +0 \\ \hline \end{array}$

29. $\begin{array}{r} 2 \\ +1 \\ \hline \end{array}$
30. $\begin{array}{r} 0 \\ +6 \\ \hline \end{array}$
31. $\begin{array}{r} 4 \\ +3 \\ \hline \end{array}$
32. $\begin{array}{r} 6 \\ +2 \\ \hline \end{array}$
33. $\begin{array}{r} 4 \\ +5 \\ \hline \end{array}$
34. $\begin{array}{r} 1 \\ +6 \\ \hline \end{array}$
35. $\begin{array}{r} 4 \\ +6 \\ \hline \end{array}$

36. $\begin{array}{r} 4 \\ +4 \\ \hline \end{array}$
37. $\begin{array}{r} 1 \\ +7 \\ \hline \end{array}$
38. $\begin{array}{r} 2 \\ +7 \\ \hline \end{array}$
39. $\begin{array}{r} 1 \\ +2 \\ \hline \end{array}$
40. $\begin{array}{r} 7 \\ +3 \\ \hline \end{array}$
41. $\begin{array}{r} 6 \\ +3 \\ \hline \end{array}$
42. $\begin{array}{r} 0 \\ +1 \\ \hline \end{array}$

43. $\begin{array}{r} 1 \\ +4 \\ \hline \end{array}$
44. $\begin{array}{r} 7 \\ +2 \\ \hline \end{array}$
45. $\begin{array}{r} 6 \\ +4 \\ \hline \end{array}$
46. $\begin{array}{r} 6 \\ +0 \\ \hline \end{array}$
47. $\begin{array}{r} 3 \\ +6 \\ \hline \end{array}$
48. $\begin{array}{r} 2 \\ +8 \\ \hline \end{array}$
49. $\begin{array}{r} 2 \\ +3 \\ \hline \end{array}$

50. $\begin{array}{r} 5 \\ +1 \\ \hline \end{array}$
51. $\begin{array}{r} 0 \\ +7 \\ \hline \end{array}$
52. $\begin{array}{r} 7 \\ +1 \\ \hline \end{array}$
53. $\begin{array}{r} 5 \\ +3 \\ \hline \end{array}$
54. $\begin{array}{r} 1 \\ +9 \\ \hline \end{array}$
55. $\begin{array}{r} 3 \\ +4 \\ \hline \end{array}$
56. $\begin{array}{r} 1 \\ +8 \\ \hline \end{array}$

PROBLEM SOLVING • APPLICATIONS

Find the sums.

57. Lily bought 3 bags of carrots. Simon bought 4 bags of carrots. How many bags did they buy in all?

58. Mavis had 7 heads of lettuce in her garden. Bianca had 3. How many did they have all together?

59. Jimmie sold 4 melons on Monday. He sold 4 on Tuesday. How many did he sell in both days?

★ 60. Kim gave 2 oranges to Billy. He also gave 3 to Tara and 4 to Ned. How many oranges did he give away?

3

Sums to 18

There are 7 children jumping rope. Then 6 more children join them. How many children jump rope in all?

The table shows:

$$7 + 6 = 13$$

13 children jump rope.

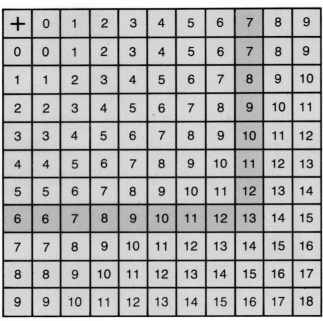

+	0	1	2	3	4	5	6	7	8	9
0	0	1	2	3	4	5	6	7	8	9
1	1	2	3	4	5	6	7	8	9	10
2	2	3	4	5	6	7	8	9	10	11
3	3	4	5	6	7	8	9	10	11	12
4	4	5	6	7	8	9	10	11	12	13
5	5	6	7	8	9	10	11	12	13	14
6	6	7	8	9	10	11	12	13	14	15
7	7	8	9	10	11	12	13	14	15	16
8	8	9	10	11	12	13	14	15	16	17
9	9	10	11	12	13	14	15	16	17	18

There are 6 children jumping rope. Then 7 more children join them. How many children jump rope in all?

Use the table to check this sum.

$$6 + 7 = 13$$

13 children jump rope.

You can add two numbers in any order. The sum is always the same.

Practice ● Add. Use the table to check.

1. $9 + 3 = $?
   $3 + 9 = $?

2. $6 + 5 = $?
   $5 + 6 = $?

3. $8 + 7 = $?
   $7 + 8 = $?

4. $\begin{array}{r} 7 \\ +6 \end{array}$ $\begin{array}{r} 6 \\ +7 \end{array}$

5. $\begin{array}{r} 6 \\ +0 \end{array}$ $\begin{array}{r} 0 \\ +6 \end{array}$

6. $\begin{array}{r} 9 \\ +7 \end{array}$ $\begin{array}{r} 7 \\ +9 \end{array}$

7. $\begin{array}{r} 8 \\ +9 \end{array}$ $\begin{array}{r} 9 \\ +8 \end{array}$

4

Mixed Practice ● Add. Use the table to check.

8. $5 + 9 =$ ___?___
   $9 + 5 =$ ___?___

9. $3 + 5 =$ ___?___
   $5 + 3 =$ ___?___

10. $4 + 8 =$ ___?___
    $8 + 4 =$ ___?___

11. $0 + 3 =$ ___?___
    $3 + 0 =$ ___?___

12. $9 + 8 =$ ___?___
    $8 + 9 =$ ___?___

13. $6 + 7 =$ ___?___
    $7 + 6 =$ ___?___

14. $7 + 9 =$ ___?___
    $9 + 7 =$ ___?___

15. $4 + 7 =$ ___?___
    $7 + 4 =$ ___?___

16. $8 + 6 =$ ___?___
    $6 + 8 =$ ___?___

17. 2
    $+8$

18. 8
    $+2$

19. 5
    $+8$

20. 8
    $+5$

21. 9
    $+4$

22. 4
    $+9$

23. 2
    $+2$

24. 7
    $+5$

25. 5
    $+7$

26. 1
    $+9$

27. 9
    $+1$

28. 8
    $+3$

29. 3
    $+8$

30. 9
    $+2$

31. 4
    $+7$

32. 8
    $+8$

33. 6
    $+0$

34. 5
    $+9$

35. 7
    $+8$

36. 9
    $+6$

37. 4
    $+5$

38. 7
    $+7$

39. 5
    $+2$

40. 1
    $+8$

41. 4
    $+7$

42. 9
    $+9$

43. 5
    $+6$

44. 0
    $+8$

45. 8
    $+6$

46. 4
    $+0$

47. 3
    $+6$

48. 6
    $+6$

49. 7
    $+1$

50. 9
    $+3$

51. 4
    $+4$

PROBLEM SOLVING ● APPLICATIONS

52. There are 7 children playing soccer. Then 6 more join them. How many children are playing soccer?

53. Yoshi swims 7 laps a day. Jolon swims 6 laps a day. How many laps do they swim in all?

54. Carlos jogged 9 times around the block. Diego jogged 8 times around the block. How many times in all did they jog?

★ 55. Jake made 5 goals. Susan made 4, and Liz made 6. How many goals did they make all together?

5

Addition Facts Drill

Add.

1. 6
   +5

2. 3
   +9

3. 1
   +5

4. 7
   +1

5. 4
   +2

6. 5
   +8

7. 8
   +8

8. 2
   +4

9. 9
   +1

10. 0
    +4

11. 3
    +5

12. 6
    +8

13. 9
    +7

14. 1
    +3

15. 4
    +7

16. 5
    +5

17. 8
    +5

18. 2
    +8

19. 7
    +4

20. 6
    +0

21. 3
    +4

22. 2
    +7

23. 0
    +3

24. 9
    +0

25. 6
    +2

26. 9
    +6

27. 2
    +0

28. 1
    +8

29. 5
    +3

30. 0
    +5

31. 8
    +2

32. 7
    +9

33. 5
    +6

34. 1
    +2

35. 0
    +9

36. 1
    +1

37. 4
    +5

38. 6
    +9

39. 3
    +0

40. 7
    +7

41. 0
    +8

42. 3
    +2

43. 8
    +7

44. 3
    +7

45. 9
    +3

46. 2
    +5

47. 3
    +3

48. 0
    +1

49. 6
    +7

50. 4
    +1

51. 4
    +8

52. 7
    +6

53. 0
    +2

54. 5
    +4

55. 9
    +9

56. 4
    +0

57. 7
    +5

58. 1
    +9

59. 8
    +4

60. 1
    +4

61. 5
    +2

62. 4
    +6

63. 2
    +1

64. 6
    +6

65. 5
    +9

66. 8
    +1

6

67. $\begin{array}{r}2\\+3\\\hline\end{array}$	68. $\begin{array}{r}6\\+1\\\hline\end{array}$	69. $\begin{array}{r}9\\+5\\\hline\end{array}$	70. $\begin{array}{r}1\\+0\\\hline\end{array}$	71. $\begin{array}{r}5\\+7\\\hline\end{array}$	72. $\begin{array}{r}2\\+2\\\hline\end{array}$
73. $\begin{array}{r}9\\+8\\\hline\end{array}$	74. $\begin{array}{r}4\\+4\\\hline\end{array}$	75. $\begin{array}{r}0\\+6\\\hline\end{array}$	76. $\begin{array}{r}8\\+3\\\hline\end{array}$	77. $\begin{array}{r}2\\+9\\\hline\end{array}$	78. $\begin{array}{r}3\\+6\\\hline\end{array}$
79. $\begin{array}{r}5\\+1\\\hline\end{array}$	80. $\begin{array}{r}6\\+3\\\hline\end{array}$	81. $\begin{array}{r}1\\+7\\\hline\end{array}$	82. $\begin{array}{r}9\\+2\\\hline\end{array}$	83. $\begin{array}{r}8\\+0\\\hline\end{array}$	84. $\begin{array}{r}6\\+4\\\hline\end{array}$
85. $\begin{array}{r}8\\+6\\\hline\end{array}$	86. $\begin{array}{r}7\\+2\\\hline\end{array}$	87. $\begin{array}{r}4\\+9\\\hline\end{array}$	88. $\begin{array}{r}0\\+7\\\hline\end{array}$	89. $\begin{array}{r}5\\+0\\\hline\end{array}$	90. $\begin{array}{r}2\\+6\\\hline\end{array}$
91. $\begin{array}{r}7\\+3\\\hline\end{array}$	92. $\begin{array}{r}8\\+9\\\hline\end{array}$	93. $\begin{array}{r}1\\+6\\\hline\end{array}$	94. $\begin{array}{r}3\\+1\\\hline\end{array}$	95. $\begin{array}{r}4\\+3\\\hline\end{array}$	96. $\begin{array}{r}3\\+8\\\hline\end{array}$
97. $\begin{array}{r}9\\+4\\\hline\end{array}$	98. $\begin{array}{r}7\\+0\\\hline\end{array}$	99. $\begin{array}{r}7\\+8\\\hline\end{array}$	100. $\begin{array}{r}8\\+4\\\hline\end{array}$		

PROBLEM SOLVING • APPLICATIONS

Add. Use the code to answer the riddles.

5	6	7	8	9	10	11	12	13	14	15	16	17	18
D	S	U	I	Z	N	L	O	E	R	A	H	B	T

★ 101. What can you do to keep a skunk from smelling?

$\begin{array}{r}7\\+9\end{array}$	$\begin{array}{r}8\\+4\end{array}$	$\begin{array}{r}5\\+6\end{array}$	$\begin{array}{r}4\\+1\end{array}$
16			
H			

$\begin{array}{r}3\\+5\end{array}$	$\begin{array}{r}9\\+9\end{array}$	$\begin{array}{r}2\\+4\end{array}$

$\begin{array}{r}7\\+3\end{array}$	$\begin{array}{r}6\\+6\end{array}$	$\begin{array}{r}5\\+1\end{array}$	$\begin{array}{r}9\\+4\end{array}$

★ 102. What do you call a sleeping bull?

$\begin{array}{r}8\\+7\end{array}$

$\begin{array}{r}9\\+8\end{array}$	$\begin{array}{r}4\\+3\end{array}$	$\begin{array}{r}7\\+4\end{array}$	$\begin{array}{r}3\\+8\end{array}$	$\begin{array}{r}0\\+5\end{array}$	$\begin{array}{r}3\\+9\end{array}$	$\begin{array}{r}6\\+3\end{array}$	$\begin{array}{r}5\\+8\end{array}$	$\begin{array}{r}8\\+6\end{array}$

Grouping Addends

Jane has 3 games on the top shelf, 2 games on the middle shelf, and 4 games on the bottom shelf. How many games does she have in all?

Add: 3 + 2 + 4 = ___?___

$$(3 + 2) + 4 = ?$$
$$5 \quad + 4 = 9$$

Jane has 9 games in all.

$$3 + (2 + 4) = ?$$
$$3 + \quad 6 \quad = 9$$

Hint: ( ) means do this first.

You can group addends in different ways. The sum is always the same.

Here is another way to add three numbers.

You can add down

$$\begin{array}{r} 3 \\ 2 \end{array} \Big\} 5$$
$$+4$$
$$\overline{9}$$

OR you can add up.

$$3$$
$$\begin{array}{r} 2 \\ +4 \end{array} \Big\} 6$$
$$\overline{9}$$

Practice • Add down. Check by adding up.

1.	2.	3.	4.	5.	6.	7.
2	1	6	4	3	1	4
4	5	3	0	5	5	2
+4	+3	+4	+5	+4	+1	+9

Mixed Practice • Add.

8.	9.	10.	11.	12.	13.	14.
4	3	6	5	6	6	3
2	4	2	2	1	3	4
+3	+4	+3	+4	+5	+3	+5

8

15. 6	16. 7	17. 6	18. 4	19. 5	20. 3	21. 5
3	2	1	1	2	5	1
+0	+6	+7	+8	+7	+1	+0

Add. Look for tens.

$$\left.\begin{array}{r} 2 \\ 6 \\ +4 \end{array}\right\} 10$$
$$\overline{12}$$

22. 7	23. 2	24. 3	25. 6	26. 3
3	8	5	2	2
+6	+1	+5	+4	+7

Add.

27. $(4 + 3) + 5 = $ _____?_____

28. $4 + (3 + 5) = $ _____?_____

29. $(8 + 2) + 6 = $ _____?_____

30. $8 + (2 + 6) = $ _____?_____

31. $(6 + 3) + 2 = $ _____?_____

32. $6 + (3 + 2) = $ _____?_____

PROBLEM SOLVING • APPLICATIONS

Find the missing scores.

	★33. Sue	★34. Tom	★35. Rob	★36. Rosa	★37. Pam	★38. Joe
First throw	5	3	?	8	2	?
Second throw	?	2	6	1	?	4
Third throw	4	?	3	?	7	2
Total	16	11	12	17	18	14

PROBLEM SOLVING • STRATEGIES

Addition

The four steps below can help you solve problems.

Read this problem and see how.

Penny has 6 bird stamps.
Jim has 8 bird stamps.
How many stamps do they have in all?

Step 1 Read the problem.
What does it ask?

To find how many in all.

Step 2 Make a plan.

You can add.
$6 + 8 = ?$

Step 3 Find the answer.

$$\begin{array}{r} 6 \\ +8 \\ \hline 14 \end{array}$$

Step 4 Check the answer.

Add the other way.

$$\begin{array}{r} 8 \\ +6 \\ \hline 14 \checkmark \end{array}$$

They have 14 stamps in all.

Solve. Use the four steps to help you.

1. A hen lays 6 eggs.
   Another hen lays 5 eggs.
   How many eggs do they lay in all?

   Add up to check.

2. A bird sings 8 times on Monday. It sings 7 times on Tuesday.
   How many times does the bird sing in all?

3. A myna bird says 7 words.
   Another bird says 4 other words.
   How many words do they say in all?

4. Bert had 3 duck eggs.
He got 5 more duck eggs.
How many duck eggs does
he have?

5. Liz sees 4 robins.
She sees 8 bluejays.
How many birds does she
see in all?

Solve.

6. One nest has 5 eggs.
Another nest has 2 eggs.
How many eggs are there in
all?

7. A farmer has 7 turkeys.
She also has 9 chickens.
How many birds does she
have?

**Make a plan before you try to
find an answer.**

8. A blackbird lays 6 eggs.
A robin lays 4 eggs.
How many eggs did the
two birds lay?

9. Remi sees 8 birds on a
fence.
She also sees 3 birds in a
tree.
How many birds does Remi
see?

10. An eagle made 4 trips from
his nest on Monday. He
made 5 trips on Tuesday.
How many trips did he
make?

11. There are 9 red birds in a
large tree. There are 3
brown birds in the tree.
How many birds are in the
tree?

12. Ari sees 6 robins.
Lisa sees 6 bluebirds.
How many birds do they
see altogether?

★ 13. Cora finds 8 baby birds in a
nest. Eric finds 0 baby
birds. How many baby
birds do they find?

★ 14. Kente keeps 2 birds in one
cage and 6 in another. Bill
keeps 2 birds in a cage.
How many birds do they
keep in cages?

Subtraction Facts to 10

There are 8 apples.
The children eat 5 apples.
How many apples are left?

You subtract to find how many are left.

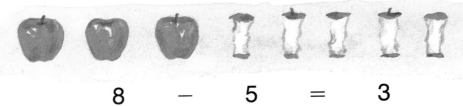

$$8 - 5 = 3$$

There are 3 apples left.

Here are two ways to show subtraction.

$$8 - 5 = 3 \longleftarrow \textbf{difference}$$

$$\begin{array}{r} 8 \\ -5 \\ \hline 3 \end{array}$$

The **difference** is the answer in subtraction.

Practice ● Subtract.

1. $8 - 1 = $ ____?____

2. $6 - 5 = $ ____?____

3. $9 - 2 = $ ____?____

4. $6 - 4 = $ ____?____

5. $4 - 2 = $ ____?____

6. $5 - 0 = $ ____?____

7. $10 - 2 = $ ____?____

8. $7 - 7 = $ ____?____

9. $4 - 1 = $ ____?____

Mixed Practice ● Subtract.

10. $7 - 5 = $ ____?____

11. $4 - 1 = $ ____?____

12. $5 - 5 = $ ____?____

12

13. $6 - 3 = \underline{\quad?\quad}$ 14. $9 - 1 = \underline{\quad?\quad}$ 15. $3 - 2 = \underline{\quad?\quad}$

16. $8 - 4 = \underline{\quad?\quad}$ 17. $10 - 8 = \underline{\quad?\quad}$ 18. $9 - 5 = \underline{\quad?\quad}$

19. $4 - 3 = \underline{\quad?\quad}$ 20. $8 - 0 = \underline{\quad?\quad}$ 21. $9 - 7 = \underline{\quad?\quad}$

22. $\begin{array}{r} 2 \\ -1 \\ \hline \end{array}$ 23. $\begin{array}{r} 10 \\ -\ 5 \\ \hline \end{array}$ 24. $\begin{array}{r} 3 \\ -1 \\ \hline \end{array}$ 25. $\begin{array}{r} 9 \\ -4 \\ \hline \end{array}$ 26. $\begin{array}{r} 8 \\ -2 \\ \hline \end{array}$ 27. $\begin{array}{r} 6 \\ -2 \\ \hline \end{array}$ 28. $\begin{array}{r} 9 \\ -2 \\ \hline \end{array}$

29. $\begin{array}{r} 7 \\ -2 \\ \hline \end{array}$ 30. $\begin{array}{r} 10 \\ -\ 4 \\ \hline \end{array}$ 31. $\begin{array}{r} 8 \\ -8 \\ \hline \end{array}$ 32. $\begin{array}{r} 7 \\ -4 \\ \hline \end{array}$ 33. $\begin{array}{r} 5 \\ -4 \\ \hline \end{array}$ 34. $\begin{array}{r} 10 \\ -\ 6 \\ \hline \end{array}$ 35. $\begin{array}{r} 8 \\ -1 \\ \hline \end{array}$

36. $\begin{array}{r} 8 \\ -5 \\ \hline \end{array}$ 37. $\begin{array}{r} 9 \\ -6 \\ \hline \end{array}$ 38. $\begin{array}{r} 10 \\ -\ 7 \\ \hline \end{array}$ 39. $\begin{array}{r} 5 \\ -3 \\ \hline \end{array}$ 40. $\begin{array}{r} 7 \\ -2 \\ \hline \end{array}$ 41. $\begin{array}{r} 9 \\ -0 \\ \hline \end{array}$ 42. $\begin{array}{r} 6 \\ -4 \\ \hline \end{array}$

43. $\begin{array}{r} 6 \\ -6 \\ \hline \end{array}$ 44. $\begin{array}{r} 8 \\ -6 \\ \hline \end{array}$ 45. $\begin{array}{r} 5 \\ -2 \\ \hline \end{array}$ 46. $\begin{array}{r} 9 \\ -6 \\ \hline \end{array}$ 47. $\begin{array}{r} 3 \\ -1 \\ \hline \end{array}$ 48. $\begin{array}{r} 10 \\ -\ 9 \\ \hline \end{array}$ 49. $\begin{array}{r} 7 \\ -4 \\ \hline \end{array}$

50. $\begin{array}{r} 6 \\ -1 \\ \hline \end{array}$ 51. $\begin{array}{r} 10 \\ -\ 2 \\ \hline \end{array}$ 52. $\begin{array}{r} 7 \\ -0 \\ \hline \end{array}$ 53. $\begin{array}{r} 8 \\ -7 \\ \hline \end{array}$ 54. $\begin{array}{r} 10 \\ -\ 3 \\ \hline \end{array}$ 55. $\begin{array}{r} 9 \\ -3 \\ \hline \end{array}$ 56. $\begin{array}{r} 5 \\ -1 \\ \hline \end{array}$

PROBLEM SOLVING • APPLICATIONS

57. Tony baked 9 cherry pies. He gave 6 away. How many did he have left?

58. Clara made 7 bowls of dough. She used 4 of them to make bread. How many bowls did she have left?

59. Terry had 8 pots of pumpkin mix. He used 5. How many did he have left?

★ 60. Esther made 2 loaves of white bread and 3 loaves of whole wheat bread. She also made 4 loaves of rye bread. How many more loaves of rye bread did she make than whole wheat?

13

Subtraction Facts to 18

Lori plants 12 trees. Ben plants 8 trees.
How many more trees does Lori plant?

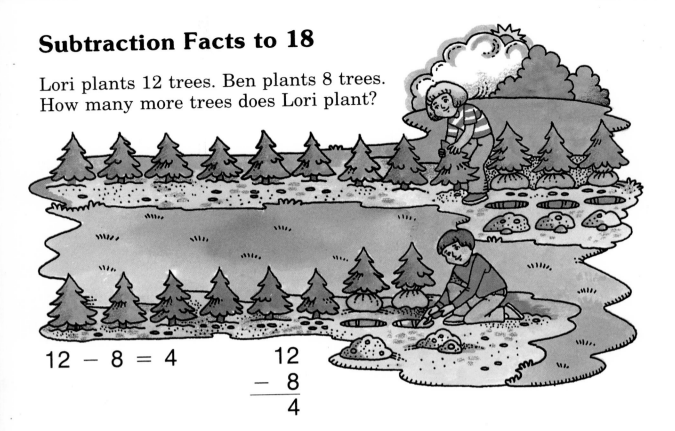

$$12 - 8 = 4$$

$$\begin{array}{r} 12 \\ -\ 8 \\ \hline 4 \end{array}$$

Lori plants 4 more trees.

More Examples

$$\begin{array}{r} 15 \\ -\ 6 \\ \hline 9 \end{array} \qquad \begin{array}{r} 12 \\ -\ 7 \\ \hline 5 \end{array} \qquad \begin{array}{r} 11 \\ -\ 3 \\ \hline 8 \end{array} \qquad \begin{array}{r} 14 \\ -\ 8 \\ \hline 6 \end{array} \qquad \begin{array}{r} 15 \\ -\ 6 \\ \hline 9 \end{array}$$

Practice • Subtract.

1. $\begin{array}{r} 13 \\ -\ 9 \\ \hline \end{array}$ 2. $\begin{array}{r} 16 \\ -\ 7 \\ \hline \end{array}$ 3. $\begin{array}{r} 11 \\ -\ 6 \\ \hline \end{array}$ 4. $\begin{array}{r} 14 \\ -\ 9 \\ \hline \end{array}$ 5. $\begin{array}{r} 11 \\ -\ 2 \\ \hline \end{array}$ 6. $\begin{array}{r} 12 \\ -\ 3 \\ \hline \end{array}$

7. $\begin{array}{r} 12 \\ -\ 9 \\ \hline \end{array}$ 8. $\begin{array}{r} 16 \\ -\ 8 \\ \hline \end{array}$ 9. $\begin{array}{r} 18 \\ -\ 9 \\ \hline \end{array}$ 10. $\begin{array}{r} 13 \\ -\ 4 \\ \hline \end{array}$ 11. $\begin{array}{r} 12 \\ -\ 5 \\ \hline \end{array}$ 12. $\begin{array}{r} 11 \\ -\ 7 \\ \hline \end{array}$

13. $\begin{array}{r} 13 \\ -\ 6 \\ \hline \end{array}$ 14. $\begin{array}{r} 17 \\ -\ 8 \\ \hline \end{array}$ 15. $\begin{array}{r} 14 \\ -\ 7 \\ \hline \end{array}$ 16. $\begin{array}{r} 11 \\ -\ 4 \\ \hline \end{array}$ 17. $\begin{array}{r} 12 \\ -\ 7 \\ \hline \end{array}$ 18. $\begin{array}{r} 16 \\ -\ 9 \\ \hline \end{array}$

Mixed Practice • Subtract.

19. $\begin{array}{r} 15 \\ -\ 8 \\ \hline \end{array}$
20. $\begin{array}{r} 11 \\ -\ 5 \\ \hline \end{array}$
21. $\begin{array}{r} 12 \\ -\ 4 \\ \hline \end{array}$
22. $\begin{array}{r} 11 \\ -\ 8 \\ \hline \end{array}$
23. $\begin{array}{r} 14 \\ -\ 5 \\ \hline \end{array}$
24. $\begin{array}{r} 13 \\ -\ 7 \\ \hline \end{array}$

25. $\begin{array}{r} 10 \\ -\ 7 \\ \hline \end{array}$
26. $\begin{array}{r} 15 \\ -\ 9 \\ \hline \end{array}$
27. $\begin{array}{r} 17 \\ -\ 9 \\ \hline \end{array}$
28. $\begin{array}{r} 14 \\ -\ 6 \\ \hline \end{array}$
29. $\begin{array}{r} 13 \\ -\ 7 \\ \hline \end{array}$
30. $\begin{array}{r} 13 \\ -\ 6 \\ \hline \end{array}$

Complete the number sentences.

31. $13 - 7 = $?
32. $17 - 9 = $?
33. $15 - 6 = $?

34. $15 - 8 = $?
35. $16 - 7 = $?
36. $14 - 5 = $?

PROBLEM SOLVING • APPLICATIONS

Use the table. Who planted more trees? How many more?

⋆ 37. Judy or Bill

⋆ 38. Juan or Frank

⋆ 39. Mary or Frank

⋆ 40. Mia or Bill

Trees Planted

Mary	13
Frank	8
Bill	9
Judy	4
Mia	14
Juan	17

Midchapter Review

1. $\begin{array}{r} 2 \\ +9 \\ \hline \end{array}$
2. $\begin{array}{r} 7 \\ +8 \\ \hline \end{array}$
3. $\begin{array}{r} 9 \\ +6 \\ \hline \end{array}$
4. $\begin{array}{r} 4 \\ +7 \\ \hline \end{array}$
5. $\begin{array}{r} 3 \\ +9 \\ \hline \end{array}$
6. $\begin{array}{r} 6 \\ +5 \\ \hline \end{array}$

7. $\begin{array}{r} 14 \\ -\ 8 \\ \hline \end{array}$
8. $\begin{array}{r} 9 \\ -3 \\ \hline \end{array}$
9. $\begin{array}{r} 14 \\ -\ 9 \\ \hline \end{array}$
10. $\begin{array}{r} 17 \\ -\ 9 \\ \hline \end{array}$
11. $\begin{array}{r} 15 \\ -\ 6 \\ \hline \end{array}$
12. $\begin{array}{r} 13 \\ -\ 8 \\ \hline \end{array}$

Families of Facts

Write 0 to 9 on three strips of paper.
Write 10 to 18 on a fourth strip.
Cut each strip apart.
Label two pieces of paper as shown.
Use your number cards to make
true number sentences.

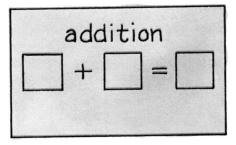

By moving around the digits 2, 3, and 5,
you can make

two true addition sentences
and
two true subtraction sentences.

These four number sentences make up a
family of facts.

Family of Facts

$2 + 3 = 5$

$3 + 2 = 5$

$5 - 2 = 3$

$5 - 3 = 2$

Practice • Complete the number sentences.

1. $4 + 2 = 6$
    $2 + 4 = 6$
    $6 - 2 = 4$
    $6 - 4 = ?$

2. $8 - 3 = 5$
    $8 - 5 = 3$
    $5 + 3 = 8$
    $3 + 5 = ?$

3. $7 + 4 = 11$
    $11 - 4 = 7$
    $4 + 7 = 11$
    $11 - 7 = ?$

Mixed Practice ● Complete the number sentences.

4. $3 + 4 = 7$
   $4 + 3 = 7$
   $7 - 4 = 3$
   $7 - 3 = \underline{\quad?\quad}$

5. $16 - 7 = 9$
   $16 - 9 = 7$
   $9 + 7 = 16$
   $7 + 9 = \underline{\quad?\quad}$

6. $5 + 8 = 13$
   $13 - 8 = 5$
   $8 + 5 = 13$
   $13 - 5 = \underline{\quad?\quad}$

7. $10 - 4 = 6$
   $10 - 6 = 4$
   $6 + 4 = 10$
   $4 + 6 = \underline{\quad?\quad}$

8. $3 + 8 = 11$
   $11 - 8 = 3$
   $11 - 3 = 8$
   $8 + 3 = \underline{\quad?\quad}$

9. $5 + 9 = 14$
   $9 + 5 = 14$
   $14 - 9 = 5$
   $14 - 5 = \underline{\quad?\quad}$

10. $8 + 4 = \underline{\quad?\quad}$

    $\underline{\quad?\quad} - 8 = 4$

11. $\underline{\quad?\quad} + 3 = 9$

    $\underline{\quad?\quad} - 6 = 3$

12. $11 - 9 = \underline{\quad?\quad}$

    $2 + 9 = \underline{\quad?\quad}$

Write the missing number sentences.

13. $5 + 7 = 12$
    $7 + 5 = 12$
    $12 - 7 = 5$
    $?$

14. $15 - 8 = 7$
    $15 - 7 = 8$
    $7 + 8 = 15$
    $?$

15. $13 - 4 = 9$
    $4 + 9 = 13$
    $9 + 4 = 13$
    $?$

PROBLEM SOLVING ● APPLICATIONS

Use the three numbers.
Write two addition sentences and two subtraction sentences.

★ 16.

| 7 | 6 | 13 |

★ 17.

| 5 | 11 | 6 |

★ 18.

| 15 | 6 | 9 |

★ 19.

| 8 | 14 | 6 |

★ 20.

| 9 | 4 | 13 |

★ 21.

| 15 | 8 | 7 |

★ 22.

| 9 | 17 | 8 |

★ 23.

| 12 | 5 | 7 |

Missing Addends

There are 5 marbles in one box. Some marbles are in the other box. There are 7 marbles in all. How many marbles are in the other box?

$$5 + \underline{\quad ? \quad} = 7$$

Solve using subtraction.

If $5 + \underline{\quad ? \quad} = 7$, then $7 - 5 = \underline{\quad ? \quad}$

So $7 - 5 = \underline{\quad 2 \quad}$

There are 2 marbles in the other box.

More Examples How many marbles in the other box?

If $4 + \underline{\quad ? \quad} = 13$,
then $13 - 4 = \underline{\quad ? \quad}$
So $13 - 4 = 9$

There are 9 marbles in the other box.

If $5 + \underline{\quad ? \quad} = 14$,
then $14 - 5 = \underline{\quad ? \quad}$
So $14 - 5 = 9$

There are 9 marbles in the other box.

Practice ● Find the missing addends.

       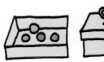

1. $3 + \underline{\quad ? \quad} = 7$ 2. $\underline{\quad ? \quad} + 2 = 8$ 3. $4 + \underline{\quad ? \quad} = 13$

4. $\underline{\quad ? \quad} + 5 = 8$ 5. $\underline{\quad ? \quad} + 6 = 15$ 6. $\underline{\quad ? \quad} + 4 = 12$

7. $6 + \underline{\quad ? \quad} = 10$ 8. $3 + \underline{\quad ? \quad} = 12$ 9. $5 + \underline{\quad ? \quad} = 11$

10. $\underline{\quad ? \quad} + 7 = 13$ 11. $\underline{\quad ? \quad} + 9 = 14$ 12. $\underline{\quad ? \quad} + 8 = 17$

More Practice • Find the missing addends.

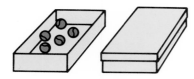 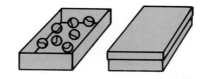 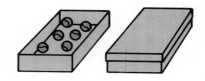

13. $5 + \underline{\quad?\quad} = 13$ **14.** $7 + \underline{\quad?\quad} = 14$ **15.** $6 + \underline{\quad?\quad} = 12$

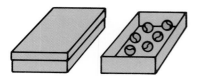 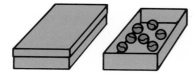 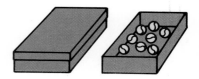

16. $\underline{\quad?\quad} + 6 = 11$ **17.** $\underline{\quad?\quad} + 7 = 10$ **18.** $\underline{\quad?\quad} + 8 = 15$

19. $8 + \underline{\quad?\quad} = 12$ **20.** $5 + \underline{\quad?\quad} = 12$ **21.** $6 + \underline{\quad?\quad} = 14$

22. $8 + \underline{\quad?\quad} = 13$ **23.** $7 + \underline{\quad?\quad} = 16$ **24.** $4 + \underline{\quad?\quad} = 9$

25. $6 + \underline{\quad?\quad} = 13$ **26.** $8 + \underline{\quad?\quad} = 15$ **27.** $7 + \underline{\quad?\quad} = 15$

28. $\underline{\quad?\quad} + 9 = 12$ **29.** $\underline{\quad?\quad} + 6 = 14$ **30.** $\underline{\quad?\quad} + 6 = 10$

31. $\underline{\quad?\quad} + 3 = 8$ **32.** $\underline{\quad?\quad} + 8 = 16$ **33.** $\underline{\quad?\quad} + 6 = 15$

PROBLEM SOLVING • APPLICATIONS

★ **34.** Josh had 7 trucks in his room. He had some more in the yard. In all he has 16 trucks. How many trucks are in the yard?

★ **35.** Anita has 13 space figures. She keeps 5 in a small box. The rest of the figures are in her desk. How many figures are in her desk?

Skills Maintenance

1. $\begin{array}{r} 3 \\ +6 \\ \hline \end{array}$ **2.** $\begin{array}{r} 1 \\ +9 \\ \hline \end{array}$ **3.** $\begin{array}{r} 2 \\ +5 \\ \hline \end{array}$ **4.** $\begin{array}{r} 7 \\ +3 \\ \hline \end{array}$ **5.** $\begin{array}{r} 4 \\ +4 \\ \hline \end{array}$ **6.** $\begin{array}{r} 2 \\ +7 \\ \hline \end{array}$ **7.** $\begin{array}{r} 5 \\ +0 \\ \hline \end{array}$

8. $\begin{array}{r} 3 \\ +4 \\ \hline \end{array}$ **9.** $\begin{array}{r} 4 \\ +2 \\ \hline \end{array}$ **10.** $\begin{array}{r} 1 \\ +6 \\ \hline \end{array}$ **11.** $\begin{array}{r} 6 \\ +4 \\ \hline \end{array}$ **12.** $\begin{array}{r} 2 \\ +3 \\ \hline \end{array}$ **13.** $\begin{array}{r} 2 \\ +8 \\ \hline \end{array}$ **14.** $\begin{array}{r} 2 \\ +2 \\ \hline \end{array}$

Subtraction Facts Drill

Subtract.

1. $\begin{array}{r} 6 \\ -1 \\ \hline \end{array}$	2. $\begin{array}{r} 10 \\ -6 \\ \hline \end{array}$	3. $\begin{array}{r} 4 \\ -0 \\ \hline \end{array}$	4. $\begin{array}{r} 6 \\ -5 \\ \hline \end{array}$	5. $\begin{array}{r} 10 \\ -1 \\ \hline \end{array}$	6. $\begin{array}{r} 11 \\ -7 \\ \hline \end{array}$
7. $\begin{array}{r} 7 \\ -4 \\ \hline \end{array}$	8. $\begin{array}{r} 2 \\ -0 \\ \hline \end{array}$	9. $\begin{array}{r} 11 \\ -6 \\ \hline \end{array}$	10. $\begin{array}{r} 3 \\ -0 \\ \hline \end{array}$	11. $\begin{array}{r} 12 \\ -3 \\ \hline \end{array}$	12. $\begin{array}{r} 12 \\ -8 \\ \hline \end{array}$
13. $\begin{array}{r} 12 \\ -5 \\ \hline \end{array}$	14. $\begin{array}{r} 3 \\ -1 \\ \hline \end{array}$	15. $\begin{array}{r} 14 \\ -5 \\ \hline \end{array}$	16. $\begin{array}{r} 8 \\ -1 \\ \hline \end{array}$	17. $\begin{array}{r} 4 \\ -4 \\ \hline \end{array}$	18. $\begin{array}{r} 10 \\ -5 \\ \hline \end{array}$
19. $\begin{array}{r} 9 \\ -7 \\ \hline \end{array}$	20. $\begin{array}{r} 9 \\ -8 \\ \hline \end{array}$	21. $\begin{array}{r} 3 \\ -2 \\ \hline \end{array}$	22. $\begin{array}{r} 14 \\ -7 \\ \hline \end{array}$	23. $\begin{array}{r} 7 \\ -5 \\ \hline \end{array}$	24. $\begin{array}{r} 13 \\ -6 \\ \hline \end{array}$
25. $\begin{array}{r} 11 \\ -8 \\ \hline \end{array}$	26. $\begin{array}{r} 8 \\ -6 \\ \hline \end{array}$	27. $\begin{array}{r} 10 \\ -4 \\ \hline \end{array}$	28. $\begin{array}{r} 9 \\ -6 \\ \hline \end{array}$	29. $\begin{array}{r} 11 \\ -9 \\ \hline \end{array}$	30. $\begin{array}{r} 8 \\ -0 \\ \hline \end{array}$
31. $\begin{array}{r} 5 \\ -0 \\ \hline \end{array}$	32. $\begin{array}{r} 7 \\ -3 \\ \hline \end{array}$	33. $\begin{array}{r} 12 \\ -4 \\ \hline \end{array}$	34. $\begin{array}{r} 4 \\ -1 \\ \hline \end{array}$	35. $\begin{array}{r} 7 \\ -7 \\ \hline \end{array}$	36. $\begin{array}{r} 11 \\ -2 \\ \hline \end{array}$
37. $\begin{array}{r} 11 \\ -3 \\ \hline \end{array}$	38. $\begin{array}{r} 7 \\ -0 \\ \hline \end{array}$	39. $\begin{array}{r} 15 \\ -8 \\ \hline \end{array}$	40. $\begin{array}{r} 7 \\ -6 \\ \hline \end{array}$	41. $\begin{array}{r} 13 \\ -9 \\ \hline \end{array}$	42. $\begin{array}{r} 8 \\ -7 \\ \hline \end{array}$
43. $\begin{array}{r} 6 \\ -6 \\ \hline \end{array}$	44. $\begin{array}{r} 8 \\ -4 \\ \hline \end{array}$	45. $\begin{array}{r} 9 \\ -3 \\ \hline \end{array}$	46. $\begin{array}{r} 9 \\ -2 \\ \hline \end{array}$	47. $\begin{array}{r} 17 \\ -9 \\ \hline \end{array}$	48. $\begin{array}{r} 13 \\ -4 \\ \hline \end{array}$
49. $\begin{array}{r} 10 \\ -3 \\ \hline \end{array}$	50. $\begin{array}{r} 14 \\ -6 \\ \hline \end{array}$	51. $\begin{array}{r} 7 \\ -1 \\ \hline \end{array}$	52. $\begin{array}{r} 17 \\ -8 \\ \hline \end{array}$	53. $\begin{array}{r} 11 \\ -5 \\ \hline \end{array}$	54. $\begin{array}{r} 16 \\ -8 \\ \hline \end{array}$
55. $\begin{array}{r} 16 \\ -7 \\ \hline \end{array}$	56. $\begin{array}{r} 11 \\ -4 \\ \hline \end{array}$	57. $\begin{array}{r} 8 \\ -2 \\ \hline \end{array}$	58. $\begin{array}{r} 9 \\ -5 \\ \hline \end{array}$	59. $\begin{array}{r} 15 \\ -7 \\ \hline \end{array}$	60. $\begin{array}{r} 13 \\ -7 \\ \hline \end{array}$
61. $\begin{array}{r} 18 \\ -9 \\ \hline \end{array}$	62. $\begin{array}{r} 7 \\ -2 \\ \hline \end{array}$	63. $\begin{array}{r} 5 \\ -3 \\ \hline \end{array}$	64. $\begin{array}{r} 12 \\ -9 \\ \hline \end{array}$	65. $\begin{array}{r} 6 \\ -4 \\ \hline \end{array}$	66. $\begin{array}{r} 4 \\ -3 \\ \hline \end{array}$

67. 6 -0	68. 15 $-\ 6$	69. 16 $-\ 9$	70. 15 $-\ 9$	71. 10 $-$
73. 10 $-\ 9$	74. 12 $-\ 6$	75. 1 -0	76. 6 -2	77. 8 -5
79. 14 $-\ 8$	80. 3 -3	81. 8 -3	82. 9 -9	83. 8 -8	84. -3
85. 2 -2	86. 12 $-\ 4$	87. 14 $-\ 9$	88. 12 $-\ 7$	89. 13 $-\ 8$	90. 10 $-\ 8$
91. 9 -0	92. 5 -5	93. 2 -1	94. 5 -2	95. 1 -1	96. 9 -4
97. 5 -4	98. 9 -1	99. 4 -2	100. 10 $-\ 2$	

PROBLEM SOLVING • APPLICATIONS

Subtract across and then subtract down.

101.
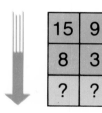

102.
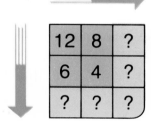

103.
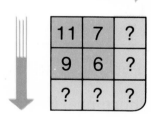

104.
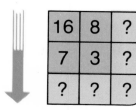

★ **105.**
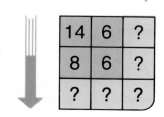

★ **106.**
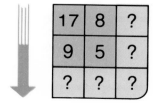

Three Uses of Subtraction

Three Uses of Subtraction
- to find how many are left
- to find how many more are needed
- to compare

Read each problem carefully.

There are 9 balloons in the parade. You see 4 come down the avenue. How many are left to come?

14 bands are needed in the parade. 6 are on the way. How many more are needed?

8 trumpet players and 5 drummers are in a band. How many more trumpet players than drummers are there?

Subtract.

to find how many more are left.
$$\begin{array}{r} 9 \\ -\ 4 \\ \hline 5 \end{array}$$
There are 5 balloons left to come.

to find how many more are needed.
$$\begin{array}{r} 14 \\ -\ 6 \\ \hline 8 \end{array}$$
8 more bands are needed.

to compare.
$$\begin{array}{r} 8 \\ -\ 5 \\ \hline 3 \end{array}$$
There are 3 more trumpet players.

Can you use subtraction to solve? Write YES or NO.

1. There are 18 people on a float. Then 9 people get off. How many people are on the float now?

Read the problem carefully.

2. There are 14 bands in the parade. Now 8 are here. How many more bands are yet to come?

3. First 8 people are sitting on the grass. Then 9 more people join them. How many people are sitting now?

Solve.

4. Today 17 people buy balloons. Only 8 people buy flags. How many more people buy balloons than flags?

5. At first 12 people help sell food. Soon 4 people take a break. How many people are left to help?

6. Ramona counts 14 horses. She sees that 5 horses have brown saddles. How many horses do not have brown saddles?

7. A band has 11 flute players. There are 4 tuba players. How many more flute players are there?

8. On a float 13 people ride. Beside the float 6 people walk. How many more people ride the float than walk?

When you subtract, always make sure the greater number is on the top.

9. In an old car 9 people ride. Of them, 2 are children. How many are not children?

10. Maria has 11 friends at the parade. She wants to buy each one an apple. She buys 8. How many more apples does she need?

11. First 12 clowns are marching in a row. Then 7 run off into the crowd. Now 2 come back. How many are marching now?

12. First 14 Girl Scout troops march. Behind them 6 Boy Scout troops and 3 Cub Scout troops march. How many more Girl Scout troops march than Boy Scout and Cub Scout troops?

Add. (pages 2–5, 8–9)

1. $3 + 5 = $ _____?_____

2. $6 + 4 = $ _____?_____

3. $9 + 1 = $ _____?_____

4. $\begin{array}{r} 4 \\ +3 \\ \hline \end{array}$

5. $\begin{array}{r} 5 \\ +2 \\ \hline \end{array}$

6. $\begin{array}{r} 8 \\ +2 \\ \hline \end{array}$

7. $\begin{array}{r} 6 \\ +5 \\ \hline \end{array}$

8. $\begin{array}{r} 9 \\ +7 \\ \hline \end{array}$

9. $\begin{array}{r} 8 \\ +3 \\ \hline \end{array}$

10. $\begin{array}{r} 5 \\ +8 \\ \hline \end{array}$

11. $\begin{array}{r} 7 \\ +6 \\ \hline \end{array}$

12. $\begin{array}{r} 6 \\ 1 \\ +4 \\ \hline \end{array}$

13. $\begin{array}{r} 3 \\ 5 \\ +8 \\ \hline \end{array}$

14. $\begin{array}{r} 5 \\ 4 \\ +7 \\ \hline \end{array}$

15. $\begin{array}{r} 4 \\ 0 \\ +5 \\ \hline \end{array}$

Subtract. (pages 12–15)

16. $6 - 4 = $ _____?_____

17. $9 - 5 = $ _____?_____

18. $10 - 1 = $ _____?_____

19. $\begin{array}{r} 8 \\ -3 \\ \hline \end{array}$

20. $\begin{array}{r} 9 \\ -8 \\ \hline \end{array}$

21. $\begin{array}{r} 7 \\ -7 \\ \hline \end{array}$

22. $\begin{array}{r} 14 \\ -5 \\ \hline \end{array}$

23. $\begin{array}{r} 17 \\ -9 \\ \hline \end{array}$

24. $\begin{array}{r} 14 \\ -7 \\ \hline \end{array}$

25. $\begin{array}{r} 18 \\ -9 \\ \hline \end{array}$

26. $\begin{array}{r} 16 \\ -9 \\ \hline \end{array}$

27. $\begin{array}{r} 15 \\ -6 \\ \hline \end{array}$

28. $\begin{array}{r} 13 \\ -5 \\ \hline \end{array}$

29. $\begin{array}{r} 12 \\ -9 \\ \hline \end{array}$

30. $\begin{array}{r} 11 \\ -2 \\ \hline \end{array}$

Find the missing addends. (pages 18–19)

31. $3 + $ _____?_____ $= 9$

32. $8 + $ _____?_____ $= 14$

33. $7 + $ _____?_____ $= 10$

34. _____?_____ $+ 0 = 5$

35. _____?_____ $+ 9 = 17$

36. _____?_____ $+ 4 = 12$

Solve.

37. Steve had 9 crayons. His mother gave him 4 more. How many does he have now? (p. 10)

38. Karen had 6 pencils. She gave 2 of them away. How many does she have left? (p. 22)

Bar Graphs

Jennifer asked her friends to choose their favorite sport.

Jennifer made this bar graph.

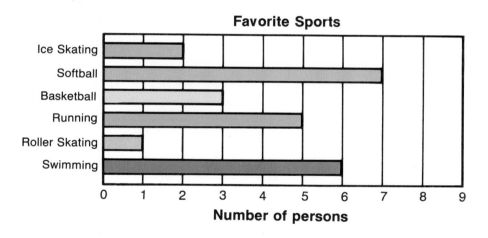

1. Which sport had the most votes?
2. Which sport had the fewest votes?
3. Which sport had more votes
   ice skating or running?
   swimming or softball?
4. How many votes were there for
   basketball?   ice skating?   roller skating?

Ask your friends to choose their favorite sport.
Make a bar graph.

25

TEST

Add.

1. $5 + 1 = \underline{\quad ? \quad}$

2. $3 + 3 = \underline{\quad ? \quad}$

3. $7 + 2 = \underline{\quad ? \quad}$

4. $\begin{array}{r} 6 \\ +3 \\ \hline \end{array}$

5. $\begin{array}{r} 4 \\ +2 \\ \hline \end{array}$

6. $\begin{array}{r} 5 \\ +5 \\ \hline \end{array}$

7. $\begin{array}{r} 9 \\ +4 \\ \hline \end{array}$

8. $\begin{array}{r} 5 \\ +7 \\ \hline \end{array}$

9. $\begin{array}{r} 6 \\ +8 \\ \hline \end{array}$

10. $\begin{array}{r} 7 \\ +9 \\ \hline \end{array}$

11. $\begin{array}{r} 9 \\ +2 \\ \hline \end{array}$

12. $\begin{array}{r} 2 \\ 5 \\ +7 \\ \hline \end{array}$

13. $\begin{array}{r} 8 \\ 1 \\ +1 \\ \hline \end{array}$

14. $\begin{array}{r} 6 \\ 2 \\ +8 \\ \hline \end{array}$

15. $\begin{array}{r} 3 \\ 5 \\ +9 \\ \hline \end{array}$

Subtract.

16. $8 - 7 = \underline{\quad ? \quad}$

17. $10 - 6 = \underline{\quad ? \quad}$

18. $9 - 1 = \underline{\quad ? \quad}$

19. $\begin{array}{r} 9 \\ -4 \\ \hline \end{array}$

20. $\begin{array}{r} 10 \\ -\ 3 \\ \hline \end{array}$

21. $\begin{array}{r} 8 \\ -5 \\ \hline \end{array}$

22. $\begin{array}{r} 13 \\ -\ 4 \\ \hline \end{array}$

23. $\begin{array}{r} 12 \\ -\ 6 \\ \hline \end{array}$

24. $\begin{array}{r} 14 \\ -\ 8 \\ \hline \end{array}$

25. $\begin{array}{r} 13 \\ -\ 8 \\ \hline \end{array}$

26. $\begin{array}{r} 11 \\ -\ 4 \\ \hline \end{array}$

27. $\begin{array}{r} 13 \\ -\ 9 \\ \hline \end{array}$

28. $\begin{array}{r} 17 \\ -\ 8 \\ \hline \end{array}$

29. $\begin{array}{r} 11 \\ -\ 3 \\ \hline \end{array}$

30. $\begin{array}{r} 16 \\ -\ 8 \\ \hline \end{array}$

Find the missing addends.

31. $9 + \underline{\quad ? \quad} = 14$

32. $7 + \underline{\quad ? \quad} = 11$

33. $8 + \underline{\quad ? \quad} = 17$

34. $\underline{\quad ? \quad} + 6 = 11$

35. $\underline{\quad ? \quad} + 8 = 15$

36. $\underline{\quad ? \quad} + 9 = 16$

Solve.

37. Tim sold 9 granola bars. His sister sold 6 bars. How many did they sell in all?

38. Samantha had a box of 8 granola bars. There are only 5 left. How many has she sold?

More Than One Answer

Each puppet holds the same cards.
The cards show whole numbers.
They are the numbers 0 to 20.

Give Lurch Less two numbers.
Give him 3 + 2.

He gives you all the numbers
less than the sum.
He gives you 0, 1, 2, 3, and 4.

Give Lurch Less the sum.
What numbers will he give you?

**LURCH
LESS**

1. $2 + 2$ 2. $4 + 1$ 3. $5 + 4$

4. $1 + 6$ 5. $3 + 0$ 6. $4 + 2$

7. $3 + 5$ 8. $6 + 4$ 9. $0 + 7$

10. $4 + 8$ 11. $9 + 2$ 12. $6 + 3$

Give Gregor Great two numbers.
Give him 9 + 7.

He gives you all the numbers
greater than the sum to 20.

He gives you 17, 18, 19, and 20.

**GREGOR
GREAT**

Give Gregor Great the sum. What numbers will he give you?

13. $9 + 9$ 14. $6 + 8$ 15. $8 + 7$

16. $8 + 8$ 17. $9 + 6$ 18. $9 + 8$

19. $8 + 5$ 20. $7 + 7$ 21. $9 + 3$

22. $5 + 9$ 23. $5 + 5$ 24. $8 + 2$

CALCULATOR

Using a Calculator

A calculator is a machine for working with numbers.
A calculator, like a wagon, is a helpful tool.

A calculator has *buttons.* You push the buttons. If you want numbers, you push *number* buttons.

If you want to *calculate,* you push a *command* button.

⁷ ⁸ ⁹
⁴ ⁵ ⁶
¹ ² ³
⁰

(÷) DIVIDE

(×) TIMES

(−) MINUS

(+) PLUS

(=) EQUALS

If you put in a number or a command by pushing a button, the number or command is called *input.*

First you turn the calculator *on*. 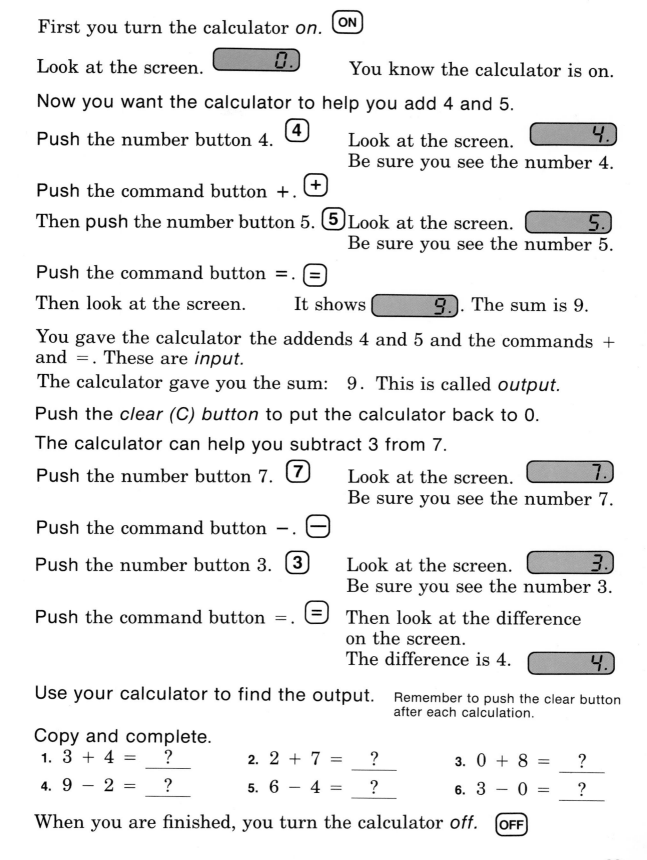 ON

Look at the screen. `0.` You know the calculator is on.

Now you want the calculator to help you add 4 and 5.

Push the number button 4. (4)   Look at the screen. `4.`
Be sure you see the number 4.

Push the command button +. (+)

Then push the number button 5. (5) Look at the screen. `5.`
Be sure you see the number 5.

Push the command button =. (=)

Then look at the screen.   It shows `9.`. The sum is 9.

You gave the calculator the addends 4 and 5 and the commands + and =. These are *input*.
The calculator gave you the sum: 9. This is called *output*.

Push the *clear (C) button* to put the calculator back to 0.

The calculator can help you subtract 3 from 7.

Push the number button 7. (7)   Look at the screen. `7.`
Be sure you see the number 7.

Push the command button −. (−)

Push the number button 3. (3)   Look at the screen. `3.`
Be sure you see the number 3.

Push the command button =. (=)   Then look at the difference on the screen.
The difference is 4. `4.`

Use your calculator to find the output.   Remember to push the clear button after each calculation.

Copy and complete.

1. $3 + 4 =$ __?__   2. $2 + 7 =$ __?__   3. $0 + 8 =$ __?__

4. $9 - 2 =$ __?__   5. $6 - 4 =$ __?__   6. $3 - 0 =$ __?__

When you are finished, you turn the calculator *off*. (OFF)

Choose the correct answers.

1. $5 + 4 =$ ___?___

   A. 8
   B. 6
   C. 9
   D. not here

2.
$$\begin{array}{r} 5 \\ +9 \\ \hline \end{array}$$

   A. 12
   B. 14
   C. 4
   D. not here

3.
$$\begin{array}{r} 7 \\ +8 \\ \hline \end{array}$$

   A. 15
   B. 18
   C. 13
   D. not here

4.
$$\begin{array}{r} 7 \\ 6 \\ +3 \\ \hline \end{array}$$

   A. 10
   B. 16
   C. 15
   D. not here

5. $8 +$ ___?___ $= 14$

   A. 8
   B. 12
   C. 3
   D. not here

6. $9 - 9 =$ ___?___

   A. 6
   B. 0
   C. 18
   D. not here

7. $12 - 6 =$ ___?___

   A. 0
   B. 6
   C. 7
   D. not here

8.
$$\begin{array}{r} 18 \\ -\ 9 \\ \hline \end{array}$$

   A. 11
   B. 13
   C. 9
   D. not here

9.
$$\begin{array}{r} 16 \\ -\ 9 \\ \hline \end{array}$$

   A. 7
   B. 13
   C. 10
   D. not here

10. There are 8 pears in a basket. Jane puts in 2 more pears. How many pears in all?

   A. 6
   B. 4
   C. 10
   D. not here

11. Rod has 11 strawberries. He eats 4 of them. How many strawberries are left?

   A. 15
   B. 7
   C. 6
   D. not here

Numeration and Place Value

Tens ● **Hundreds**
● **Comparing and Ordering Numbers** ● **Rounding**
● **Thousands** ● **Reading and Writing Numbers**
● **Ten Thousands and Hundred Thousands** ● **Ordinals**
● **Problem Solving: What Is the Question?**
● **Even and Odd Numbers** ● **Roman Numerals**

Tens

We use ten digits to name numbers.

0   1   2   3   4   5   6   7   8   9

We use only ten digits because we group by tens.

Ten ones make one ten.

Write the number to show
how many blocks.

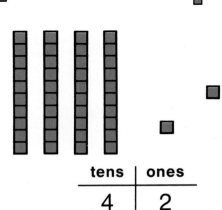

Read. ⟶ forty-two

Write. ⟶ 42

tens	ones
4	2

Practice • Write the numbers.

1.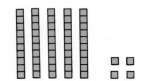

2.

3.

4.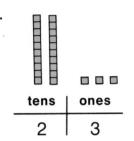

tens	ones
2	3

5.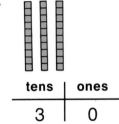

tens	ones
3	0

6.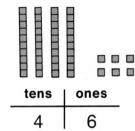

tens	ones
4	6

7. 6 tens 5 ones

8. 1 ten 8 ones

9. 2 tens 4 ones

10. thirty-three

11. seventy-six

12. fifty-nine

Mixed Practice ● Write the numbers.

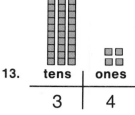

13.

tens	ones
3	4

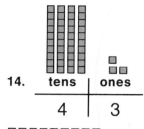

14.

tens	ones
4	3

15.

tens	ones
2	0

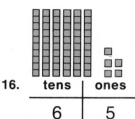

16.

tens	ones
6	5

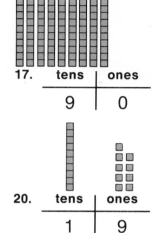

17.

tens	ones
9	0

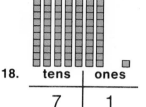

18.

tens	ones
7	1

19.

tens	ones
8	6

20.

tens	ones
1	9

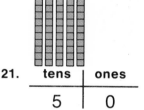

21.

tens	ones
5	0

22. 5 tens 3 ones   23. 3 tens 6 ones   24. 9 tens 2 ones

25. 4 tens 9 ones   26. 8 tens 1 one   27. 7 tens 8 ones

28. 2 tens 5 ones   29. 6 tens 4 ones   30. 4 tens 7 ones

31. 8 tens 0 ones   32. 1 ten 6 ones   33. 7 tens 3 ones

34. forty-one   35. seventy-five   36. eighteen

37. sixty-three   38. twenty-six   39. ninety-four

40. fifty-eight   41. eighty-two   42. thirty-seven

43. seventy   44. thirty-five   45. sixty-six

PROBLEM SOLVING ● APPLICATIONS

Use both digits. Name two different numbers.

★ 46. 4 and 6   ★ 47. 8 and 2   ★ 48. 9 and 1

★ 49. 7 and 2   ★ 50. 9 and 5   ★ 51. 6 and 8

Hundreds

Ten tens make one hundred.

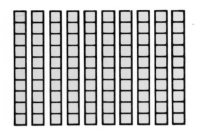

hundreds	tens	ones
1	0	0

Write the number
that shows how many blocks.

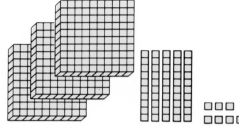

Read. $\longrightarrow$ three hundred fifty-seven

Write. $\longrightarrow$ 357

hundreds	tens	ones
3	5	7

Practice • Write the numbers.

1.
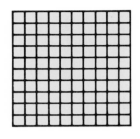

2.

3.
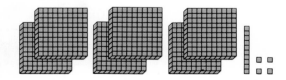

4.

5.

hundreds	tens	ones
1	3	6

6.

hundreds	tens	ones
3	4	5

7. 5 hundreds 7 tens 2 ones

8. 2 hundreds 9 tens 4 ones

9. six hundred twenty-eight

10. four hundred twelve

Mixed Practice ● Write the numbers.

11.
hundreds	tens	ones
2	5	1

12.
hundreds	tens	ones
4	0	2

13.
hundreds	tens	ones
9	2	3

14.
hundreds	tens	ones
7	6	8

15. 5 hundreds 8 tens 0 ones

16. 6 hundreds 0 tens 3 ones

17. 8 hundreds 3 tens 9 ones

18. 4 hundreds 6 tens 7 ones

19. seven hundred

20. nine hundred three

21. five hundred ninety

22. three hundred sixty-two

23. eight hundred fifty-four

24. six hundred eleven

Write in words.

★ 25. 152   ★ 26. 640   ★ 27. 321   ★ 28. 738

PROBLEM SOLVING ● APPLICATIONS

Complete the table.

		Name 1 more	Name 10 more	Name 100 more
29.	571	572	?	671
30.	400	?	410	?
31.	899	?	909	?
32.	879	?	?	?

Comparing and Ordering Numbers

The cat always wants the greater amount.

4 is greater than 2.
4 > 2

2 is less than 4.
2 < 4

Use > or < to make a true sentence.

64 46

Think: 6 tens is greater than 4 tens. So 64 > 46

Use > or < to make a true sentence. 325 ● 328

Think: Same number of hundreds.
Same number of tens.
Compare the ones. 5 < 8 So 325 < 328

Write in order from least to greatest. 265, 253, 257

Think: 253 < 257 257 < 265 So 253, 257, 265

Practice ● Name the greater number.

1. 5 or 8
2. 73 or 37
3. 420 or 399

Write > or <.

4. 11 ● 9
5. 15 ● 48
6. 98 ● 103

36

Mixed Practice ● Name the greater number.

7. 4 or 2

8. 32 or 52

9. 66 or 63

10. 236 or 128

11. 464 or 467

12. 829 or 832

Write > or <.

13. 0 ⬤ 3

14. 1 ⬤ 6

15. 9 ⬤ 5

16. 27 ⬤ 17

17. 61 ⬤ 59

18. 96 ⬤ 99

19. 53 ⬤ 56

20. 45 ⬤ 40

21. 68 ⬤ 65

22. 399 ⬤ 412

23. 217 ⬤ 236

24. 143 ⬤ 146

25. 715 ⬤ 709

26. 624 ⬤ 525

27. 832 ⬤ 836

28. 367 ⬤ 357

29. 371 ⬤ 370

30. 582 ⬤ 549

Write in order from least to greatest.

31. 343, 323, 363

32. 571, 568, 570

33. 401, 398, 390

34. 220, 230, 226

35. 658, 651, 655

36. 842, 846, 839

PROBLEM SOLVING ● APPLICATIONS

Use the three cards. Name all the numbers you can.
Write the numbers in order from least to greatest.

★ 37. | 1 | 2 | 3 |

★ 38. | 3 | 7 | 1 |

★ 39. | 6 | 4 | 9 |

Skills Maintenance

1. 9
   −8

2. 10
   − 2

3. 7
   −4

4. 9
   −3

5. 14
   − 7

6. 13
   − 8

7. 5
   −3

8. 4
   −1

9. 10
   − 7

10. 7
   −1

11. 6
   −3

12. 9
   −2

Rounding

Round 28 to the nearest ten.
28 is between 20 and 30.

It is nearer to 30.
28 rounded to the nearest ten
is 30.

Round 232 to the nearest
hundred.

232 is between 200 and 300.
It is nearer to 200.
232 rounded to the nearest
hundred is 200.

Round 35 to the nearest ten.
35 is halfway between 30 and 40.

Round 35 up to 40.
35 rounded to the nearest ten
is 40.

Round 650 to the nearest
hundred.

650 is halfway between 600
and 700.
Round 650 up to 700.
650 rounded to the nearest
hundred is 700.

Practice • Round to the nearest ten.

1. 26

Round to the nearest hundred.

3. 534

2. 82

4. 750

Mixed Practice • Round to the nearest ten.

5. 19

Round to the nearest hundred.

7. 468

6. 73

8. 351

Round to the nearest ten.

9. 47   10. 55   11. 52   12. 48   13. 43   14. 56

15. 64   16. 11   17. 33   18. 79   19. 25   20. 67

Round to the nearest hundred.

21. 172   22. 437   23. 585   24. 763   25. 214   26. 328

27. 350   28. 141   29. 604   30. 597   ★31. 5,869   ★32. 6,734

PROBLEM SOLVING • APPLICATIONS

33. Connie was asked to round 461 to the nearest hundred. What was her answer?

34. Carmen was asked to round 335 to the nearest hundred. Her answer was 300. Was she right?

★35. There were 2,715 stamps in Rollo's stamp book. Round the number of stamps to the nearest hundred. What is the answer?

★36. There were 4,867 people at the stamp fair. Round this number to the nearest hundred. About how many people were at the stamp fair?

Midchapter Review

Write the numbers.

1. 5 tens 8 ones   2. 7 tens 3 ones   3. 1 ten 9 ones

4. 6 hundreds 9 tens 1 one   5. 4 hundreds 0 tens 5 ones

6. twenty-two   7. eighty-seven   8. thirty-six

9. three hundred seventeen   10. seven hundred fifty-one

Write > or <.

11. 75 ⬤ 84   12. 62 ⬤ 60   13. 28 ⬤ 25

14. 490 ⬤ 409   15. 718 ⬤ 699   16. 352 ⬤ 355

Thousands

Ten hundreds make one thousand.

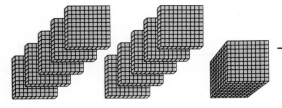

thousands	hundreds	tens	ones
1	0	0	0

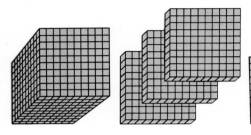

thousands	hundreds	tens	ones
1	3	2	4

Write the number to show how many blocks.

Write. ⟶ 1,324 ⟵ **Hint:** Use a comma to separate thousands from hundreds.

Read. ⟶ one thousand, three hundred twenty-four

Practice • Write the numbers.

1.
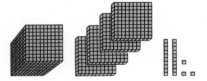

2.
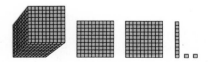

3.

4.

5.

thousands	hundreds	tens	ones
1	3	1	5

6.

thousands	hundreds	tens	ones
2	0	4	6

7. 6 thousands 9 hundreds 4 tens 8 ones

8. 2 thousands 0 hundreds 6 tens 3 ones

Mixed Practice • Write the numbers.

9. thousands	hundreds	tens	ones
2	2	0	4

10. thousands	hundreds	tens	ones
3	1	5	7

11. thousands	hundreds	tens	ones
9	0	6	0

12. thousands	hundreds	tens	ones
8	4	9	1

13. 3 thousands 8 hundreds 6 tens 2 ones

14. 5 thousands 7 hundreds 2 tens 0 ones

15. 1 thousand 3 hundreds 7 tens 4 ones

16. 6 thousands 0 hundreds 4 tens 8 ones

17. 7 thousands 6 hundreds 1 ten 5 ones

18. 4 thousands 2 hundreds 8 tens 7 ones

19. 9 thousands 1 hundred 5 tens 6 ones

Write the numbers.

★ 20. 4 thousands
5 hundreds
7 tens
2 ones

★ 21. 3 thousands
0 hundreds
6 tens
2 ones

★ 22. 3 thousands
6 hundreds
5 tens
8 ones

PROBLEM SOLVING • APPLICATIONS

Complete the table.

		Name 100 more	Name 1,000 more
23.	4,362	?	5,362
24.	8,073	8,173	?
25.	2,800	?	3,800
26.	4,001	?	5,001
27.	5,164	5,264	?
28.	8,143	?	9,143
29.	5,000	5,100	?
30.	562	662	?
31.	7,222	?	8,222
32.	6,999	?	7,999

Reading and Writing Numbers

There are 1,440 minutes in a day.

thousands	hundreds	tens	ones
1	4	4	0

Read. ⟶ one thousand,
four hundred forty

Write. ⟶ 1,440

There are 8,760 hours in a year.

thousands	hundreds	tens	ones
8	7	6	0

Read. ⟶ eight thousand, seven hundred sixty

Write. ⟶ 8,760

Practice ● Read the numbers.

1. 6,421   2. 3,605   3. 7,014   4. 2,050   5. 9,126

Write the numbers.

6. five thousand, two hundred sixty-seven

7. three thousand, seven hundred nine

8. six thousand, twenty-four

42

Mixed Practice ● Read the numbers.

9. 4,125   10. 1,254   11. 8,302   12. 6,097   13. 5,690

14. 2,041   15. 4,176   16. 3,580   17. 2,738   18. 6,305

19. 7,913   20. 5,269   21. 9,401   22. 3,424   23. 1,870

Write the numbers.

24. seven thousand, five hundred sixty-four

25. four thousand, one hundred twenty-five

26. nine thousand, three hundred seventy-one

27. six thousand, forty-two

28. one thousand, nine hundred eighty

29. eight thousand, two hundred six

30. two thousand, two

31. three thousand, five hundred sixteen

32. five thousand, seven hundred

33. eight thousand, thirty-nine

34. one thousand, two hundred thirty-four

PROBLEM SOLVING ● APPLICATIONS
Name 100 less.

35. 4,362   36. 8,173   37. 6,930   38. 4,201   39. 8,999

Name 1,000 less.

40. 5,164   41. 8,143   42. 5,000   43. 5,627   44. 2,806

Write in words.

★ 45. 1,232   ★ 46. 947   ★ 47. 7,406   ★ 48. 8,451   ★ 49. 5,401

Ten Thousands and Hundred Thousands

There were 25,915 people at a concert.

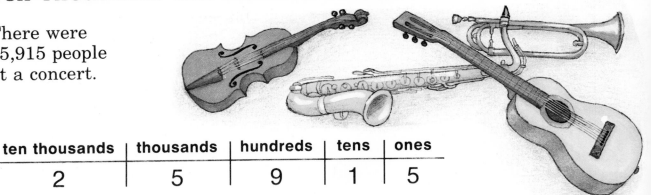

ten thousands	thousands	hundreds	tens	ones
2	5	9	1	5

Read. ⟶ twenty-five thousand, nine hundred fifteen

Write. ⟶ **25,915**

406,395 people could not get tickets.

hundred thousands	ten thousands	thousands	hundreds	tens	ones
4	0	6	3	9	5

Read. ⟶ four hundred six thousand, three hundred ninety-five

Write. ⟶ **406,395**

Practice • Read the numbers.

1. 67,458   2. 72,016   3. 931,582   4. 320,584

Write the numbers.

5. thirty-two thousand, four hundred twenty-eight

6. fifty-seven thousand, eighty-five

7. seventeen thousand, two hundred thirty

8. two hundred fifty-four thousand, six hundred ninety-five

9. one hundred twenty thousand, eight hundred forty-six

10. five hundred six thousand, three hundred seventeen

Mixed Practice • Read the numbers.

11. 31,647   12. 27,133   13. 60,261   14. 86,594

15. 18,021   16. 52,700   17. 29,175   18. 93,086

19. 246,143   20. 132,480   21. 527,348   22. 192,709

23. 309,627   24. 953,074   25. 780,890   26. 974,918

Write the numbers.

27. thirty-one thousand, six hundred twenty-one

28. fifty-eight thousand, nine hundred seventy-two

29. ninety-six thousand, forty-five

30. eighteen thousand, four hundred thirty-six

31. twenty thousand, seven hundred eighty

32. three hundred seventy-five thousand, two hundred thirty-six

33. seven hundred thirty-two thousand, one hundred fifty-four

34. one hundred eighty-nine thousand, five hundred two

35. five hundred sixty thousand, four hundred seventy-six

36. nine hundred twenty-one thousand, seventy-five

Write in words.

★ 37. 86,002   ★ 38. 40,693   ★ 39. 704,031   ★ 40. 999,999

PROBLEM SOLVING • APPLICATIONS

Complete the patterns.

41. 10, 20, 30, ___?___, ___?___, ___?___, ___?___, ___?___, ___?___, ___?___

42. 100, 200, ___?___, ___?___, 500, ___?___, ___?___, ___?___, ___?___, ___?___

43. 1,000, 2,000, ___?___, ___?___, ___?___, ___?___, ___?___, ___?___, ___?___, ___?___

★ 44. 150, 250, 350, ___?___, ___?___, ___?___, ___?___, ___?___, ___?___, ___?___

Ordinals

July fourth is on a Thursday.
The seventh day of the month is a Sunday.

The second Tuesday of the month is July 9.
The fifth Wednesday is July 31.

Which Thursday of the month is July 25?

SUNDAY	MONDAY	TUESDAY	WEDNESDAY	THURSDAY	FRIDAY	SATURDAY
	1	2	3	4	5	6
7	8	9	10	11	12	13
14	15	16	17	18	19	20
21	22	23	24	25	26	27
28	29	30	31			

JULY · 1776

Practice ● Use the calendar.

On which day of the week is
1. July third?   2. July eighth?   3. July twelfth?

What is the date of the
4. first Tuesday?   5. second Thursday?   6. fourth Monday?

Mixed Practice ● Use the calendar.

On which day of the week is
7. July first?   8. July sixth?   9. July fifteenth?

10. July eleventh?   11. July ninth?   12. July seventh?

46

What is the date of the

13. first Sunday?   14. second Friday?   15. third Sunday?

16. fifth Wednesday?   17. third Tuesday?   18. fourth Thursday?

19. Which Sunday of the month is July 14?

20. Which Friday of the month is July 26?

21. Which Thursday of the month is July 18?

22. Which Saturday of the month is July 20?

The first month of the year is January. Which month is

23. second?   24. third?   25. fourth?

26. fifth?   27. sixth?   28. seventh?

29. eighth?   30. ninth?   31. tenth?

32. eleventh?   33. twelfth?

34. 2 months before the eighth month?

35. 5 months before the tenth month?

36. 3 months after the fourth month?

37. 8 months after the third month?

Find each date for this year. Name the holiday.

★ 38. The first Monday in the ninth month

★ 39. The fourth Thursday in the eleventh month

PROBLEM SOLVING • APPLICATIONS

Use the calendar on the opposite page.

★ 40. What date is the second Tuesday after the first Thursday?

★ 41. What date is the third Monday after the second Sunday?

PROBLEM SOLVING • STRATEGIES

What Is the Question?

You must read problems
carefully to find out what
question is being asked.
Read these sentences.

Jenna sees 6 clowns.
Randy sees 5 more clowns.

Which question could you ask about what they see?

  a. How many clowns are left?
  b. How many clowns do they see in all?

Question **b** asks about what Jenna and Randy see.

Use question **b**   6   Add the other way   5
to solve the problem. +5   to check.   +6
Add to solve.   ——   ——
                        11   11 √

They see 11 clowns in all.

Tell which question you could ask.

1. Clair sees 12 balloons. Then
   5 balloons fly away.

   a. How many balloons are
      left?
   b. How many balloons in all?

2. Angie watches 8 tigers.
   Ben watches 3 ponies.

   a. How many animals are
      left?
   b. How many animals do
      they watch all together?

3. We see 6 dogs do tricks.
   Now 2 of the dogs run away.

   a. How many dogs are there
      in all?
   b. How many dogs stay?

**Read each problem carefully
to find out the question that
is being asked.**

Add to solve.

4. Anna watches 4 tigers. Pat watches 8 dogs. How many animals do they watch?

5. A woman does 7 magic tricks. A man does 6 magic tricks. How many tricks do they do in all?

Read each problem again. Check your answer.

---

6. There are 3 bears in the circus tent. Then 5 more bears walk in. How many bears are there in all?

7. Mr. Han buys 5 red balloons. Then he buys 6 blue balloons. How many balloons does he buy?

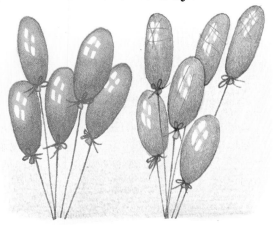

8. Sara counts 4 elephants and 5 lions. How many animals does she count?

Subtract to solve.

9. Paula sees 8 dogs dancing. Then 4 dogs sit down. How many dogs are still dancing?

10. Jimmy brings 15 peanuts to feed the elephants. He gives them 9 peanuts. How many peanuts are left?

11. A man pulls 7 doves out of a hat. 3 doves fly away. How many doves are left?

12. Marcy counts 11 horses. 7 horses trot away. How many horses are there now?

★ **13.** Ms. Ramos sees 8 clowns in a tiny car. 1 clown gets out. Then another clown gets out. How many clowns are still in the car?

★ **14.** There are 9 elephants in a ring. Then 3 elephants run out of the ring. How many elephants are still in the ring?

REVIEW

Write the numbers. (pages 32–35)

1.
tens	ones
2	1

2.
tens	ones
3	7

3.
tens	ones
4	0

4.
hundreds	tens	ones
5	6	4

5.
hundreds	tens	ones
7	0	8

6. 1 ten 5 ones

7. twenty-seven

8. sixty

9. 4 hundreds 9 tens 0 ones

10. one hundred forty-six

11. 6 hundreds 0 tens 6 ones

12. five hundred seventy

13. 7 hundreds 4 tens 9 ones

14. seven hundred sixteen

Write > or <. (pages 36–37)

15. 8 > 4

16. 67 > 63

17. 75 < 80

18. 456 < 716

19. 945 > 944

20. 292 > 285

21. 4,718 > 4,708

22. 3,659 < 3,700

23. 9,866 < 9,868

Round to the nearest ten. (pages 38–39)

24. 21   25. 78   26. 52   27. 14   28. 67

Round to the nearest hundred.

29. 110   30. 273   31. 550   32. 726   33. 891

Write the letter. (pages 46–47)

Which letter is

DINOSAUR

34. second?   35. seventh?   36. fifth?   37. fourth?

PROJECT

Even and Odd Numbers

Even numbers show pairs.

6

Odd numbers always show one left over.

5

Make a table to show even and odd numbers.

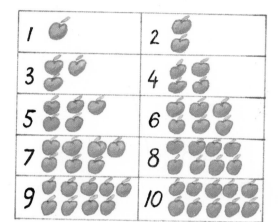

An even number ends in 0, 2, __?__ , __?__ , or __?__ .
An odd number ends in 1, 3, __?__ , __?__ , or __?__ .

Write EVEN or ODD.

1. 15   2. 18   3. 36   4. 30   5. 75   6. 84

7. 102   8. 223   9. 609   10. 461   11. 144   12. 518

List the even numbers between

13. 11 and 19.   14. 51 and 59.   15. 75 and 83.   16. 121 and 129.

List the odd numbers between

17. 30 and 40.   18. 90 and 100.   19. 28 and 38.   20. 250 and 260.

Tell how many. Then write EVEN or ODD.

21. days in a week

22. nickels in a dollar

23. days in this month

24. days in this year

TEST

Write the numbers.

1.
tens	ones
5	2

2.
tens	ones
7	0

3.
hundreds	tens	ones
2	1	8

4.
hundreds	tens	ones
4	6	6

5.
thousands	hundreds	tens	ones
6	7	1	0

6. 5 tens 7 ones

7. thirty-four

8. 3 hundreds 8 tens 4 ones

9. 3 thousands 6 ones

10. 4 thousands 3 hundreds 9 tens

11. eight hundred seventy-two

12. seven thousand, two hundred fourteen

13. twenty-seven thousand, three hundred nine

14. nine hundred fifty-two thousand, one hundred eight

15. seven hundred forty thousand

Write > or <.

16. 109 ⬤ 100

17. 8,910 ⬤ 9,001

18. 3,649 ⬤ 3,650

Round to the nearest ten.

19. 38

20. 42

21. 25

22. 78

23. 71

Round to the nearest hundred.

24. 250

25. 415

26. 697

27. 545

28. 749

Write the letter.   Monkey

Which letter is

29. second?

30. fourth?

31. first?

32. sixth?

Roman Numerals

The numbers on the clock are **Roman numerals.**

I is 1.

V is 5.

VI is 5 + 1. It is 6.

IV is 5 − 1. It is 4.

X is 10.

What is **XI**?
What is **IX**?

XX is 20.

What is **XXX**?

What number is named?

1. **I**

2. **V**

3. **X**

4. **III**

5. **VII**

6. **IV**

7. **IX**

8. **VI**

9. **VIII**

10. **XI**

11. **XII**

12. **XIII**

13. **XIV**

14. **XV**

15. **XVI**

16. **XX**

17. **XXI**

18. **XXII**

19. **XXIII**

20. **XXIV**

21. **XXV**

22. Write the Roman numerals from one to thirty.

CALCULATOR

Greater Numbers

Another way to say you input a number is to say you *enter* a number.

Enter the number 53.

Think: 5 tens and 3 ones make 53.

Push the number button 5. ⑤

Look at the screen. `5.`

Push the number button 3. ③

Look at the screen. `53.`

Enter the number 5,098.

Think: 5 thousands and 0 hundreds and 9 tens and 8 ones.

Push 5. Look at the screen. `5.`

Push 0. Look at the screen. `50.`

Push 9. Look at the screen. `509.`

Push 8. Look at the screen. `5098.`

The calculator has no comma.

Input these numbers. Clear the screen after each entry.

1. 123,456   Did you get `123456.`?

2. 4,287,392   Remember, calculators have no commas.

3. 246,802   4. 741,369   5. 852,963

6. 789,456   7. 321,654   8. 861,943

What do you do if you push the wrong button?
You erase by pushing the *clear (C)* button. [c]

You want to enter 246. Push 2, and then push 4.

Now make a mistake by pushing 7. `247.`

Push the clear button to erase. Now enter 246 correctly.

Enter these numbers by pushing the correct buttons.

9. two hundred twelve

Did you push [2] [1] [2] ?

10. fifteen thousand

11. ten thousand thirty-six

12. nine hundred seventy-six

13. one thousand two hundred

Remember to push the *clear* button if you make a mistake.

14. twenty-three thousand four hundred fifty-six

15. ninety-eight thousand seven hundred sixty-five

An *entry* is the result of pushing any number or command button.
The calculator also has a *clear entry (CE)* button. [CE]
Use it when you make a mistake with your last entry.
You want to add 1 + 2 + 3 + 4.
Push 1 + 2 + 3 + 5. Pushing 5 is a mistake.
The calculator has already added 1 + 2 + 3 and saved the answer.
How can you correct only the last entry?
Push the clear entry (CE) button.
This button sets the screen to 0 and saves the answer to 1 + 2 + 3.

Here is what you do after pushing 5 as a mistake:

Push CE to set the screen to 0. `0.`

Push 4.

Push =. You see the answer on the screen. `10.`

What happens if you input this number: 123,456,789,012?
The calculator stops.
Sometimes the numbers on the screen blink on and off.
When a number is too great to input, the calculator *overflows*.
16. How many digits can the screen show without overflowing?
Remember to turn the calculator off.

Choose the correct answers.

1.
```
   8
   6
 + 5
```
A. 20
B. 19
C. 17
D. not here

2.
```
  17
 − 9
```
A. 12
B. 26
C. 8
D. not here

3. $9 + \underline{\quad?\quad} = 16$

A. 8
B. 13
C. 9
D. not here

4. Write the number.

thirty-five

A. 35
B. 305
C. 25
D. not here

5. Write the number.

sixteen thousand, four hundred two

A. 1,642
B. 16,402
C. 16,442
D. not here

6. Compare.

45 ◯ 54

A. >
B. <
C. =
D. not here

7. Compare.

7180 ◯ 7108

A. >
B. <
C. =
D. not here

8. Round 52 to the nearest ten.

A. 60
B. 500
C. 50
D. not here

9. Round 268 to the nearest hundred.

A. 260
B. 300
C. 270
D. not here

10. What is the fifth month of the year?

A. August
C. November
B. May
D. not here

11. Brian has 18 pencils. He gives 9 pencils to Twanda. How many pencils does he have left?

A. 9
C. 11
B. 27
D. not here

Addition

Adding Two-Digit Numbers • Regrouping Ones • Regrouping Ones and Tens • Adding Three-Digit Numbers • Problem Solving: Estimating Sums • Regrouping More Than Once • Regrouping Ones, Tens, and Hundreds • Adding Money • Adding More Than Two Addends • Adding Greater Numbers

Adding Two-Digit Numbers

Bob and Cindy are picking tomatoes from the garden. Bob picks 32 tomatoes. Cindy picks 54 tomatoes. How many tomatoes do they pick in all?

32 + 54 = ?

Add the ones.
Then add the tens.

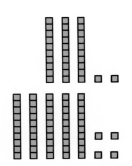

tens	ones
3	2
+5	4
8	6

START ↓

Bob and Cindy pick 86 tomatoes in all.

Practice • Add.

1. 48 +41	2. 12 +45	3. 33 +61	4. 12 + 4	5. 83 +11	6. 28 +20
7. 62 +17	8. 38 +40	9. 96 + 3	10. 24 +54	11. 43 +54	12. 31 +28

Mixed Practice • Add.

13. 50 +39	14. 12 +16	15. 53 +26	16. 34 +41	17. 82 + 7	18. 26 +73
19. 45 +33	20. 16 +61	21. 27 +31	22. 84 +10	23. 25 +72	24. 62 +36

25. 51
+18

26. 68
+ 1

27. 64
+15

28. 40
+56

29. 32
+22

30. 71
+ 4

31. 47
+52

32. 24
+63

33. 82
+16

34. 30
+39

35. 78
+11

36. 56
+23

37. 13
+75

38. 60
+29

39. 91
+ 8

40. 25
+64

41. 32
+67

42. 45
+42

43. 34
+33

44. 71
+28

45. 27
+32

46. 43
+15

47. 6
+90

48. 50
+37

49. $65 + 22 =$?

50. $35 + 43 =$?

51. $51 + 47 =$?

52. $24 + 73 =$?

53. $62 + 33 =$?

54. $14 + 32 =$?

55. $63 + 12 =$?

56. $45 + 21 =$?

57. $46 + 53 =$?

Find the missing digits.

★ 58.
  ▨ 5
+ 7 ▨
  9 6

★ 59.
  6 ▨
+ ▨ 6
  8 9

★ 60.
  ▨ 8
+ 6 ▨
  9 8

★ 61.
  2 5
+ ▨ ▨
  5 8

★ 62.
  ▨ ▨
+ 3 2
  7 9

PROBLEM SOLVING • APPLICATIONS

63. Cindy pulls 43 weeds from the pepper plants. She pulls 36 weeds from the tomato plants. How many weeds does she pull in all?

64. Bob picks 26 pea pods. Cindy picks 43 pea pods. How many pea pods do they pick in all?

65. Leon has 14 heads of lettuce in one row. He has 21 heads of lettuce in another row. How many heads of lettuce does he have in all?

★ 66. Ken bought 32 pepper plants. Terry bought 24, and Tony got 33. How many plants did they buy in all?

Regrouping Ones

Mr. Caruso sells 27 plants in the morning.
He sells 16 more in the afternoon.
How many plants does he sell in all?

27 + 16 = ?

Step 1
Add the ones.
Regroup 13 as 1
ten 3 ones.

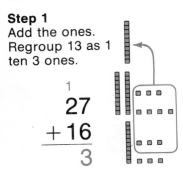

$$\begin{array}{r} 1 \\ 27 \\ +16 \\ \hline 3 \end{array}$$

Step 2
Add the tens.

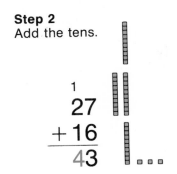

$$\begin{array}{r} 1 \\ 27 \\ +16 \\ \hline 43 \end{array}$$

Mr. Caruso sells 43 plants in all.

More Examples

$$\begin{array}{r} 1 \\ 5 \\ +48 \\ \hline 53 \end{array} \qquad \begin{array}{r} 1 \\ 63 \\ +\ 7 \\ \hline 70 \end{array} \qquad \begin{array}{r} 1 \\ 37 \\ +48 \\ \hline 85 \end{array} \qquad \begin{array}{r} 1 \\ 87 \\ +\ 9 \\ \hline 96 \end{array}$$

Practice • Add.

1.
$$\begin{array}{r} 35 \\ +27 \\ \hline \end{array}$$
2.
$$\begin{array}{r} 8 \\ +36 \\ \hline \end{array}$$
3.
$$\begin{array}{r} 75 \\ +15 \\ \hline \end{array}$$
4.
$$\begin{array}{r} 36 \\ +\ 7 \\ \hline \end{array}$$
5.
$$\begin{array}{r} 29 \\ +56 \\ \hline \end{array}$$
6.
$$\begin{array}{r} 42 \\ +\ 9 \\ \hline \end{array}$$

7.
$$\begin{array}{r} 15 \\ +35 \\ \hline \end{array}$$
8.
$$\begin{array}{r} 32 \\ +49 \\ \hline \end{array}$$
9.
$$\begin{array}{r} 47 \\ +16 \\ \hline \end{array}$$
10.
$$\begin{array}{r} 8 \\ +62 \\ \hline \end{array}$$
11.
$$\begin{array}{r} 25 \\ +57 \\ \hline \end{array}$$
12.
$$\begin{array}{r} 67 \\ +\ 8 \\ \hline \end{array}$$

Mixed Practice • Add.

13.
$$\begin{array}{r} 16 \\ +76 \\ \hline \end{array}$$
14.
$$\begin{array}{r} 25 \\ +26 \\ \hline \end{array}$$
15.
$$\begin{array}{r} 15 \\ +28 \\ \hline \end{array}$$
16.
$$\begin{array}{r} 3 \\ +68 \\ \hline \end{array}$$
17.
$$\begin{array}{r} 66 \\ +29 \\ \hline \end{array}$$
18.
$$\begin{array}{r} 18 \\ +16 \\ \hline \end{array}$$

19.
$$\begin{array}{r} 28 \\ +63 \\ \hline \end{array}$$
20.
$$\begin{array}{r} 38 \\ +\ 8 \\ \hline \end{array}$$
21.
$$\begin{array}{r} 4 \\ +79 \\ \hline \end{array}$$
22.
$$\begin{array}{r} 59 \\ +31 \\ \hline \end{array}$$
23.
$$\begin{array}{r} 16 \\ +67 \\ \hline \end{array}$$
24.
$$\begin{array}{r} 43 \\ +\ 7 \\ \hline \end{array}$$

25.	39 +44	26.	8 +54	27.	31 +67	28.	29 + 3	29.	49 +25	30.	84 + 7
31.	9 +59	32.	23 +65	33.	75 + 9	34.	7 +27	35.	41 +34	36.	47 + 5
37.	27 +48	38.	55 +29	39.	28 +61	40.	47 +32	41.	49 +25	42.	61 +29

43. 36 + 18 = ___?___   44. 18 + 78 = ___?___   45. 16 + 6 = ___?___

46. 52 + 17 = ___?___   47. 83 + 9 = ___?___   48. 38 + 46 = ___?___

49. 28 + 34 = ___?___   50. 25 + 63 = ___?___   51. 42 + 9 = ___?___

Use the numbers in the INPUT column.
Follow the rule. List the OUTPUT.

★ 52.
ADD 29

INPUT	OUTPUT
6	35
49	?
17	?
55	?

★ 53.
ADD 54

INPUT	OUTPUT
37	?
18	?
26	?
9	?

★ 54.
ADD 36

INPUT	OUTPUT
55	?
27	?
8	?
46	?

PROBLEM SOLVING • APPLICATIONS

55. Mrs. Johnson buys 25 red roses. She buys 36 white roses. How many roses does she have in all?

There are 58 red clay flowerpots, 7 red plastic flowerpots, and 25 green plastic flowerpots.

★ 56. How many red flowerpots are there?

★ 57. How many plastic flowerpots are there?

★ 58. How many flowerpots are there in all?

Regrouping Ones and Tens

The students in Room A made 43 programs.
The students in Room B made 75 programs.
How many programs did they make in all?

$43 + 75 = ?$

Regrouping Tens

Step 1 Add the ones.

$$\begin{array}{r} 43 \\ +75 \\ \hline 8 \end{array}$$

Step 2 Add the tens. Regroup 11 tens as 1 hundred 1 ten.

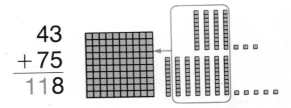

$$\begin{array}{r} 43 \\ +75 \\ \hline 118 \end{array}$$

The students made 118 programs in all.

Regrouping Ones and Tens

Step 1 Add the ones. Regroup 14 ones as 1 ten 4 ones.

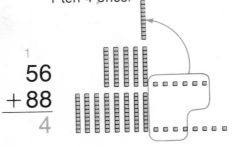

$$\begin{array}{r} 1 \\ 56 \\ +88 \\ \hline 4 \end{array}$$

Step 2 Add the tens. Regroup 14 tens as 1 hundred 4 tens.

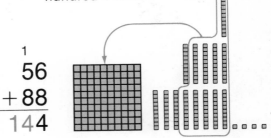

$$\begin{array}{r} 1 \\ 56 \\ +88 \\ \hline 144 \end{array}$$

Practice ● Add.

1. $\begin{array}{r} 58 \\ +61 \\ \hline \end{array}$
2. $\begin{array}{r} 57 \\ +92 \\ \hline \end{array}$
3. $\begin{array}{r} 86 \\ +43 \\ \hline \end{array}$
4. $\begin{array}{r} 70 \\ +51 \\ \hline \end{array}$
5. $\begin{array}{r} 65 \\ +92 \\ \hline \end{array}$
6. $\begin{array}{r} 44 \\ +63 \\ \hline \end{array}$

7. $\begin{array}{r} 78 \\ +34 \\ \hline \end{array}$
8. $\begin{array}{r} 79 \\ +52 \\ \hline \end{array}$
9. $\begin{array}{r} 65 \\ +47 \\ \hline \end{array}$
10. $\begin{array}{r} 92 \\ +79 \\ \hline \end{array}$
11. $\begin{array}{r} 56 \\ +99 \\ \hline \end{array}$
12. $\begin{array}{r} 83 \\ +37 \\ \hline \end{array}$

Mixed Practice ● Add.

13. $\begin{array}{r} 42 \\ +75 \\ \hline \end{array}$
14. $\begin{array}{r} 57 \\ +81 \\ \hline \end{array}$
15. $\begin{array}{r} 69 \\ +60 \\ \hline \end{array}$
16. $\begin{array}{r} 23 \\ +84 \\ \hline \end{array}$
17. $\begin{array}{r} 45 \\ +91 \\ \hline \end{array}$
18. $\begin{array}{r} 77 \\ +62 \\ \hline \end{array}$

19. $\begin{array}{r} 56 \\ +78 \\ \hline \end{array}$
20. $\begin{array}{r} 49 \\ +83 \\ \hline \end{array}$
21. $\begin{array}{r} 92 \\ +18 \\ \hline \end{array}$
22. $\begin{array}{r} 76 \\ +34 \\ \hline \end{array}$
23. $\begin{array}{r} 54 \\ +68 \\ \hline \end{array}$
24. $\begin{array}{r} 78 \\ +59 \\ \hline \end{array}$

25. $\begin{array}{r} 74 \\ +83 \\ \hline \end{array}$
26. $\begin{array}{r} 90 \\ +58 \\ \hline \end{array}$
27. $\begin{array}{r} 65 \\ +32 \\ \hline \end{array}$
28. $\begin{array}{r} 83 \\ +71 \\ \hline \end{array}$
29. $\begin{array}{r} 37 \\ +56 \\ \hline \end{array}$
30. $\begin{array}{r} 26 \\ +95 \\ \hline \end{array}$

31. $\begin{array}{r} 58 \\ +93 \\ \hline \end{array}$
32. $\begin{array}{r} 75 \\ +52 \\ \hline \end{array}$
33. $\begin{array}{r} 94 \\ +28 \\ \hline \end{array}$
34. $\begin{array}{r} 46 \\ +52 \\ \hline \end{array}$
35. $\begin{array}{r} 27 \\ +85 \\ \hline \end{array}$
36. $\begin{array}{r} 40 \\ +78 \\ \hline \end{array}$

37. $56 + 74 = $?
38. $32 + 57 = $?
39. $78 + 64 = $?

40. $93 + 55 = $?
41. $68 + 94 = $?
42. $17 + 81 = $?

43. $80 + 74 = $?
44. $83 + 49 = $?
45. $47 + 65 = $?

Add. Name the greater sum.

★ 46. $\begin{array}{r} 76 \\ +48 \\ \hline \end{array}$ $\begin{array}{r} 33 \\ +84 \\ \hline \end{array}$

★ 47. $\begin{array}{r} 27 \\ +98 \\ \hline \end{array}$ $\begin{array}{r} 57 \\ +66 \\ \hline \end{array}$

★ 48. $\begin{array}{r} 48 \\ +56 \\ \hline \end{array}$ $\begin{array}{r} 69 \\ +34 \\ \hline \end{array}$

PROBLEM SOLVING ● APPLICATIONS

49. The students put on a play for 67 people on Friday. On Saturday 79 people saw the play. How many people in all saw the play?

50. The students set up 75 chairs in the auditorium. They set up 40 more chairs. How many chairs did they set up in all?

51. The students served 48 glasses of juice on Friday. They served 65 glasses on Saturday. How much juice did they serve?

★ 52. The students in Room A made 57 costumes for the play. Room B made 23. Room C made 22. How many costumes were made in all?

Adding Three-Digit Numbers

There are 232 pencil erasers.
There are 158 ink erasers. How
many erasers are there in all?

$232 + 158 = ?$

Step 1
Add the ones.
Regroup 10 ones.

$$\begin{array}{r} 1 \\ 232 \\ +158 \\ \hline 0 \end{array}$$

Step 2
Add the tens.

$$\begin{array}{r} 1 \\ 232 \\ +158 \\ \hline 90 \end{array}$$

Step 3
Add the
hundreds.

$$\begin{array}{r} 1 \\ 232 \\ +158 \\ \hline 390 \end{array}$$

There are 390 erasers in all.

Practice ● Add.

1. $\begin{array}{r} 123 \\ +617 \\ \hline \end{array}$
2. $\begin{array}{r} 184 \\ +113 \\ \hline \end{array}$
3. $\begin{array}{r} 424 \\ +258 \\ \hline \end{array}$
4. $\begin{array}{r} 260 \\ +517 \\ \hline \end{array}$
5. $\begin{array}{r} 529 \\ +265 \\ \hline \end{array}$
6. $\begin{array}{r} 303 \\ +314 \\ \hline \end{array}$

7. $\begin{array}{r} 225 \\ +466 \\ \hline \end{array}$
8. $\begin{array}{r} 637 \\ +256 \\ \hline \end{array}$
9. $\begin{array}{r} 507 \\ +381 \\ \hline \end{array}$
10. $\begin{array}{r} 311 \\ +137 \\ \hline \end{array}$
11. $\begin{array}{r} 328 \\ +242 \\ \hline \end{array}$
12. $\begin{array}{r} 614 \\ +180 \\ \hline \end{array}$

Mixed Practice ● Add.

13. $\begin{array}{r} 628 \\ +203 \\ \hline \end{array}$
14. $\begin{array}{r} 352 \\ +145 \\ \hline \end{array}$
15. $\begin{array}{r} 764 \\ +126 \\ \hline \end{array}$
16. $\begin{array}{r} 278 \\ +406 \\ \hline \end{array}$
17. $\begin{array}{r} 154 \\ +532 \\ \hline \end{array}$
18. $\begin{array}{r} 465 \\ +327 \\ \hline \end{array}$

19. $\begin{array}{r} 589 \\ +210 \\ \hline \end{array}$
20. $\begin{array}{r} 652 \\ +137 \\ \hline \end{array}$
21. $\begin{array}{r} 302 \\ +239 \\ \hline \end{array}$
22. $\begin{array}{r} 754 \\ +138 \\ \hline \end{array}$
23. $\begin{array}{r} 604 \\ +289 \\ \hline \end{array}$
24. $\begin{array}{r} 257 \\ +632 \\ \hline \end{array}$

25. $\begin{array}{r} 607 \\ +286 \\ \hline \end{array}$
26. $\begin{array}{r} 357 \\ +41 \\ \hline \end{array}$
27. $\begin{array}{r} 234 \\ +624 \\ \hline \end{array}$
28. $\begin{array}{r} 63 \\ +29 \\ \hline \end{array}$
29. $\begin{array}{r} 648 \\ +325 \\ \hline \end{array}$
30. $\begin{array}{r} 471 \\ +523 \\ \hline \end{array}$

31. 544	32. 347	33. 22	34. 256	35. 623	36. 15
+329	+102	+68	+425	+252	+75

37. $438 + 257 = $?   38. $369 + 504 = $?   39. $718 + 152 = $?

40. $568 + 310 = $?   41. $42 + 37 = $?   42. $326 + 667 = $?

43. $243 + 135 = $?   44. $267 + 313 = $?   45. $493 + 405 = $?

46. $638 + 44 = $?   47. $586 + 307 = $?   48. $278 + 517 = $?

Estimate each sum to the nearest hundred. Name the greatest sum in each row.

★ 49. a. $208 + 346 = $?   b. $527 + 263 = $?   c. $152 + 419 = $?

★ 50. a. $769 + 123 = $?   b. $433 + 358 = $?   c. $346 + 202 = $?

★ 51. a. $375 + 108 = $?   b. $624 + 267 = $?   c. $481 + 122 = $?

PROBLEM SOLVING • APPLICATIONS

52. Sara had 48 pencils. She receives 144 more. How many pencils does she have now?

★ 53. There are 237 notebooks in the storeroom. There are 128 notebooks in the store. To the nearest ten, how many books are there in all?

Midchapter Review

Add.

1. 73	2. 436	3. 623	4. 54	5. 48
+24	+251	+ 56	+ 7	+27

6. 89	7. 536	8. 145	9. 564	10. 48
+46	+208	+847	+312	+41

PROBLEM SOLVING • STRATEGIES

Estimating Sums

Estimating is guessing about how many.

Carol and Ed sell tickets to the school play. Carol sells 52 tickets. Ed sells 37 tickets. About how many do they sell in all?

They sell about 90 tickets in all.

Now read this problem.

On Monday 187 people see the play.
On Tuesday 124 people see the play.

Estimate the sum.

Round to the nearest ten.

$$52 \longrightarrow 50$$
$$+37 \longrightarrow +40$$
$$\overline{ \quad 90}$$

Round to the nearest hundred.

$$187 \longrightarrow 200$$
$$+124 \longrightarrow +100$$
$$\overline{ \quad 300}$$

About how many people see the play in all?
Estimate the sum to find out about how many in all.

About 300 people see the play in all.

Estimate each answer. Round to the nearest ten or hundred.

1. Donya sets up 240 chairs for the school play. Maria sets up 185 chairs. About how many chairs do they set up all together?

When numbers end in 5, round up.

2. There are 29 students in Mr. Lee's class. There are 38 in Miss Brown's class. About how many students are there in all?

3. There are 16 students in the play. There are 42 more students that help with the play. About how many work on the play in all?

66

Estimate each answer.

4. There are 15 people waiting to buy tickets. Then 18 more people join them. About how many people are waiting to buy tickets?

Make sure you are adding the correct numbers.

---

5. There are 179 people sitting on the left side of the room. Then 134 people sit on the right side. About how many people are in the room?

6. There are 11 songs in the first act of the play. There are 14 songs in the second act. About how many songs are in the play?

7. On Monday 193 people see the play. On Tuesday 186 people see the play. About how many people see the play in all?

8. The first act is 29 minutes long. The second act is 32 minutes long. About how many minutes are both acts?

9. The students practice for 45 minutes on Thursday. They practice 51 minutes on Friday. About how many minutes did they practice all together?

10. The students sell 61 boxes of popcorn on Monday. They sell 52 boxes on Tuesday. About how many boxes do they sell in all?

★ 11. Raymond sings for 17 minutes. Beth sings for 12 minutes and Anita sings for 5. About how many minutes do they sing in all?

★ 12. Boyd helps 25 people find their seats. Taro helps 24 people and Alani helps 28. About how many people do they help?

Regrouping More Than Once

Andrea is working on a puzzle.
She has 542 pieces put together.
There are 296 more pieces in
the box. How many pieces does
the puzzle have?

542 + 296 = ?

Step 1
Add the ones.

$$\begin{array}{r} 542 \\ +296 \\ \hline 8 \end{array}$$

Step 2
Add the tens.
Regroup 13 tens as
1 hundred 3 tens.

$$\begin{array}{r} 1 \\ 542 \\ +296 \\ \hline 38 \end{array}$$

Step 3
Add the hundreds.

$$\begin{array}{r} 1 \\ 542 \\ +296 \\ \hline 838 \end{array}$$

The puzzle has 838 pieces.

Add: 423 + 289.

Step 1
Add the ones.
Regroup 12 ones
as 1 ten 2 ones.

$$\begin{array}{r} 1 \\ 423 \\ +289 \\ \hline 2 \end{array}$$

Step 2
Add the tens.
Regroup 11 tens as
1 hundred 1 ten.

$$\begin{array}{r} 1\ 1 \\ 423 \\ +289 \\ \hline 12 \end{array}$$

Step 3
Add the hundreds.

$$\begin{array}{r} 1\ 1 \\ 423 \\ +289 \\ \hline 712 \end{array}$$

Practice • Add.

1. $\begin{array}{r} 349 \\ +285 \\ \hline \end{array}$
2. $\begin{array}{r} 563 \\ +164 \\ \hline \end{array}$
3. $\begin{array}{r} 256 \\ +478 \\ \hline \end{array}$
4. $\begin{array}{r} 97 \\ +132 \\ \hline \end{array}$
5. $\begin{array}{r} 736 \\ +198 \\ \hline \end{array}$
6. $\begin{array}{r} 458 \\ +\ 64 \\ \hline \end{array}$

7. $\begin{array}{r} 673 \\ +156 \\ \hline \end{array}$
8. $\begin{array}{r} 271 \\ +559 \\ \hline \end{array}$
9. $\begin{array}{r} 42 \\ +269 \\ \hline \end{array}$
10. $\begin{array}{r} 276 \\ +482 \\ \hline \end{array}$
11. $\begin{array}{r} 197 \\ +\ 53 \\ \hline \end{array}$
12. $\begin{array}{r} 281 \\ +\ 67 \\ \hline \end{array}$

Mixed Practice ● Add.

13. 364
    +463

14. 374
    +177

15. 185
    +651

16. 263
    +287

17. 535
    + 96

18. 93
    +543

19. 505
    +197

20. 471
    +468

21. 497
    +424

22. 75
    +162

23. 238
    +593

24. 172
    +774

25. 75
    +298

26. 392
    +504

27. 243
    + 82

28. 468
    + 32

29. 108
    +386

30. 741
    +166

31. 685
    +245

32. 597
    +365

33. 86
    +842

34. 284
    + 89

35. 516
    +346

36. 252
    +476

37. 437
    +168

38. 218
    +652

39. 35
    +897

40. 370
    +269

41. 966
    + 7

42. 524
    +296

★ 43. 247 + 654 = ___?___

★ 44. 75 + 406 = ___?___

★ 45. 172 + 86 = ___?___

★ 46. 246 + 689 = ___?___

★ 47. 354 + 492 = ___?___

★ 48. 587 + 259 = ___?___

PROBLEM SOLVING ● APPLICATIONS

Add across and down.

★ 49.

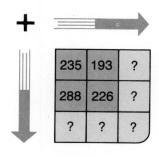

235	193	?
288	226	?
?	?	?

★ 50.

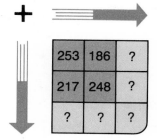

253	186	?
217	248	?
?	?	?

51. Ming Ling has a puzzle with 474 pieces. Nora has a puzzle with 285 pieces. How many pieces are there in all?

52. There are 166 large puzzles in the store. There are 148 small puzzles. How many puzzles are there in all?

Regrouping Ones, Tens, and Hundreds

Tyrone has 673 tiles to make a picture. He buys 454 more tiles. How many tiles does he have in all?

$673 + 454 = ?$

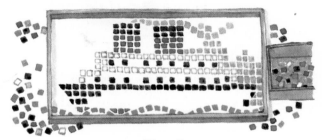

Step 1
Add the ones.

$$\begin{array}{r} 673 \\ +454 \\ \hline 7 \end{array}$$

Step 2
Add the tens.
Regroup 12 tens as 1 hundred 2 tens.

$$\begin{array}{r} \overset{1}{6}73 \\ +454 \\ \hline 27 \end{array}$$

Step 3
Add the hundreds.
Regroup 11 hundreds as 1 thousand 1 hundred.

$$\begin{array}{r} \overset{1}{6}73 \\ +454 \\ \hline 1,127 \end{array}$$

Tyrone has 1,127 tiles in all.

Add: 785 + 449.

Step 1
Add the ones.
Regroup 14 ones as 1 ten 4 ones.

$$\begin{array}{r} 78\overset{1}{5} \\ +449 \\ \hline 4 \end{array}$$

Step 2
Add the tens.
Regroup 13 tens as 1 hundred 3 tens.

$$\begin{array}{r} \overset{1}{7}8\overset{1}{5} \\ +449 \\ \hline 34 \end{array}$$

Step 3
Add the hundreds.
Regroup 12 hundreds as 1 thousand 2 hundreds.

$$\begin{array}{r} \overset{1}{7}8\overset{1}{5} \\ +449 \\ \hline 1,234 \end{array}$$

Practice • Add.

1. $\begin{array}{r} 786 \\ +640 \\ \hline \end{array}$
2. $\begin{array}{r} 528 \\ +846 \\ \hline \end{array}$
3. $\begin{array}{r} 471 \\ +745 \\ \hline \end{array}$
4. $\begin{array}{r} 895 \\ +381 \\ \hline \end{array}$
5. $\begin{array}{r} 587 \\ +758 \\ \hline \end{array}$
6. $\begin{array}{r} 656 \\ +681 \\ \hline \end{array}$

7. $\begin{array}{r} 575 \\ +469 \\ \hline \end{array}$
8. $\begin{array}{r} 734 \\ +768 \\ \hline \end{array}$
9. $\begin{array}{r} 596 \\ +692 \\ \hline \end{array}$
10. $\begin{array}{r} 785 \\ +927 \\ \hline \end{array}$
11. $\begin{array}{r} 667 \\ +459 \\ \hline \end{array}$
12. $\begin{array}{r} 535 \\ +639 \\ \hline \end{array}$

Mixed Practice ● Add.

13. 866 +156	14. 761 +807	15. 446 +631	16. 290 +711	17. 818 +785	18. 672 +890
19. 945 +489	20. 950 + 94	21. 838 +265	22. 899 +260	23. 691 +636	24. 350 +890
25. 382 +895	26. 170 +516	27. 699 +421	28. 157 +824	29. 981 + 29	30. 702 +917
31. 409 +896	32. 503 +561	33. 402 +779	34. 527 +765	35. 517 +400	36. 771 +229

37. 816 + 950 = ___?___   38. 627 + 681 = ___?___   39. 81 + 603 = ___?___

40. 868 + 828 = ___?___   41. 683 + 794 = ___?___   42. 600 + 179 = ___?___

43. 205 + 355 = ___?___   44. 899 + 423 = ___?___   45. 952 + 61 = ___?___

Find the missing digit.

★ 46. 793 + 6▧6 = 1,409   ★ 47. 671 + 2▧6 = 957

PROBLEM SOLVING ● APPLICATIONS

48. Elaine used 732 blue tiles and 489 red tiles. How many tiles did she use in all?

49. Philip has 557 blue tiles in one box. He has 463 blue tiles in another box. How many blue tiles does he have in all?

★ 50. Each sum stands for a letter. Find the sums. Put them in order from the greatest to the least.
Then solve the riddle.

What falls but never gets hurt?

166 +643	642 +254	635 +387	793 +762
N	I	A	R

71

Adding Money

Steven buys a kite for $4.38 and string for $2.65. How much does he spend?

$4.38 + $2.65 = ?

Add amounts of money as if you were adding whole numbers. Remember to write the dollar sign and the cents point in your answer.

Think:
$$438 + 265$$

Write:
$$\$4.38 + 2.65 = \$7.03$$

Steven spends $7.03.
Now estimate to see if your answer makes sense.
To estimate money, round to the nearest dollar.

Think: Round $4.38 to $4.00.
Round $2.65 to $3.00.
Add.

Write:
$$\$4.38 \longrightarrow \$4.00$$
$$+ \; 2.65 \longrightarrow + \; 3.00$$
$$\$7.00$$

Steven spends about $7.00.
Does your answer, $7.03, make sense?

Practice • Add.

1. $ .43
   + .49

2. $ .39
   + .82

3. $ .74
   + .98

4. $6.58
   + 2.74

5. $3.46
   + 5.66

6. $5.31
   + 1.79

7. $3.64
   + 4.58

8. $3.17
   + .96

9. $ .85
   + 7.76

10. $6.62
    + 1.58

Mixed Practice ● Add.

11. $\begin{array}{r} \$ \ .28 \\ + \ \ .75 \\ \hline \end{array}$

12. $\begin{array}{r} \$9.56 \\ + \ 4.84 \\ \hline \end{array}$

13. $\begin{array}{r} \$2.19 \\ + \ 4.92 \\ \hline \end{array}$

14. $\begin{array}{r} \$ \ .45 \\ + \ \ .85 \\ \hline \end{array}$

15. $\begin{array}{r} \$ \ .63 \\ + \ 2.88 \\ \hline \end{array}$

16. $\begin{array}{r} \$5.47 \\ + \ \ .84 \\ \hline \end{array}$

17. $\begin{array}{r} \$5.81 \\ + \ 1.39 \\ \hline \end{array}$

18. $\begin{array}{r} \$ \ .43 \\ + \ \ .78 \\ \hline \end{array}$

19. $\begin{array}{r} \$7.69 \\ + \ 6.91 \\ \hline \end{array}$

20. $\begin{array}{r} \$6.46 \\ + \ \ .76 \\ \hline \end{array}$

21. $\begin{array}{r} \$6.35 \\ + \ 2.18 \\ \hline \end{array}$

22. $\begin{array}{r} \$3.04 \\ + \ 5.97 \\ \hline \end{array}$

23. $\begin{array}{r} \$ \ .63 \\ + \ 5.77 \\ \hline \end{array}$

24. $\begin{array}{r} \$ \ .57 \\ + \ \ .60 \\ \hline \end{array}$

25. $\begin{array}{r} \$7.64 \\ + \ 1.69 \\ \hline \end{array}$

★ 26. $5.32 + $8.79 = ____?____

★ 27. $ .85 + $ .37 = ____?____

★ 28. $6.40 + $1.75 = ____?____

★ 29. $3.42 + $3.69 = ____?____

PROBLEM SOLVING ● APPLICATIONS

Buy both. How much do they cost?

30.
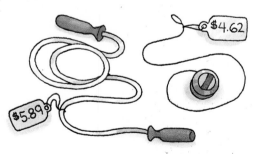

31.

32.

33.

Write a plus (+) sign to make a true sentence.

$$1 \quad 7 + 8 \quad 6 \quad 2 = 879$$

★ 34. 4   6   4   9   5 = 559

★ 35. 4   6   8   7   9 = 925

★ 36. 7   2   2   7   2 = 344

★ 37. 3   2   7   8   5 = 412

Adding More Than Two Addends

Ramón scores 336 points on the first throw. Then he scores 28 points and 452 points. How many points does Ramón score in all?

$336 + 28 + 452 = ?$

Step 1
Add the ones.
Regroup 16 as 1 ten 6 ones.

```
    1
  336
   28
+ 452
    6
```

Step 2
Add the tens.
Regroup 11 tens as 1 hundred 1 ten.

```
  1 1
  336
   28
+ 452
   16
```

Step 3
Add the hundreds.

```
  1 1
  336
   28
+ 452
  816
```

Ramón scores 816 points.

Practice • Add.

1.	2.	3.	4.	5.	6.
27	43	25	37	43	2
36	18	11	4	15	29
+12	+24	+13	+18	+38	+22

7.	8.	9.	10.	11.	12.
325	498	745	536	257	647
182	213	526	170	6	394
+345	+234	+ 84	+262	+ 92	+211

More Practice • Add.

13.	14.	15.	16.	17.	18.
35	24	48	39	56	40
12	56	13	4	25	14
+48	+17	+24	+45	+17	+13

74

19. 359 179 +231	20. 883 120 +458	21. 247 167 + 73	22. 19 584 +174	23. 236 506 +347	24. 6 574 + 57
25. 481 42 +605	26. 363 68 + 8	27. 652 989 +144	28. 3 355 + 71	29. 85 227 + 4	30. 452 66 + 7
31. 538 6 +272	32. 34 197 +708	★33. 368 67 735 +204	★34. 436 540 75 +189	★35. 287 463 38 + 4	★36. 75 884 96 +351

PROBLEM SOLVING • APPLICATIONS

How many points were scored

37. in Game 1?   38. in Game 2?

39. in Game 3?

How many points were scored by

★ 40. the Eagles?   ★ 41. the Falcons?

★ 42. the Cardinals?

	GAMES		
	1	2	3
EAGLES	116	75	131
FALCONS	93	126	140
CARDINALS	127	118	89

Skills Maintenance

1. 15 +15	2. 29 +32	3. 33 +47	4. 41 +29	5. 58 + 4	6. 65 +19
7. 77 +45	8. 64 +29	9. 78 +17	10. 58 +86	11. 43 + 9	12. 76 +14
13. 5 +56	14. 37 +79	15. 27 +54	16. 8 +39	17. 65 +28	18. 46 +46

Adding Greater Numbers

Mr. Robbins has 2,986 white chickens and 1,857 brown chickens. How many chickens does he have in all?

2,986 + 1,857 = ?

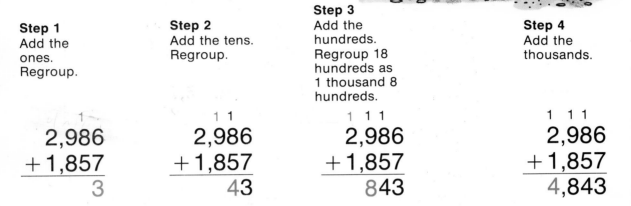

Step 1
Add the ones. Regroup.

```
  1
2,986
+1,857
    3
```

Step 2
Add the tens. Regroup.

```
 1 1
2,986
+1,857
   43
```

Step 3
Add the hundreds. Regroup 18 hundreds as 1 thousand 8 hundreds.

```
 1 1 1
2,986
+1,857
  843
```

Step 4
Add the thousands.

```
 1 1 1
2,986
+1,857
4,843
```

Mr. Robbins has 4,843 chickens in all.

Practice • Add.

1. 2,459 + 2,842
2. 1,654 + 6,457
3. 1,252 + 7,866
4. 8,342 + 918
5. 4,475 + 3,329

6. 5,374 + 1,749
7. 659 + 8,375
8. 3,865 + 2,565
9. 2,296 + 838
10. 4,785 + 2,956

11. 1,447 + 2,193
12. 7,223 + 1,168
13. 1,647 + 4,494
14. 6,977 + 1,641
15. 1,573 + 913

Mixed Practice • Add.

16. 6,356 + 1,955
17. 2,359 + 4,015
18. 6,047 + 2,569
19. 3,651 + 2,857
20. 7,454 + 1,769

21. 5,271 + 3,809
22. 1,982 + 6,887
23. 2,573 + 1,837
24. 4,356 + 3,895
25. 1,647 + 4,416

26. 3,745
    +2,387

27. 6,914
    + 217

28. 7,581
    +1,739

29. 2,857
    +1,266

30. 5,584
    +3,283

31. 8,657
    +1,184

32. 4,945
    +3,735

33. 6,782
    +2,379

34. 7,553
    + 558

35. 2,138
    +6,148

36. 2,384
    1,962
    + 148

37.   87
    3,423
    + 406

38. 1,634
    2,971
    +3,584

★39. 9,293
    1,486
    + 752

★40. 6,045
    3,782
    +4,957

★41. 3,618
    +7,685

★42. 6,274
    +6,274

★43. 9,563
    +3,659

★44. 5,748
    +8,285

★45. 7,835
    +9,375

46. $32.76 + $18.68 = ___?___

47. $53.94 + $28.78 = ___?___

48. $61.27 + $15.93 = ___?___

49. $49.48 + $35.67 = ___?___

50. $23.70 + $19.96 = ___?___

51. $81.64 + $7.44 = ___?___

PROBLEM SOLVING ● APPLICATIONS

52. Mr. Robbins collects 3,654 eggs on Monday. He collects 3,867 eggs on Tuesday. How many eggs does he collect in all?

53. There are 4,843 chickens on Mr. Robbins's farm. Mr. Robbins buys 2,575 more chickens for the farm. How many chickens are there in all?

★54. Mr. Robbins sold 6,478 eggs on Wednesday. He sold 7,589 on Friday. How many eggs did he sell in all?

★55. Mr. Robbins's chickens laid 3,879 eggs on Saturday. The hens laid 4,219 eggs on Monday and 4,627 on Wednesday. How many eggs did they lay in all?

77

REVIEW

Add. (pages 58–63)

1. 42
+ 6

2. 83
+10

3. 26
+51

4. 24
+37

5. 66
+ 9

6. 54
+36

7. 73
+48

8. 45
+55

9. 62
+79

10. 83
+29

Estimate the sum. Then add. Compare. (pages 64–67)

11. 257
+301

12. 469
+223

13. 726
+154

14. 564
+229

Add. (pages 68–77)

15. 453
+697

16. $2.59
+ .72

17. $ .58
+ .45

18. $7.99
+ 1.99

19. 3,812
+1,697

20. 6,789
+2,594

21. 1,262
+ 778

22. 63
12
+40

23. 109
275
+ 61

24. 341
188
+425

Solve.

25. There are two class trips. Now 48 pupils go to the museum. Another 57 pupils go to the zoo. How many pupils go on trips? (p. 62)

26. There are 283 boys and 309 girls in Grand School. How many pupils are there in all? (p. 64)

27. There are 217 pupils in the lunchroom. There are 175 pupils on the playground. There are 187 pupils in classrooms. How many pupils are there in all? (p. 74)

28. The girls in Grand School save $48.91. The boys save $41.69. How much do they save in all? (p. 72)

Do You Have the Right Number?

This is part of a page from a phone book. Read it carefully.

Backus, Donald 1475 First Ave. 745–9399
Baco, Martha Z. 342 West Jones St. 489–8635
Bacon, C. 252 Ridge Ave. 684–2903
Bada, José 617 West Chuck St. 863–0367
Bader, Ethel 165 James St. 874–1937
Badia, Maria 568 Seventh Ave. 795–0198
Bady, R. 486 East Gulf St. 533–8329
Baer, Abel 92 River Drive. 878–6777

Add the first three digits of the following phone numbers. The first one has been done for you.

1. (Baco, Martha Z.) + (Bady, R.)   = <u> **1,022** </u>

    +

2. (Baer, Abel) + (Bader, Ethel)   = <u> ? </u>

3. (Bada, José) + (Backus, Donald) = <u> ? </u>

4. (Bacon, C.) + (Badia, Maria)   = <u> ? </u>

5. (Bada, José) + (Badia, Maria)   = <u> ? </u>

6. (Bady, R.) + (Bader, Ethel)   = <u> ? </u>

Write the last name of the person whose phone number begins with the number.

7. 878 _____   8. 745 _____

9. 863 _____   10. 795 _____

TEST

Add.

1. 46
+32

2. 31
+58

3. 72
+16

4. 54
+29

5. 18
+66

6. 77
+ 5

7. 36
+84

8. 62
+49

9. 94
+35

10. 61
+84

Estimate the sum. Then add. Compare.

11. 266
+426

12. 429
+158

13. 112
+387

14. 607
+335

15. 552
+138

Add.

16. 157
+194

17. 328
+277

18. 454
+ 89

19. 960
+384

20. 497
+557

21. 247
+864

22. $3.17
+ 6.95

23. $ .72
+ .45

24. $6.53
+ .70

25. 7,206
+ 949

26. 3,178
+2,517

27. 4,226
+1,835

28. 627
41
+153

29. 206
171
+488

30. 535
279
+162

Solve.

31. You have 27 shells in your collection. You find 17 more. How many shells do you have in all?

32. You have $2.15 in your bank. You earn $1.07. How much do you have in all?

33. You have 149 football cards, 67 baseball cards, and 83 hockey cards. How many cards do you have?

34. You have 4,325 bottle caps. Your friend has 2,682. How many bottle caps do you and your friend have?

The Least Number of Coins

	Quarter	Dime	Nickel	Penny
39¢	1	1		4
73¢				
91¢				
57¢				
48¢				
65¢				
84¢				
77¢				
42¢				
33¢				
69¢				
23¢				
52¢				

You must pay each amount. Find the least number of coins you can use.

Copy and complete the chart.

These coins are worth 25¢.
Find 11 more groups of coins
also worth 25¢. Copy and complete the chart.

Dimes		1									
Nickels	5	3									
Pennies											

81

COMPUTER

Computer Input and Output

Computers are more powerful and more helpful than calculators.
You can add five one-digit numbers on a calculator in ten seconds.
A computer can add hundreds of thousands of numbers in less
    than one second.
So a computer is much faster than a calculator.

A computer can handle input (numbers or commands) and output
    (numbers) much faster than a calculator can.
Computers can also handle letters and words as input and output.

Like calculators, computers must be told what to do at each step.
Computers cannot think. People must think for them.
A *programmer* is a person who thinks for computers.
A *program* is a list of step-by-step input to a computer.
Programmers write programs.
A computer *stores* a program in its *storage,* or *memory.*
Then the computer works with, or *processes,* the program.
The computer produces answers, or *results,* as output.
Here is a picture of what the whole process looks like.

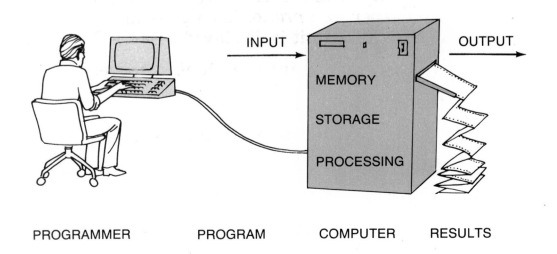

PROGRAMMER   PROGRAM   COMPUTER   RESULTS

There are many forms of input.

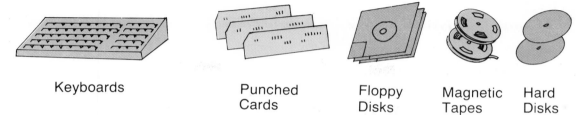

| Keyboards | Punched Cards | Floppy Disks | Magnetic Tapes | Hard Disks |

Keyboards are like typewriters and calculators. One
key must be pressed for each number or letter.
Punched cards are cards with holes punched in them.
80 numbers or letters can be input from each card.
Floppy disks, or diskettes, hold as much input as
thousands of cards.
Magnetic tapes are like recording or cassette tapes.
A reel of tape holds as much input as thousands of cards.
Hard disks hold as much input as many floppy disks or
magnetic tapes. They are very fast and very expensive.

There are many forms of output.

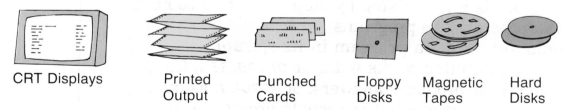

| CRT Displays | Printed Output | Punched Cards | Floppy Disks | Magnetic Tapes | Hard Disks |

CRT stands for **C**athode **R**ay **T**ube. It is like a TV
tube. Numbers and words on a CRT are called a *display.*
Output printed on paper by a *printer* is long-lasting.
Output is printed faster than it is displayed on a CRT.

The other outputs are like the inputs described above.

Copy and complete.

1. A person who thinks for computers is called a __?__ .

2. A list of step-by-step input to a computer is called a __?__ .

3. A computer stores programs in its __?__ , or __?__ .

4. Two forms of computer input are __?__ and __?__ .

5. Two forms of computer output are __?__ and __?__ .

Choose the correct answers.

1. $9 + \underline{\quad ? \quad} = 17$

   A. 8
   B. 26
   C. 7
   D. not here

2. $\begin{array}{r} 7 \\ 4 \\ +6 \\ \hline \end{array}$

    A. 11
    B. 19
    C. 18
    D. not here

3. Write the number.

   fourteen thousand,
   four hundred seven

   A. 14,477
   B. 144,407
   C. 14,407
   D. not here

4. Round 725 to the nearest hundred.

   A. 700
   B. 800
   C. 850
   D. not here

5. Compare.

   9,801 ⬤ 9,810

   A. >
   B. =
   C. <
   D. not here

6. $\begin{array}{r} 287 \\ +695 \\ \hline \end{array}$

    A. 882
    B. 928
    C. 982
    D. not here

7. $\begin{array}{r} 79 \\ +87 \\ \hline \end{array}$

    A. 167
    B. 156
    C. 165
    D. not here

8. $\begin{array}{r} 4,987 \\ +\quad 586 \\ \hline \end{array}$

    A. 5,473
    B. 5,437
    C. 5,573
    D. not here

9. $\begin{array}{r} \$1.56 \\ +\quad 9.57 \\ \hline \end{array}$

    A. $11.13
    B. $10.21
    C. $11.23
    D. not here

10. Carmen went to the zoo. She saw 6 lions and 8 bears. How many animals did she see in all?

    A. 2
    B. 14
    C. 15
    D. not here

11. Keith bought a football for $6.72 and a book for $3.50. How much did he spend?

    A. 1,022
    B. $10.22
    C. $11.23
    D. not here

Subtraction

Subtracting Two-Digit Numbers

Mickey works at the animal shelter.
She has 36 puppy treats.
She gives 24 of them to the dogs.
How many puppy treats does
Mickey have left?

36 − 24 = ?

Step 1
Subtract the ones.

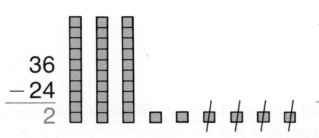

$$\begin{array}{r} 36 \\ -24 \\ \hline 2 \end{array}$$

Step 2
Subtract the tens.

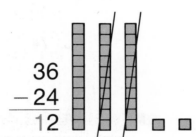

$$\begin{array}{r} 36 \\ -24 \\ \hline 12 \end{array}$$

Mickey has 12 puppy treats left.

Practice • Subtract.

1. $\begin{array}{r} 65 \\ -52 \\ \hline \end{array}$	2. $\begin{array}{r} 89 \\ -46 \\ \hline \end{array}$	3. $\begin{array}{r} 56 \\ -46 \\ \hline \end{array}$	4. $\begin{array}{r} 98 \\ -37 \\ \hline \end{array}$	5. $\begin{array}{r} 62 \\ -40 \\ \hline \end{array}$	6. $\begin{array}{r} 73 \\ -\ 1 \\ \hline \end{array}$
7. $\begin{array}{r} 83 \\ -21 \\ \hline \end{array}$	8. $\begin{array}{r} 76 \\ -12 \\ \hline \end{array}$	9. $\begin{array}{r} 84 \\ -\ 3 \\ \hline \end{array}$	10. $\begin{array}{r} 98 \\ -15 \\ \hline \end{array}$	11. $\begin{array}{r} 56 \\ -\ 5 \\ \hline \end{array}$	12. $\begin{array}{r} 24 \\ -11 \\ \hline \end{array}$

Mixed Practice • Subtract.

13. $\begin{array}{r} 39 \\ -17 \\ \hline \end{array}$	14. $\begin{array}{r} 69 \\ -\ 8 \\ \hline \end{array}$	15. $\begin{array}{r} 84 \\ -14 \\ \hline \end{array}$	16. $\begin{array}{r} 83 \\ -22 \\ \hline \end{array}$	17. $\begin{array}{r} 84 \\ -\ 2 \\ \hline \end{array}$	18. $\begin{array}{r} 53 \\ -20 \\ \hline \end{array}$
19. $\begin{array}{r} 98 \\ -75 \\ \hline \end{array}$	20. $\begin{array}{r} 93 \\ -62 \\ \hline \end{array}$	21. $\begin{array}{r} 46 \\ -\ 3 \\ \hline \end{array}$	22. $\begin{array}{r} 63 \\ -60 \\ \hline \end{array}$	23. $\begin{array}{r} 78 \\ -24 \\ \hline \end{array}$	24. $\begin{array}{r} 75 \\ -25 \\ \hline \end{array}$

25. $\begin{array}{r}57\\-33\end{array}$	26. $\begin{array}{r}98\\-50\end{array}$	27. $\begin{array}{r}78\\-13\end{array}$	28. $\begin{array}{r}97\\-42\end{array}$	29. $\begin{array}{r}82\\-21\end{array}$	30. $\begin{array}{r}56\\-45\end{array}$
31. $\begin{array}{r}49\\-13\end{array}$	32. $\begin{array}{r}57\\-\ 7\end{array}$	33. $\begin{array}{r}52\\-42\end{array}$	34. $\begin{array}{r}76\\-45\end{array}$	35. $\begin{array}{r}98\\-23\end{array}$	36. $\begin{array}{r}43\\-20\end{array}$
37. $\begin{array}{r}89\\-62\end{array}$	38. $\begin{array}{r}68\\-51\end{array}$	39. $\begin{array}{r}78\\-\ 7\end{array}$	40. $\begin{array}{r}57\\-31\end{array}$	41. $\begin{array}{r}67\\-16\end{array}$	42. $\begin{array}{r}89\\-79\end{array}$
43. $\begin{array}{r}96\\-22\end{array}$	44. $\begin{array}{r}86\\-85\end{array}$	45. $\begin{array}{r}53\\-53\end{array}$	46. $\begin{array}{r}69\\-63\end{array}$	47. $\begin{array}{r}58\\-27\end{array}$	48. $\begin{array}{r}96\\-64\end{array}$

49. $69 - 45 = $? 50. $53 - 13 = $? 51. $97 - 25 = $?

52. $68 - 4 = $? 53. $74 - 42 = $? 54. $80 - 30 = $?

Find the missing numbers.

★ 55. $87 - 2\blacksquare = 65$ ★ 56. $49 - 1\blacksquare = 33$ ★ 57. $38 - 2\blacksquare = 12$

PROBLEM SOLVING • APPLICATIONS

58. Mickey orders 87 bags of dry dog food. She uses 24 bags. How many bags of dog food are left?

59. There are 90 vitamins in a large jar. The doctor takes 20 vitamins from the jar. How many vitamins are left in the jar?

60. The animal shelter has 56 flea collars. Mickey sells 24 of them. How many collars are left?

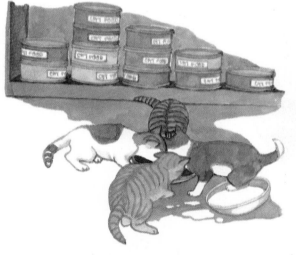

★ 61. There are 24 cans of cat food on a shelf. There are 48 on another shelf. Daphne uses 10 to feed the cats. How many cans are left?

Regrouping Tens

Angela has 65 stamps. She sends 27 stamps to a friend. How many stamps are left?

$65 - 27 = ?$

Step 1
Regroup 6 tens 5 ones as 5 tens 15 ones.

```
 5 15
  6̶5̶
-27
```
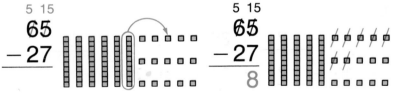

Step 2
Subtract the ones.

```
 5 15
  6̶5̶
-27
   8
```

Step 3
Subtract the tens.

```
 5 15
  6̶5̶
-27
  38
```

Angela has 38 stamps left.

You can use addition to check your answer.

```
  1
 38
+27
 65
```

Practice ● Subtract.

1. 62 −15	2. 51 −24	3. 25 − 8	4. 34 −27	5. 73 −39	6. 46 −18
7. 73 −48	8. 33 −15	9. 50 −27	10. 31 − 4	11. 42 −36	12. 62 − 5

Mixed Practice ● Subtract.

13. $\begin{array}{r} 34 \\ -17 \\ \hline \end{array}$
14. $\begin{array}{r} 91 \\ -59 \\ \hline \end{array}$
15. $\begin{array}{r} 50 \\ -31 \\ \hline \end{array}$
16. $\begin{array}{r} 74 \\ -59 \\ \hline \end{array}$
17. $\begin{array}{r} 94 \\ -25 \\ \hline \end{array}$
18. $\begin{array}{r} 92 \\ -39 \\ \hline \end{array}$

19. $\begin{array}{r} 90 \\ -12 \\ \hline \end{array}$
20. $\begin{array}{r} 61 \\ -35 \\ \hline \end{array}$
21. $\begin{array}{r} 61 \\ -28 \\ \hline \end{array}$
22. $\begin{array}{r} 75 \\ -\ 6 \\ \hline \end{array}$
23. $\begin{array}{r} 56 \\ -19 \\ \hline \end{array}$
24. $\begin{array}{r} 78 \\ -29 \\ \hline \end{array}$

25. $\begin{array}{r} 42 \\ -38 \\ \hline \end{array}$
26. $\begin{array}{r} 95 \\ -72 \\ \hline \end{array}$
27. $\begin{array}{r} 70 \\ -18 \\ \hline \end{array}$
28. $\begin{array}{r} 83 \\ -79 \\ \hline \end{array}$
29. $\begin{array}{r} 60 \\ -\ 9 \\ \hline \end{array}$
30. $\begin{array}{r} 86 \\ -11 \\ \hline \end{array}$

31. $\begin{array}{r} 83 \\ -\ 4 \\ \hline \end{array}$
32. $\begin{array}{r} 61 \\ -17 \\ \hline \end{array}$
33. $\begin{array}{r} 27 \\ -16 \\ \hline \end{array}$
34. $\begin{array}{r} 83 \\ -26 \\ \hline \end{array}$
35. $\begin{array}{r} 34 \\ -\ 6 \\ \hline \end{array}$
36. $\begin{array}{r} 57 \\ -29 \\ \hline \end{array}$

37. $83 - 26 =$?
38. $76 - 27 =$?
39. $62 - 48 =$?

40. $74 - 67 =$?
41. $55 - 18 =$?
42. $41 - 8 =$?

43. $92 - 38 =$?
44. $75 - 46 =$?
45. $80 - 57 =$?

Find the missing numbers.

⋆ 46. $38 +$? $= 46$ ⋆ 47. $27 +$? $= 32$ ⋆ 48. $17 +$? $= 66$

⋆ 49. $39 +$? $= 48$ ⋆ 50. $45 +$? $= 50$ ⋆ 51. $7 +$? $= 23$

PROBLEM SOLVING ● APPLICATIONS

52. A stamp album has 48 pages. Jeffrey has filled 39 pages. How many pages are left to fill?

53. Samantha has 64 stamps in a box. She puts 47 stamps into an album. How many stamps are left in the box?

54. Monica had 57 stamps. She gave a friend 9 stamps. How many stamps did she have left?

55. Mark had 82 stamps. He lost 23 of them. How many did he have left?

Subtracting Three-Digit Numbers

Mrs. Chu made 358 grain snacks for the fair. She sold 232 snacks. How many snacks did she have left?

$358 - 232 = ?$

Step 1
Subtract
the ones.

```
  358
- 232
-----
    6
```

Step 2
Subtract
the tens.

```
  358
- 232
-----
   26
```

Step 3
Subtract the
hundreds.

```
  358
- 232
-----
  126
```

Mrs. Chu had 126 snacks left.

Sometimes you need to regroup tens before you subtract.

Subtract: $653 - 418$.

Step 1
Regroup 5
tens 3 ones
as 4 tens 13 ones.

```
  4 13
  653
- 418
-----
```

Step 2
Subtract the
ones.

```
  4 13
  653
- 418
-----
     5
```

Step 3
Subtract the
tens.

```
  4 13
  653
- 418
-----
    35
```

Step 4
Subtract the
hundreds.

```
  4 13
  653
- 418
-----
   235
```

Practice • Subtract.

1. 476	2. 758	3. 835	4. 847	5. 792	6. 561
−212	−604	−217	−610	−125	−435

7. 985	8. 560	9. 829	10. 676	11. 313	12. 457
−502	−457	−219	− 49	−205	−329

Mixed Practice • Subtract.

13. $\begin{array}{r} 864 \\ -652 \\ \hline \end{array}$
14. $\begin{array}{r} 289 \\ -126 \\ \hline \end{array}$
15. $\begin{array}{r} 942 \\ -435 \\ \hline \end{array}$
16. $\begin{array}{r} 486 \\ -159 \\ \hline \end{array}$
17. $\begin{array}{r} 638 \\ -\ 25 \\ \hline \end{array}$
18. $\begin{array}{r} 793 \\ -588 \\ \hline \end{array}$

19. $\begin{array}{r} 379 \\ -156 \\ \hline \end{array}$
20. $\begin{array}{r} 842 \\ -\ 38 \\ \hline \end{array}$
21. $\begin{array}{r} 450 \\ -132 \\ \hline \end{array}$
22. $\begin{array}{r} 529 \\ -419 \\ \hline \end{array}$
23. $\begin{array}{r} 891 \\ -858 \\ \hline \end{array}$
24. $\begin{array}{r} 782 \\ -\ 56 \\ \hline \end{array}$

25. $\begin{array}{r} 944 \\ -631 \\ \hline \end{array}$
26. $\begin{array}{r} 672 \\ -465 \\ \hline \end{array}$
27. $\begin{array}{r} 185 \\ -174 \\ \hline \end{array}$
28. $\begin{array}{r} 247 \\ -138 \\ \hline \end{array}$
29. $\begin{array}{r} 739 \\ -528 \\ \hline \end{array}$
30. $\begin{array}{r} 868 \\ -149 \\ \hline \end{array}$

31. $\begin{array}{r} 282 \\ -154 \\ \hline \end{array}$
32. $\begin{array}{r} 420 \\ -208 \\ \hline \end{array}$
33. $\begin{array}{r} 981 \\ -570 \\ \hline \end{array}$
34. $\begin{array}{r} 635 \\ -527 \\ \hline \end{array}$
35. $\begin{array}{r} 162 \\ -\ 36 \\ \hline \end{array}$
36. $\begin{array}{r} 381 \\ -264 \\ \hline \end{array}$

37. $863 - 542 = $ ___?___
38. $291 - 175 = $ ___?___
39. $756 - 27 = $ ___?___

40. $958 - 349 = $ ___?___
41. $833 - 721 = $ ___?___
42. $317 - 209 = $ ___?___

Find the missing numbers.

★ 43. ▉ $64 - 76 = 488$
★ 44. ▉ $26 - 108 = 118$
★ 45. ▉ $80 - 453 = 227$

PROBLEM SOLVING • APPLICATIONS

46. The food stand had 160 orange drinks. Of these, 135 orange drinks were sold. How many orange drinks were left?

★ 47. There were 150 frozen yogurt bars. Only 19 bars were sold in the morning. Then 25 bars were sold in the afternoon. How many bars were left?

Skills Maintenance

1. $\begin{array}{r} 347 \\ +426 \\ \hline \end{array}$
2. $\begin{array}{r} 519 \\ +238 \\ \hline \end{array}$
3. $\begin{array}{r} 206 \\ +587 \\ \hline \end{array}$
4. $\begin{array}{r} 125 \\ +\ 35 \\ \hline \end{array}$
5. $\begin{array}{r} 815 \\ +493 \\ \hline \end{array}$
6. $\begin{array}{r} 128 \\ +747 \\ \hline \end{array}$

7. $\begin{array}{r} 215 \\ +\ 68 \\ \hline \end{array}$
8. $\begin{array}{r} 517 \\ +207 \\ \hline \end{array}$
9. $\begin{array}{r} 956 \\ +\ 24 \\ \hline \end{array}$
10. $\begin{array}{r} 104 \\ +787 \\ \hline \end{array}$
11. $\begin{array}{r} 257 \\ +138 \\ \hline \end{array}$
12. $\begin{array}{r} 432 \\ +\ 58 \\ \hline \end{array}$

PROBLEM SOLVING · STRATEGIES

Add or Subtract?

You must read a problem carefully to know whether to add or subtract.
An addition problem may ask how many in all or how many all together.

A subtraction problem may ask how many are left or how many more.

Read the problems.

On Monday 1,286 people rode on the boat. On Tuesday 2,237 people rode. How many people rode in all?

$$\begin{array}{r} 1,286 \\ +\,2,237 \\ \hline 3,523 \end{array}$$

3,523 people rode in all.

There were 384 people on the boat. Then 287 people got off to see the statue. How many people are left on the boat?

$$\begin{array}{r} 384 \\ -\,287 \\ \hline 97 \end{array}$$

97 people are left on the boat.

How would you solve the problem? Write ADD or SUBTRACT.

1. Now 208 people are inside the crown. Another 117 wait outside the statue. How many people is that all together?

Read each problem carefully to decide whether to add or subtract.

2. There are 1,343 people standing in line. There are 257 people not in line. How many more people stand in line?

3. First 462 people were inside the statue. Then 256 people leave. How many people are left inside?

Solve.

4. Now 508 people walk up the steps. Of these, 289 are students. How many are not students?

5. The base has 167 steps. The statue has 168 steps. How many steps are there in all?

6. There are 168 steps from the foot to the head. Ming has climbed 79 steps. How many more steps must she climb?

7. There are 25 windows in the crown. People look out of 5 windows. How many windows are empty?

8. Last Friday 256 people went to the statue. This Friday 127 people came. How many more people came last Friday?

9. Mr. Weber paid $2.25 to visit the statue. Craig paid $.85. How much did they pay all together?

10. Today 486 people want to ride on the boat. Only 239 people can get on the boat. How many people will not ride on the boat?

★ 11. Mr. and Mrs. Diaz paid $4.50 to go to the statue. Mrs. Kelly paid $2.25 for herself and $.85 for her son. How much more money did the Diazes spend?

★ 12. On Monday 2,286 people rode the elevator. On Tuesday 2,916 rode, and 3,126 rode on Wednesday. How many people in all rode the elevator?

93

Regrouping Hundreds

Tom uses 329 dried beans to make a picture of a sailboat. He uses 146 beans to make the sail. How many beans does he use in the rest of the picture?

$329 - 146 = ?$

Step 1 Subtract the ones.

$$\begin{array}{r} 329 \\ -146 \\ \hline 3 \end{array}$$

Step 2 Regroup 3 hundreds 2 tens as 2 hundreds 12 tens.

$$\begin{array}{r} {\scriptstyle 2\ 12} \\ 329 \\ -146 \\ \hline 3 \end{array}$$

Step 3 Subtract the tens.

$$\begin{array}{r} {\scriptstyle 2\ 12} \\ 329 \\ -146 \\ \hline 83 \end{array}$$

Step 4 Subtract the hundreds.

$$\begin{array}{r} {\scriptstyle 2\ 12} \\ 329 \\ -146 \\ \hline 183 \end{array}$$

183 beans are in the rest of the picture.

Practice • Subtract.

1. 668 −391	**2.** 449 − 86	**3.** 833 −172	**4.** 949 −171	**5.** 551 −470	**6.** 306 −152
7. 989 −197	**8.** 919 −722	**9.** 360 −280	**10.** 556 − 61	**11.** 648 −162	**12.** 737 −276

Mixed Practice • Subtract.

13. 848 −290	**14.** 878 −697	**15.** 431 −151	**16.** 879 −180	**17.** 222 − 90	**18.** 539 −195
19. 329 − 63	**20.** 608 −585	**21.** 438 −288	**22.** 819 −338	**23.** 558 −286	**24.** 823 −570

25. 922
   −732
	26. 739
	   −674
		27. 902
		   −121
			28. 423
			   −218
				29. 868
				   −774
					30. 853
					   −193

31. 608
   − 53
	32. 879
	   −449
		33. 324
		   −153
			34. 789
			   −295
				35. 248
				   −112
					36. 511
					   −370

37. 472
   −381
	38. 875
	   − 92
		39. 446
		   −129
			40. 681
			   −490
				41. 738
				   −556
					42. 937
					   −185

43. $859 - 384 = $ ____?____ 44. $948 - 378 = $ ____?____ 45. $754 - 91 = $ ____?____

Find the missing numbers.

★ 46. $529 - 3\blacksquare 3 = 146$ ★ 47. $9\blacksquare 7 - 65 = 852$ ★ 48. $656 - 2\blacksquare 2 = 374$

PROBLEM SOLVING • APPLICATIONS

49. Tom uses 185 red beans and 217 white beans for his picture. How many more white beans does he use?

50. There are 326 pinto beans in the bag. Tom uses 83 of the beans. How many pinto beans are left?

51. Gloria needs 325 beans to make a picture. She has 250 beans. How many more beans does she need?

★ 52. There are 350 beans in a bag. Carmela used 125 beans to make a picture. She used another 75 beans on the frame. How many beans are left in the bag?

Midchapter Review

Subtract.

1. 65
  −22
	2. 286
	  − 34
		3. 789
		  −301
			4. 74
			  − 8
				5. 52
				  −36
					6. 46
					  −29

7. 90
  −18
	8. 245
	  −138
		9. 436
		  − 71
			10. 730
			  −525
				11. 339
				  − 87
					12. 826
					  −354

Regrouping More Than Once

Mr. Thompson has 634 flower seeds.
He plants 256 of the seeds.
How many seeds are left?

$634 - 256 = ?$

Step 1
Regroup 3 tens 4 ones as 2 tens 14 ones. Subtract the ones.

```
   2 14
  6 3 4
- 2 5 6
------
      8
```

Step 2
Regroup 6 hundreds 2 tens as 5 hundreds 12 tens. Subtract the tens.

```
      12
   5 2 14
  6 3 4
- 2 5 6
------
     7 8
```

Step 3
Subtract the hundreds.

```
      12
   5 2 14
  6 3 4
- 2 5 6
------
   3 7 8
```

378 seeds are left.

Use addition to check your answer.

```
  1 1
  3 7 8
+ 2 5 6
------
  6 3 4
```

Practice • Subtract.

1. 745 −657	2. 230 −142	3. 377 −299	4. 943 −246	5. 745 − 89	6. 838 −189
7. 537 −168	8. 466 −279	9. 680 − 93	10. 814 −657	11. 753 −485	12. 942 −864

Mixed Practice ● Subtract.

13. 861
   − 199

14. 951
   − 375

15. 452
   − 268

16. 960
   − 563

17. 612
   − 479

18. 363
   − 274

19. 924
   − 439

20. 855
   − 388

21. 851
   − 567

22. 630
   − 54

23. 931
   − 646

24. 641
   − 498

25. 252
   − 186

26. 826
   − 248

27. 816
   − 497

28. 582
   − 97

29. 372
   − 185

30. 436
   − 177

31. 726
   − 328

32. 80
   − 46

33. 826
   − 7

34. 340
   − 157

35. 680
   − 246

36. 563
   − 517

37. 436
   − 291

38. 324
   − 187

39. 462
   − 68

40. 420
   − 162

41. 569
   − 5

42. 327
   − 95

43. 437 − 158 = ___?___   44. 775 − 586 = ___?___   45. 313 − 185 = ___?___

46. 940 − 161 = ___?___   47. 836 − 37 = ___?___   48. 641 − 254 = ___?___

Find the missing numbers.

★ 49. 526 − ___?___ = 437   ★ 50. 754 − ___?___ = 378   ★ 51. 912 − ___?___ = 17

PROBLEM SOLVING ● APPLICATIONS

52. Martha planted 334 seeds. Only 276 grew. How many seeds did not grow?

53. Jason ordered 145 packages of seeds. Today 78 packages came. How many more packages have to come?

★ 54. Rita has 423 flower seeds. She plants 168 seeds on Thursday and 175 seeds on Friday. On Saturday she plants the rest of the seeds. How many seeds does she plant on Saturday?

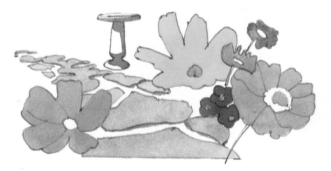

Zeros in Subtraction

Mr. Scott has 503 new trees to plant. He plants 147 of the trees. How many trees are left to plant?

$503 - 147 = ?$

Sometimes you need to regroup hundreds first to subtract ones.

Step 1
Regroup 5 hundreds
0 tens as 4 hundreds
10 tens.

$$\begin{array}{r} {\scriptstyle 4\ 10} \\ 5\cancel{0}3 \\ -147 \\ \hline \end{array}$$

Step 2
Regroup 10 tens
3 ones as 9 tens
13 ones.
Subtract the ones.

$$\begin{array}{r} {\scriptstyle\ \ \ 9} \\ {\scriptstyle 4\ \cancel{10}\ 13} \\ \cancel{5}\cancel{0}\cancel{3} \\ -147 \\ \hline 6 \end{array}$$

Step 3
Subtract the tens.

$$\begin{array}{r} {\scriptstyle\ \ \ 9} \\ {\scriptstyle 4\ \cancel{10}\ 13} \\ \cancel{5}\cancel{0}\cancel{3} \\ -147 \\ \hline 56 \end{array}$$

Step 4
Subtract the hundreds.

$$\begin{array}{r} {\scriptstyle\ \ \ 9} \\ {\scriptstyle 4\ \cancel{10}\ 13} \\ \cancel{5}\cancel{0}\cancel{3} \\ -147 \\ \hline 356 \end{array}$$

There are 356 trees left to plant.

Subtract: $700 - 238$.

Step 1
Regroup 7 hundreds
0 tens as
6 hundreds
10 tens.

$$\begin{array}{r} {\scriptstyle 6\ 10} \\ 7\cancel{0}0 \\ -238 \\ \hline \end{array}$$

Step 2
Regroup 10 tens
0 ones as
9 tens 10 ones.
Subtract the ones.

$$\begin{array}{r} {\scriptstyle\ \ \ 9} \\ {\scriptstyle 6\ \cancel{10}\ 10} \\ 7\cancel{0}\cancel{0} \\ -238 \\ \hline 2 \end{array}$$

Step 3
Subtract the tens.

$$\begin{array}{r} {\scriptstyle\ \ \ 9} \\ {\scriptstyle 6\ \cancel{10}\ 10} \\ 7\cancel{0}\cancel{0} \\ -238 \\ \hline 62 \end{array}$$

Step 4
Subtract the hundreds.

$$\begin{array}{r} {\scriptstyle\ \ \ 9} \\ {\scriptstyle 6\ \cancel{10}\ 10} \\ 7\cancel{0}\cancel{0} \\ -238 \\ \hline 462 \end{array}$$

Practice • Subtract.

1. $\begin{array}{r} 300 \\ -129 \\ \hline \end{array}$
2. $\begin{array}{r} 500 \\ -335 \\ \hline \end{array}$
3. $\begin{array}{r} 600 \\ -255 \\ \hline \end{array}$
4. $\begin{array}{r} 405 \\ -309 \\ \hline \end{array}$
5. $\begin{array}{r} 707 \\ -669 \\ \hline \end{array}$
6. $\begin{array}{r} 903 \\ -146 \\ \hline \end{array}$

7. $\begin{array}{r} 104 \\ -\ 76 \\ \hline \end{array}$
8. $\begin{array}{r} 907 \\ -189 \\ \hline \end{array}$
9. $\begin{array}{r} 506 \\ -348 \\ \hline \end{array}$
10. $\begin{array}{r} 800 \\ -656 \\ \hline \end{array}$
11. $\begin{array}{r} 404 \\ -\ 87 \\ \hline \end{array}$
12. $\begin{array}{r} 607 \\ -599 \\ \hline \end{array}$

Mixed Practice • Subtract.

13. $\begin{array}{r} 800 \\ -336 \\ \hline \end{array}$ 14. $\begin{array}{r} 500 \\ -298 \\ \hline \end{array}$ 15. $\begin{array}{r} 200 \\ -102 \\ \hline \end{array}$ 16. $\begin{array}{r} 900 \\ -117 \\ \hline \end{array}$ 17. $\begin{array}{r} 400 \\ -185 \\ \hline \end{array}$ 18. $\begin{array}{r} 700 \\ -443 \\ \hline \end{array}$

19. $\begin{array}{r} 305 \\ -288 \\ \hline \end{array}$ 20. $\begin{array}{r} 602 \\ -\ 96 \\ \hline \end{array}$ 21. $\begin{array}{r} 402 \\ -165 \\ \hline \end{array}$ 22. $\begin{array}{r} 803 \\ -514 \\ \hline \end{array}$ 23. $\begin{array}{r} 906 \\ -428 \\ \hline \end{array}$ 24. $\begin{array}{r} 501 \\ -274 \\ \hline \end{array}$

25. $\begin{array}{r} 300 \\ -\ 84 \\ \hline \end{array}$ 26. $\begin{array}{r} 602 \\ -483 \\ \hline \end{array}$ 27. $\begin{array}{r} 800 \\ -\ 56 \\ \hline \end{array}$ 28. $\begin{array}{r} 640 \\ -282 \\ \hline \end{array}$ 29. $\begin{array}{r} 700 \\ -173 \\ \hline \end{array}$ 30. $\begin{array}{r} 800 \\ -\ 74 \\ \hline \end{array}$

31. $\begin{array}{r} 704 \\ -219 \\ \hline \end{array}$ 32. $\begin{array}{r} 425 \\ -279 \\ \hline \end{array}$ 33. $\begin{array}{r} 404 \\ -159 \\ \hline \end{array}$ 34. $\begin{array}{r} 400 \\ -158 \\ \hline \end{array}$ 35. $\begin{array}{r} 900 \\ -767 \\ \hline \end{array}$ 36. $\begin{array}{r} 700 \\ -257 \\ \hline \end{array}$

37. $\begin{array}{r} 402 \\ -375 \\ \hline \end{array}$ 38. $\begin{array}{r} 900 \\ -\ 53 \\ \hline \end{array}$ 39. $\begin{array}{r} 308 \\ -299 \\ \hline \end{array}$ 40. $\begin{array}{r} 420 \\ -128 \\ \hline \end{array}$ 41. $\begin{array}{r} 600 \\ -495 \\ \hline \end{array}$ 42. $\begin{array}{r} 209 \\ -189 \\ \hline \end{array}$

43. $602 - 349 = $ __?__   44. $804 - 189 = $ __?__   45. $462 - 157 = $ __?__

Subtract. Then round to the nearest hundred.

★ 46. $700 - 436 = $ __?__   ★ 47. $900 - 134 = $ __?__   ★ 48. $705 - 278 = $ __?__

PROBLEM SOLVING • APPLICATIONS

Each number is 149 less than the number named before it.
What are the next two numbers in each pattern?

★ 49. 920   771   622   __?__   __?__

★ 50. 857   708   559   __?__   __?__

★ 51. 908   759   610   __?__   __?__

★ 52. 700   551   402   __?__   __?__

53. There are 700 trees. 447 trees have been cut down. How many trees are left?

54. There are 306 trees. Mr. Scott waters 158 of them. How many are left to water?

Subtracting Money

Loren has $5.63. He buys an angelfish for $2.87. How much money does he have left?

$5.63 − $2.87 = ?

Subtract amounts of money the same way that you subtract whole numbers. Remember to write the dollar sign and the cents point in the answer.

Think:
$$\begin{array}{r} \overset{\scriptstyle15}{} \\ \overset{4\ 5\ 13}{5\,6\,3} \\ -\ 2\,8\,7 \\ \hline 2\,7\,6 \end{array}$$

Write:
$$\begin{array}{r} \overset{\scriptstyle15}{} \\ \overset{4\ 5\ 13}{\$5.63} \\ -\ 2.87 \\ \hline \$2.76 \end{array}$$

He has $2.76 left.

Practice • Subtract. Remember to use the dollar sign and the cents point.

1. $7.25 − 3.59	2. $4.51 − 1.56	3. $3.62 − 1.84	4. $7.20 − 1.47	5. $7.00 − 2.36
6. $8.35 − 5.58	7. $6.26 − .98	8. $9.53 − 6.85	9. $5.17 − 1.79	10. $4.62 − 3.63

Mixed Practice • Subtract. Remember to use the dollar sign and the cents point.

11. $8.54 − 2.86	12. $7.85 − 6.98	13. $9.51 − 5.84	14. $3.23 − .57	15. $9.20 − 8.54
16. $7.33 − 4.59	17. $8.03 − 4.57	18. $6.32 − 2.36	19. $4.56 − .97	20. $7.61 − 6.86

21. $7.69 − .92	22. $6.23 − 3.38	23. $5.84 − .89	24. $3.62 − 1.54	25. $5.30 − 1.51
26. $9.65 − 5.87	27. $8.30 − 4.13	28. $6.00 − 5.79	29. $7.14 − 2.62	30. $4.58 − .59
31. $8.93 − 7.32	32. $7.45 − .97	33. $9.82 − 7.98	34. $4.86 − 3.67	35. $5.05 − 1.80

Subtract.

⋆ 36. $4.46 − $3.56 = ___?___   ⋆ 37. $6.49 − $ .89 = ___?___

⋆ 38. $8.22 − $4.95 = ___?___   ⋆ 39. $3.00 − $1.79 = ___?___

⋆ 40. $4.57 − $ .76 = ___?___   ⋆ 41. $9.81 − $7.59 = ___?___

PROBLEM SOLVING • APPLICATIONS

Complete the table.

	Has	Spends	Amount left
⋆42.	$3.98	$1.99	?
⋆43.	$6.55	$2.78	?
⋆44.	$7.49	$.59	?
⋆45.	$9.00	$6.88	?
⋆46.	$5.86	$4.97	?

Skills Maintenance

Write the numbers.

1. five hundred thirty-one

2. seven hundred eighty

3. one hundred nine

4. six hundred twenty-five

5. two hundred ninety-eight

6. nine hundred forty-seven

7. eight hundred fifteen

8. four hundred five

9. three hundred thirty

10. six hundred fifty-three

PROBLEM SOLVING • STRATEGIES

Estimating Differences

Sometimes you must estimate a number. You may do this to find about how many or about how much more. To do this, you must be able to round the numbers in a problem.

Read the problems.

Clarence sold 37 boxes of nails on Friday and 87 boxes on Saturday. About how many more boxes of nails did he sell on Saturday?

Estimate the difference to find about how many more were sold.

$$
\begin{array}{r}
84 \longrightarrow 80 \\
-37 \longrightarrow -40 \\
\hline
40
\end{array}
$$

Round to the nearest ten.

He sold about 40 more boxes of nails on Saturday.

At the hardware store, Ralph counts 318 boxes of screws. The store sells 179 boxes. About how many boxes of screws are left?

Estimate the difference to find about how many are left.

$$
\begin{array}{r}
318 \longrightarrow 300 \\
-179 \longrightarrow -200 \\
\hline
100
\end{array}
$$

Round to the nearest hundred.

About 100 boxes are left.

At the hardware store, Jamie spends $7.65 for paint. She spends $4.39 for brushes. About how much more does she spend for paint than for brushes?

To estimate money, round to the nearest dollar.

$$
\begin{array}{r}
\$7.65 \longrightarrow \$8.00 \\
-\ 4.39 \longrightarrow -\ 4.00 \\
\hline
\$4.00
\end{array}
$$

She spends about $4.00 more for paint.

Estimate each answer. Round to the nearest ten, hundred, or dollar.

1. Pearl spends $2.93 for bolts. Jason spends $1.58 for bolts. About how much more does Pearl spend than Jason?

Make sure you round correctly.

2. The hardware store has 88 saws and 74 drills. About how many more saws than drills does it have?

3. Reggie counts 67 saws. He sells 39 saws. About how many saws are left?

4. Kareem wants to buy a hammer that costs $6.95. He has $4.67. About how much more money does he need?

Check the estimate after you subtract.

5. Mrs. Rike has 109 cans of white paint and 187 cans of yellow paint in her store. About how many more cans of yellow paint does she have?

6. The hardware store gets 415 boxes of nails. Wendy puts 285 boxes on the shelf. About how many more boxes does she have to put on the shelf?

★ 7. The hardware store has 560 cans of paint. It sells 281 cans of wall paint and 92 cans of ceiling paint. About how many cans are left?

★ 8. Bruce gets $3.25 for helping at the hardware store. Carlos gets $16.15 for helping. About how much more does Carlos get?

Subtracting Greater Numbers

There are 4,362 seats at Bradley Park.
1,575 people are at the football game.
How many seats are empty?

$4,362 - 1,575 = ?$

Step 1
Regroup.
Subtract the
ones.

$$\begin{array}{r} {}^{5\ 12} \\ 4,3\cancel{6}\cancel{2} \\ -1,575 \\ \hline 7 \end{array}$$

Step 2
Regroup.
Subtract the
tens.

$$\begin{array}{r} {}^{15} \\ {}^{2\ 5\ 12} \\ 4,\cancel{3}\cancel{6}\cancel{2} \\ -1,575 \\ \hline 87 \end{array}$$

Step 3
Regroup.
Subtract the
hundreds.

$$\begin{array}{r} {}^{12\ 15} \\ {}^{3\ \ 2\ 5\ 12} \\ 4,\cancel{3}\cancel{6}\cancel{2} \\ -1,575 \\ \hline 787 \end{array}$$

Step 4
Subtract the
thousands.

$$\begin{array}{r} {}^{12\ 15} \\ {}^{3\ \ 2\ 5\ 12} \\ 4,\cancel{3}\cancel{6}\cancel{2} \\ -1,575 \\ \hline 2,787 \end{array}$$

There are 2,787 empty seats.

More Examples

$$\begin{array}{r} {}^{12} \\ {}^{7\ \ 2\ 14} \\ 8,\cancel{3}\cancel{4}9 \\ -2,876 \\ \hline 5,473 \end{array} \qquad \begin{array}{r} {}^{14} \\ {}^{7\ 4\ 11} \\ 6,\cancel{8}\cancel{5}\cancel{1} \\ -3,394 \\ \hline 3,457 \end{array} \qquad \begin{array}{r} {}^{15} \\ {}^{2\ 5\ 12} \\ 3,\cancel{6}\cancel{2}\cancel{8} \\ -2,758 \\ \hline 870 \end{array}$$

Practice • Subtract.

1. $\begin{array}{r} 8,247 \\ -3,569 \\ \hline \end{array}$

2. $\begin{array}{r} 5,384 \\ -2,396 \\ \hline \end{array}$

3. $\begin{array}{r} 4,763 \\ -1,385 \\ \hline \end{array}$

4. $\begin{array}{r} 9,605 \\ -8,736 \\ \hline \end{array}$

5. $\begin{array}{r} 8,536 \\ -2,773 \\ \hline \end{array}$

6. $\begin{array}{r} 7,022 \\ -1,655 \\ \hline \end{array}$

7. $\begin{array}{r} 9,418 \\ -7,839 \\ \hline \end{array}$

8. $\begin{array}{r} 6,850 \\ -\ \ 984 \\ \hline \end{array}$

9. $\begin{array}{r} 5,100 \\ -4,296 \\ \hline \end{array}$

10. $\begin{array}{r} 7,371 \\ -\ \ 693 \\ \hline \end{array}$

Mixed Practice • Subtract.

11. 7,346 −5,687	12. 5,682 − 94	13. 6,819 −3,469	14. 8,024 − 7	15. 9,251 −2,372
16. 4,430 −1,651	17. 6,174 −5,086	18. 7,603 −3,815	19. 5,765 −3,966	20. 8,595 −6,687
21. 3,727 − 848	22. 9,400 −2,616	23. 4,861 −1,883	24. 7,549 −6,389	25. 8,173 −4,184
26. 6,413 −5,555	27. 5,300 − 762	28. 3,934 −2,961	29. 9,651 −5,488	30. 7,208 −4,809
31. $59.16 − 49.26	32. $40.82 − 1.94	33. $83.47 − 66.59	34. $62.90 − 7.97	35. $95.28 − 87.19

★ 36. $7,986 - 3,927 = $ _____?_____   ★ 37. $5,914 - 4,946 = $ _____?_____

★ 38. $8,000 - 859 = $ _____?_____   ★ 39. $9,457 - 7,937 = $ _____?_____

PROBLEM SOLVING • APPLICATIONS

40. For the game on Tuesday, 2,689 tickets were sold. For the game on Friday, 3,256 tickets were sold. How many more tickets were sold for Friday?

41. We need 2,418 plastic football helmets. There are 1,852. How many more helmets are needed?

★ 42. This is a magic square. The sum of the numbers in each row, column, and diagonal is the same. The sum is called the magic sum. Find the missing numbers.

The magic sum is 1686.

379	?	651
834	562	290
473	?	745

REVIEW

Subtract. (pages 86–89)

1. 57
− 6

2. 44
−20

3. 87
−47

4. 68
−25

5. 92
−41

6. 29
−18

7. 68
− 9

8. 30
− 4

9. 84
−26

10. 77
−38

11. 55
−37

12. 31
−29

Subtract. (pages 90–91, 94–101, 104–105)

13. 749
−238

14. 691
−481

15. 578
−459

16. 943
−426

17. 862
−338

18. 623
−507

19. 417
−325

20. 338
−246

21. 756
−465

22. 869
−783

23. 623
−173

24. 777
−298

25. 372
−298

26. 645
−379

27. 926
−477

28. 737
−438

29. 800
−169

30. 403
−205

31. 600
−384

32. 708
−379

33. $6.26
− 2.58

34. $9.00
− 6.53

35. $8.65
− 6.78

36. 8,356
−1,378

37. 6,012
−3,195

38. 5,125
− 987

39. 4,202
−1,688

40. 7,500
−2,911

Solve.

41. There are 548 tickets for the play. 339 have been sold so far. How many tickets are left? (p. 92)

42. Chet spent $4.46 on lunch. He gave the cashier $5.00. How much change did he get? (p. 100)

PROJECT

Differences in Space

The Stars and Comets are going to play Space Capture.
The numbers tell the power each one has. The greater
the number is, the more power it has.

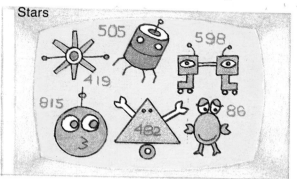

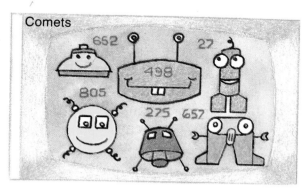

Find the difference between each one below.
If a Star is more powerful, write the difference
in the box below Stars.
If a Comet is more powerful, write the difference
in the box below Comets.

1. captures . The difference is 59.

2. captures .

3. captures .

4. captures .

5. captures .

6. captures .

STARS	COMETS
59	
?	?

Add up the numbers in each box.
The team with the most points wins.
Who won the game? By how much?

TEST

Subtract.

1. 85
  −14

2. 69
  − 7

3. 35
  −24

4. 76
  −35

5. 90
  −60

6. 48
  −23

7. 58
  − 9

8. 60
  − 7

9. 74
  −35

10. 42
  −36

11. 93
  −78

12. 87
  −39

Subtract.

13. 658
  −247

14. 586
  −329

15. 423
  −216

16. 785
  −529

17. 816
  −609

18. 634
  −428

19. 408
  −317

20. 738
  −546

21. 317
  −286

22. 829
  −577

23. 561
  −205

24. 682
  −190

25. 428
  −379

26. 372
  −175

27. 937
  −648

28. 814
  −626

29. 700
  −236

30. 407
  −389

31. 800
  −796

32. 602
  −173

33. $2.86
  − 1.97

34. $7.51
  − 2.79

35. $4.06
  − 1.78

36. 7,163
  −4,174

37. 1,600
  − 782

38. 8,248
  −6,279

39. 6,031
  −3,174

40. 4,851
  −2,868

Solve.

41. Tony needs 734 programs for the play. He has 216 now. How many more programs does he need?

42. There are 550 seats in the theater. 372 people are inside already. How many people still have to come?

Elevator Arithmetic

John and Mary use the elevator.
They enter on the main floor.
They go UP 6 floors.
They go DOWN 2 floors.
They go UP 9 floors.
They go UP 2 more floors.
They go DOWN 5 floors.
They get off the elevator.
They are on the tenth floor.

What floor are you on?
Start at the main floor each time.

1. UP 5
   UP 8
   DOWN 3
   UP 7
   DOWN 9
   FLOOR? ___?___

2. UP 12
   DOWN 4
   UP 7
   UP 2
   DOWN 8
   FLOOR? ___?___

3. UP 7
   UP 9
   DOWN 8
   DOWN 2
   UP 7
   FLOOR? ___?___

4. UP 16
   DOWN 4
   DOWN 7
   UP 6
   DOWN 2
   UP 5
   FLOOR? ___?___

5. UP 8
   DOWN 3
   UP 5
   UP 8
   DOWN 10
   UP 2
   FLOOR? ___?___

6. UP 15
   UP 2
   DOWN 6
   DOWN 3
   UP 7
   DOWN 12
   FLOOR? ___?___

18
17
16
15
14
13
12
11
10
9
8
7
6
5
4
3
2
1

Main Floor

109

CALCULATOR

Subtraction on a Calculator

Although the calculator is helpful, you can make mistakes on it.
You check *subtraction* on a calculator by using *addition*.
First turn the calculator on.

Try 555 − 222 = ?. Did you push ⑤ ⑤ ⑤ ⊖ ② ② ② ⊜?

Remember to push [CE] if you make a mistake in your last entry.

If you subtracted correctly, the screen looks like this: [*333.*]
Write down the answer, 333.

To check your subtraction, you now *add* 222 to see if you get 555.

Just push ⊕ ② ② ② ⊜. Look at the screen. [*555.*]

Since you started with 555, you know 333 is correct.

Subtract. Check your answer.

1. 963	2. 852	3. 46,954	4. 3,284
− 741	− 147	− 24,872	− 2,527

Calculators have no commas or $ signs. They do have decimal points.

Try $9.15 − $8.45 = ?.

Push ⑨ ⊙ ① ⑤ ⊖ ⑧ ⊙ ④ ⑤ ⊜. Screen: [*0.70*]

Write the answer as **$.70**, adding the $ and keeping the decimal point.

Subtract. Check your answer.

5. $3.76	6. $1.98	7. $82.67	8. $1,244.98
− 3.75	− .45	− 44.32	− 237.99

Remember to turn the calculator off.

110

Choose the correct answers.

1. 8 + 9 = ___?___

   A. 17
   B. 18
   C. 16
   D. not here

2.   7
  +8

   A. 14
   B. 13
   C. 15
   D. not here

3.   7
   5
  +4

   A. 16
   B. 12
   C. 11
   D. not here

4.   16
  − 7

   A. 23
   B. 9
   C. 8
   D. not here

5. 13 − 5 = ___?___

   A. 8
   B. 7
   C. 9
   D. not here

6. Write the number.
seventeen thousand four hundred twenty-seven

   A. 17,474
   B. 170,427
   C. 17,407
   D. not here

7. Round 749 to the nearest hundred.

   A. 800
   B. 700
   C. 750
   D. not here

8. $4.79
  + 3.45

   A. $824
   B. $8.26
   C. $8.24
   D. not here

9.   2,961
  +5,658

   A. 8,617
   B. 7,492
   C. 8,619
   D. not here

10.   951
  −678

   A. 273
   B. 279
   C. 277
   D. not here

11. $7.00
  − 4.27

   A. 273
   B. $2.73
   C. $2.27
   D. not here

12.   9,403
  −6,736

   A. 2,663
   B. 16,139
   C. 2,667
   D. not here

Skills Maintenance continued

Choose the correct answers.

13. Tanya has 6 tennis balls. Bill has 3. How many do they have all together?

    A. 3   B. 9
    C. 8   D. not here

14. Tony had 16 baseball cards. He gave 9 away. How many does he have left?

    A. 8   B. 25
    C. 7   D. not here

15. What is the seventh month of the year?

    A. August   B. September
    C. July   D. not here

16. Mia has 14 stickers. She gives 6 stickers to Shelly. How many stickers does she have left?

    A. 20   B. 9
    C. 7   D. not here

17. Jane bought a game bag for $6.39 and a headband for $2.68. How much did she spend in all?

    A. $9.07   B. $3.71
    C. $9.17   D. not here

18. David sold 217 tickets to the game on Monday. He sold 286 on Tuesday. How many tickets did he sell on both days?

    A. 530   B. 503
    C. 69   D. not here

19. There were 750 flags. Of these, 356 were sold. How many were not sold?

    A. 393   B. 394
    C. 1,106   D. not here

20. There are 3,125 seats. Now 2,769 are filled. How many seats are not filled?

    A. 354   B. 256
    C. 356   D. not here

Time and Money

$2.50 for 2 hours

Hour, Half Hour, and Quarter Hour

The short hand is the hour hand.
In one hour it moves from one number to the next number.

Read. ⟶ three o'clock
Write. ⟶ 3:00

Read. ⟶ four o'clock
Write. ⟶ 4:00

The long hand is the minute hand.
In one hour it moves around the clock once.
There are 60 minutes in an hour.
There are 30 minutes in a half hour.
There are 15 minutes in a quarter hour.

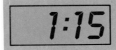

Read. ⟶ one o'clock
Write. ⟶ 1:00

Read. ⟶ quarter past one
Write. ⟶ 1:15

Read. ⟶ one thirty
Write. ⟶ 1:30

Practice • Write the time.

1.

2.

3.

4.

5.

6.

Mixed Practice ● Write the time.

7.

8.

9.

10.

11.

12.

What time will it be one hour later?

13.

14.

15.

What time was it one hour earlier?

16.

17.

18.

PROBLEM SOLVING ● APPLICATIONS

19. It takes 15 minutes for Enrico to walk from his house to school. Enrico leaves his house at seven o'clock. At what time does Enrico arrive at school?

20. Lisa begins reading at six o'clock. She reads for one-half hour. At what time is Lisa finished reading?

★ 21. Lisa goes to visit her grandmother at two o'clock. She is there for two hours. At what time does she leave?

★ 22. It is five o'clock. Enrico began working one-half hour ago. At what time did he begin?

Minutes

The long hand is the minute hand.
In 60 minutes it moves around the clock once.
In 5 minutes it moves from one number to the next number.
In 1 minute it moves from one mark to the next mark.

Read. ⟶ five
o'clock
Write. ⟶ **5:00**

Read. ⟶ five
minutes past five
Write. ⟶ **5:05**

Read. ⟶ six
minutes past five
Write. ⟶ **5:06**

When the minute hand
is between the 6 and
the 12, we can give
the time in two ways.

7:40
20 minutes to 8

Practice • Write the time.

1.

2.

3.

Write the time in two ways.

4.

5.

6.

More Practice • Write the time.

7.

8.

9.

10.

11.

12.

Write the time in two ways.

13.

14.

15.

16.

17.

18.

PROBLEM SOLVING • APPLICATIONS

Complete the sentences. Use HOURS or MINUTES.

19. Jane sleeps 9 ___?___ every night.

20. Greg played ball for 40 ___?___ yesterday.

21. Larry rides the school bus 15 ___?___ every morning.

Skills Maintenance

1. 12 − 5	2. 14 − 6	3. 17 − 9	4. 16 − 8	5. 11 − 3	6. 15 − 8
7. 18 − 9	8. 13 − 7	9. 11 − 6	10. 14 − 7	11. 16 − 7	12. 15 − 6

Time Intervals

The students in Room B see a film. The film begins at 10:10. It ends at 10:30. How many minutes long is the film?

The film is 20 minutes long.

Jason begins playing a cassette tape at 1:25. He turns off the tape player 15 minutes later. At what time does Jason turn off the tape player?

Jason turns off the tape player at 1:40.

Practice ● Complete.

How many minutes from

1.

8:15 to 8:45?

2.

4:35 to 5:00?

3.

6:50 to 7:05?

What time will it be

4.

in 20 minutes?

5.

in 35 minutes?

6.

in 10 minutes?

Mixed Practice ● Complete.

How many minutes from

7.

12:20 to 1:00?

8.

9:45 to 9:55?

9.

5:30 to 6:20?

What time will it be

10.

in 30 minutes?

11.

in 55 minutes?

12.

in 25 minutes?

PROBLEM SOLVING ● APPLICATIONS

13. John went to the doctor's office at 2:05. He saw the doctor at 2:28. How long did he wait to see the doctor?

14. Amata went to the dentist's office at 1:45. She left at 2:20. How long was she there?

★ 15. Luanne saw the dentist at 2:09. She was with the dentist for 45 minutes. At what time was she finished?

★ 16. Wyatt went to visit his grandmother. He got there at 6:45. He stayed for 45 minutes. When did he leave?

Midchapter Review

Write the time in two ways.

1.

2.

3.

PROBLEM SOLVING · STRATEGIES

Timetables

Timetables are used for many things. Some timetables tell us when and where buses and trains will stop.

Read the problem and study the timetable.

At what time does the bus stop at Green Street?

Look in the Bus Stop column to find Green Street. Then look across the line. Find the time in the Time column.

The bus stops at Green Street at 8:04.

Bus Timetable

Bus stop	Time
Bank Street	8:00
Green Street	8:04
Rose Lane	8:07
Adams Street	8:11
Star Avenue	8:16
Elm Street	8:22
Main Street	8:25

Use the timetable to answer each question.

1. At what time does the bus stop at Adams Street?

   When you use a timetable, read down to your stop. Then read across to find the time.

2. The bus is at Adams Street. What is the next stop?

3. Does the bus stop at Rose Lane or at Elm Street first?

Solve. Use the timetable to help you.

4. Eva catches the bus each day at 8:16. Where does she get on?

Check to make sure you are looking at the correct stop and time.

---

5. How long does it take the bus to go from Bank Street to Green Street?

6. Wade gets on the bus at Rose Lane. Ukat gets on at Elm Street. How many minutes after Wade does Ukat get on the bus?

7. The bus is 8 minutes late getting to Star Avenue. At what time does the bus get to Star Avenue?

8. Carrie gets on the bus at 8:00. She gets off at Main Street. How long is she on the bus?

9. On a snowy day the bus was 1 hour late at the Main Street stop. At what time did it get there?

10. Linda gets to the Adams Street bus stop at 8:02. The bus is on time. How long does Linda wait?

★ 11. The bus was late leaving Bank Street. It got to Main Street at 8:35. At what time did the bus leave Elm Street?

★ 12. Paul took 20 minutes to get to the bus. He got on the bus at Rose Lane and got off the bus at Main Street. It took him 5 minutes to walk to work. How many minutes did it take him to get to work?

Counting Money

penny
1¢ or $.01

nickel
5¢ or $.05

dime
10¢ or $.10

quarter
25¢ or $.25

half-dollar
50¢ or $.50

dollar
100¢ or $1.00

You can write an amount of money in two ways.

37¢ or $.37

Read. → thirty-seven cents

128¢ or $1.28

Read. → one dollar and twenty-eight cents

Practice • Write the amount in two ways.

1.

2.

Mixed Practice • Write the amount in two ways.

3.

4.

5.

6.

7. How many pennies should you trade for a nickel?

8. How many pennies should you trade for a quarter?

9. How many nickels should you trade for a dime?

10. How many nickels should you trade for a quarter?

11. How many dimes should you trade for a dollar?

12. How many quarters should you trade for a dollar?

Use $ and . to write the amount.

13. 6 dimes
    3 nickels
    4 pennies

14. 1 half-dollar
    4 dimes
    3 pennies

15. 2 quarters
    1 dime
    4 nickels

16. 1 dollar
    2 quarters
    4 nickels

17. 1 dollar
    1 quarter
    3 dimes
    7 pennies

18. 2 half-dollars
    3 quarters
    6 nickels
    4 pennies

PROBLEM SOLVING • APPLICATIONS

★ 19. Eartha has 1 quarter, 1 dime, and 3 nickels. Liz has 1 half-dollar, 2 dimes, and 7 pennies. How much money do they have in all?

★ 20. Jeri has 2 quarters, 1 nickel, and 6 pennies. Tom has 4 dimes, 6 nickels, and 4 pennies. How much money do they have in all?

Comparing Amounts of Money

Jim has 1 half-dollar, 1 quarter,
and 2 dimes. Does he have
enough money to buy the kite?

Jim has $.95.

$.95 > $.89.

He has enough money to
buy the kite.

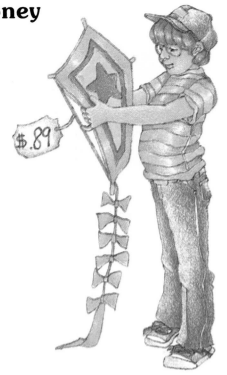

Practice • Do you have enough money to buy each item?
Write YES or NO.

1.

2.

3.
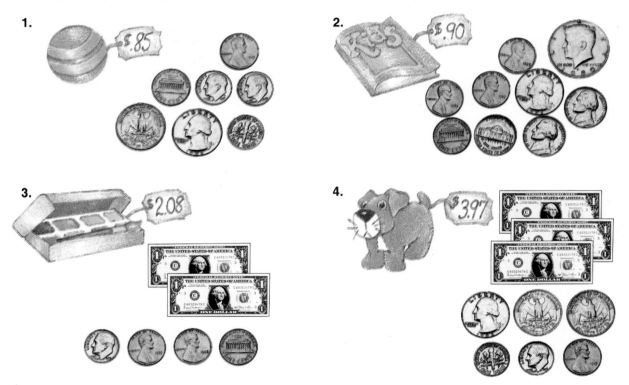

4.

124

Mixed Practice • Do you have enough money to buy each item?
Write YES or NO.

5.

6.

Use $ and . to write both amounts.
Then use > or < to show how they compare.

7. 1 quarter   2 dimes
                2 nickels

8. 2 quarters   1 half-dollar
   2 dimes   1 dime
   4 pennies   4 pennies

9. 3 dollars   3 dollars
   5 dimes   3 quarters
   1 nickel   5 pennies

★ 10. 1 dollar   1 dollar
      2 quarters   6 dimes
      1 nickel   2 nickels
      3 pennies   3 pennies

PROBLEM SOLVING • APPLICATIONS

11. Paula has 1 dollar, 2 quarters, 1 dime, and 1 nickel. Does she have enough money to buy a toy that costs $1.62?

12. Peter has 2 quarters, 3 dimes, 2 nickels, and 2 pennies. Does he have enough money to buy a battery that costs $.95?

★ 13. Peter has 72 cents. He has 5 coins. What are they?

★ 14. Pia has 46 cents. She has 4 coins. What are they?

Skills Maintenance

1. 74
   −16

2. 35
   −27

3. 60
   −26

4. 53
   − 8

5. 86
   −58

6. 47
   −19

7. 52
   − 9

8. 31
   −14

9. 75
   − 6

10. 66
    −57

11. 42
    −25

12. 83
    −38

Combinations of Coins

Roseanne buys a pin for $.58.
List the coins she gives to
the salesperson.

She gives the salesperson 2 quarters,
1 nickel, and 3 pennies.

Practice ● List the money you would give to the salesperson.
Use the fewest number of coins.

1. $.85

2. $.40

3. $.62

4. $1.65

126

Mixed Practice ● List the money you would give to the salesperson.

5.  $.63

6.  $1.17

7.  $1.39

8.  $2.07

9.  $.91

10.  $1.26

11. $1.52

12.  $2.75

Think of the number of coins needed to show the amount. What is the least number?

★ 13. $.87

★ 14. $.65

★ 15. $.92

★ 16. $.46

PROBLEM SOLVING ● APPLICATIONS

17. Wally buys beads for $.69. What coins does he give to the salesperson to pay the exact amount? List the coins.

18. Roseanne bought a pen for $1.17. List the coins she gave the salesperson to pay the exact amount.

127

PROBLEM SOLVING • STRATEGIES

Making Change

Always figure out how much change you should get back. If you must make change yourself, be sure you know how.

Pablo buys groceries for $2.67. He gives the checker $5.00. What change should he get? You can solve the problem in two ways.

Start with the cost, $2.67.
Count on to reach $5.00.

Start with————————→$2.67.
  Count 3 pennies.————→$2.70
  Count 1 nickel. ————→$2.75
  Count 1 quarter.————→$3.00
  Count 2 dollars. ————→$5.00

Subtract the cost, $2.67, from the amount given, $5.00.

$$\begin{array}{r} \$5.00 \\ -\ 2.67 \\ \hline \$2.33 \end{array}$$

Pablo should get $2.33 in change: 2 dollars, 1 quarter, 1 nickel, and 3 pennies.

What is the correct change? List the bills and coins.

1. A box of crackers costs $.79. You give the checker $1.00.

Start with	$ .79.
Count ? penny.	$ .80
Count ? dimes.	$1.00

Start with coins of the least value to make change.

2. Fish costs $2.29. You give the checker $5.00.

3. Grapes cost $1.19. You give the checker $2.00.

4. Corn costs $ .55. You give the checker $5.00.

Start with the cost. Find the correct change.
The first one has been done for you.

You buy	Cost	You give	Change				
			p	n	d	q	$
apples	$.68	$1.00	2	1	0	1	0
5. cheese	$1.73	$2.00	?	?	?	?	?
6. soup	$.85	$1.00	?	?	?	?	?
7. peas	$.54	$1.00	?	?	?	?	?
8. orange juice	$1.76	$5.00	?	?	?	?	?
9. bread	$.99	$5.00	?	?	?	?	?

Solve.

10. Mrs. Kim buys rice for $1.37. She gives the checker $2.00. What change does she get?

Check your answer by adding the change and the cost.

11. Ward buys chicken for $2.15. He gives the checker $5.00. What change does he get?

12. Elena buys meat for $3.39. She gives the checker $4.00. What change does she get?

★ 13. Miss Koto buys carrots for $1.69. Her change is 1 penny, 1 nickel, 1 quarter, and 3 dollars. What did she give the checker?

★ 14. Mr. Kim buys milk for $1.09. His change is 1 penny, 1 nickel, 1 dime, and 3 quarters. What did he give the checker?

Write the time in two ways. (pages 116–117)

1.

2.

3.

How many minutes from (pages 118–119)

4.

2:00 to 2:35?

5.

8:30 to 8:50?

6.

10:20 to 11:05?

What time will it be (pages 118–119)

7.

in 15 minutes?

8.

in 25 minutes?

9.

in 45 minutes?

Write the amount in two ways. (pages 122–123)

10.

11.

Use $ and . to write the amount. (pages 122–123)

12. 3 quarters
2 dimes

13. 7 nickels
8 pennies

14. 3 dollars
1 quarter
3 nickels
6 pennies

Solve.

15. Elbert left for the store at 2:30. He got there at 2:47. How many minutes did it take him to get to the store? (p. 118)

16. Leta has 4 quarters, 2 dimes, 3 nickels, and 7 pennies. How much money does she have? (p. 122)

Comparison Shopping

Copy the items from the shopping list.
Next to each item, write the name of the store that
has the lowest price. Then write the name of the store
that has the highest price.

Shopping list	A to Z Grocery	Phil's Foods	Plaza Market
milk	$.75	$.70	$.68
eggs	$1.29	$1.35	$1.30
apples	$.79	$.85	$.69
bread	$1.09	$1.19	$.99
cheese	$1.79	$1.69	$1.59
peas	$.59	$.75	$.69
juice	$1.29	$1.35	$1.20
butter	$2.19	$2.09	$2.15

Which store would you shop at? Why?

Find the food store ads in your local newspaper.
Choose two stores. List five items that are for sale at
both stores. List the prices of each item. Which store
has the better buys?

TEST

Write the time in two ways.

1.

2.

3.

How many minutes from

4.

4:00 to 4:10?

5.

7:15 to 7:40?

6.

1:30 to 2:10?

What time will it be

7.

in 1 hour?

8.

in 15 minutes?

9.

in 40 minutes?

Write the amount in two ways.

10.

11.

Use $ and . to write the amount.

12. 3 quarters
1 dime
3 pennies

13. 1 half-dollar
6 nickels
9 pennies

14. 2 quarters
4 dimes
3 nickels
5 pennies

Solve.

15. Joanne took her brother to the zoo. They got on the bus at 9:20. They arrived at 10:15. How many minutes did it take them to get to the zoo?

16. Waban has a half-dollar, 3 quarters, 5 nickels, and 8 pennies. How much money does he have?

A.M. and P.M.

There are 24 hours in 1 day.

A.M. means the time between midnight and noon.

P.M. means the time between noon and midnight.

Tom eats breakfast at 7:30 A.M.

Tom goes to bed at 8:15 P.M.

Write A.M. or P.M.

1. Stephanie gets home from school at 3:15 ___?___ .

2. Mr. Jackson eats dinner at 5:30 ___?___ .

3. Ann gets on the school bus at 8:00 ___?___ .

4. The sun sets at 5:45 ___?___ .

5. Recess is at 10:45 ___?___ .

6. The sun rises at 6:30 ___?___ .

7. Larry has a piano lesson at 4:00 ___?___ .

8. School begins at 8:30 ___?___ .

Write the time. Use A.M. or P.M.

9. It is 11:50 P.M. What time will it be in 20 minutes?

10. It is 11:15 A.M. What time will it be in 2 hours?

11. It is 12 noon. What time will it be in 25 minutes?

12. It is 12 midnight. What time was it 15 minutes ago?

13. It is 12:10 P.M. What time was it 20 minutes ago?

14. It is 2:00 A.M. What time was it 3 hours ago?

COMPUTER

Binary Numbers

A calculator can have any one of 10 digits in one place: 0, 1, 2, 3, 4, 5, 6, 7, 8, or 9.
These digits are used to write decimal numbers.
The word *decimal* is related to a word for *ten*.

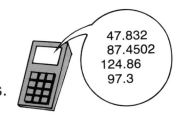

A computer can only have one of 2 digits in one place: 0 or 1.
These digits are used to write binary numbers.
The word *binary* is related to a word for *two*.

A calculator cannot add 9 + 1 and put the sum in one place.
There is no one-place number above 9 in a calculator.
A calculator must go to a second place that is called the tens place.
What a calculator calls 10 is really "one ten, no ones."
So 25 is really "two tens, five ones."

A computer cannot add 1 + 1 and put the sum in one place.
There is no one-place number above 1 in a computer.
A computer must go to a second place that is called the twos place.
What a computer calls 10 is really "one two, no ones."
So 11 is really "one two, one one."

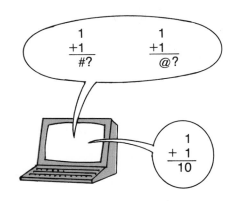

We know about **place value** for calculators.

hundred thousands	ten thousands	thousands	hundreds	tens	ones
1	0	1	0	1	0

Write: 101,010. Large decimal numbers have commas.
Read: "one hundred thousand, one thousand, and ten."
Reading other numbers: 555–1212, which is a phone number, is read "five five five one two one two."

Place value for computers is very different.

sixty–fours	thirty–twos	sixteens	eights	fours	twos	ones
1	0	1	0	1	0	1

Write: 1010101. Binary numbers do *not* have commas.
Read: "one sixty-four, one sixteen, one four, and one one."
Reading binary numbers: This number is usually read "one oh one oh one oh one."

This binary number has a decimal number value of

$$64 + 16 + 4 + 1 = 85.$$

Do you see how the binary system works?

Addition Facts for Calculators

$$\begin{array}{r} 1 \\ + 1 \\ \hline 2 \end{array} \quad \begin{array}{r} 9 \\ + 1 \\ \hline 10 \end{array} \quad \begin{array}{r} 199 \\ + 1 \\ \hline 200 \end{array} \quad \begin{array}{r} 2599 \\ + 9 \\ \hline 2608 \end{array}$$ This is *decimal* addition.

Addition Facts for Computers

$$\begin{array}{r} 1 \\ + 1 \\ \hline 10 \end{array} \quad \begin{array}{r} 10101 \\ + 1 \\ \hline 10110 \end{array} \quad \begin{array}{r} 1011111 \\ + 1 \\ \hline 1100000 \end{array} \quad \begin{array}{r} 111110 \\ + 10001 \\ \hline 1001111 \end{array}$$ This is *binary* addition.

Calculate using binary addition.

1. $\begin{array}{r} 1 \\ + 1 \\ \hline \end{array}$

2. $\begin{array}{r} 10 \\ + 1 \\ \hline \end{array}$

3. $\begin{array}{r} 101 \\ + 1 \\ \hline \end{array}$

4. $\begin{array}{r} 100111 \\ + 1 \\ \hline \end{array}$

5. $\begin{array}{r} 1001101 \\ + 1001 \\ \hline \end{array}$

6. $\begin{array}{r} 11111111 \\ + 1 \\ \hline \end{array}$

7. $\begin{array}{r} 101010101 \\ + 10101011 \\ \hline \end{array}$

8. $\begin{array}{r} 1111111111 \\ + 1111111111 \\ \hline \end{array}$

SKILLS MAINTENANCE
Chapters 1 Through 5

Choose the correct answers.

1. 8 + 4 = ___?___

- A. 32
- B. 12
- C. 21
- D. not here

2. 2 + 9 + 6 = ___?___

- A. 16
- B. 17
- C. 24
- D. not here

3. 15 − ___?___ = 6

- A. 11
- B. 8
- C. 9
- D. not here

4. Name 100 more.

600

- A. 60
- B. 600
- C. 700
- D. not here

5. Round 68 to the nearest ten.

- A. 50
- B. 60
- C. 75
- D. not here

6.
$$\begin{array}{r} 763 \\ +139 \\ \hline \end{array}$$

- A. 902
- B. 624
- C. 892
- D. not here

7. $ .39 + $7.79 = ___?___

- A. $7.18
- B. $8.09
- C. $8.18
- D. not here

8.
$$\begin{array}{r} 437 \\ -269 \\ \hline \end{array}$$

- A. 706
- B. 168
- C. 266
- D. not here

9. 3,000 − 567 = ___?___

- A. 2,543
- B. 2,633
- C. 2,433
- D. not here

10. Lucy has a puzzle with 356 pieces. Roe has a puzzle with 2,000 pieces. How many more pieces does Roe's puzzle have?

- A. 2,356
- B. 1,644
- C. 1,365
- D. not here

11. Mr. D's Department Store sold 26 games on Friday. The store sold 158 games on Saturday. How many games did the store sell in all?

- A. 184
- B. 148
- C. 132
- D. not here

Multiplication Facts

Meaning of Multiplication

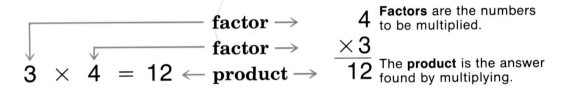

4   +   4   +   4 = 12

3 fours = 12

There are 4 tomatoes in each group.
There are 3 groups. There are 12 tomatoes.

factor →   4   **Factors** are the numbers to be multiplied.

factor →   ×3

3 × 4 = 12 ← product →   12 The **product** is the answer found by multiplying.

Practice • Complete the sentences to show how many in all.

1.

8 + 8 = ____?____
2 × 8 = ____?____

2.

3 + 3 = ____?____
2 × 3 = ____?____

3.

2 + 2 + 2 = ____?____
3 × 2 = ____?____

Mixed Practice • Complete the sentences to show how many in all.

4.

2 + 2 + 2 + 2
= ____?____
4 × 2 = ____?____

5.

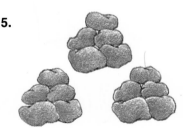

5 + 5 + 5
= ____?____
3 × 5 = ____?____

6.

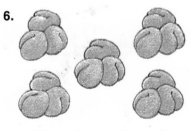

3 + 3 + 3 + 3
+ 3 = ____?____
5 × 3 = ____?____

7.

$2 + 2 + 2 + 2$
$+ 2 = $ ___?___
$5 \times 2 = $ ___?___

8.

$5 + 5 + 5 +$
$5 = $ ___?___
$4 \times 5 = $ ___?___

9.

$9 + 9 = $ ___?___
$2 \times 9 = $ ___?___

10.
$$\begin{array}{r} 6 \\ \times 4 \\ \hline \end{array}$$

11.
$$\begin{array}{r} 7 \\ \times 3 \\ \hline \end{array}$$

12.
$$\begin{array}{r} 4 \\ \times 4 \\ \hline \end{array}$$

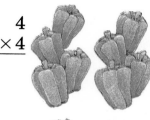

PROBLEM SOLVING • APPLICATIONS

Write an addition sentence and a multiplication sentence.

★ **13.**

★ **14.**

★ **15.**

2 as a Factor

How many
shoes in all?

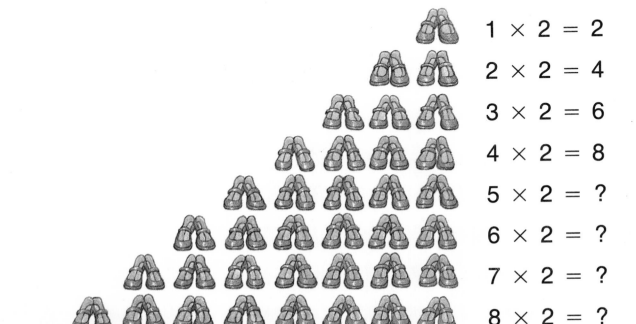

$$2 + 2 + 2 + 2 = 8$$

4 twos = 8
$4 \times 2 = 8$

There are 8 shoes in all.

$1 \times 2 = 2$

$2 \times 2 = 4$

$3 \times 2 = 6$

$4 \times 2 = 8$

$5 \times 2 = ?$

$6 \times 2 = ?$

$7 \times 2 = ?$

$8 \times 2 = ?$

$9 \times 2 = ?$

Practice • Complete the sentences to show how many in all.

1.

$2 + 2 + 2 = \underline{}$
$3 \times 2 = \underline{}$

2.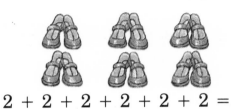

$2 + 2 + 2 + 2 + 2 + 2 = \underline{}$
$6 \times 2 = \underline{}$

3. $5 \times 2 = \underline{}$

4. $2 \times 2 = \underline{}$

5. $9 \times 2 = \underline{}$

6. $8 \times 2 = \underline{}$

7. $1 \times 2 = \underline{}$

8. $7 \times 2 = \underline{}$

Mixed Practice ● Find the products.

9. $1 \times 2 = $?

10. $7 \times 2 = $?

11. $9 \times 2 = $?

12. $3 \times 2 = $?

13. $5 \times 2 = $?

14. $8 \times 2 = $?

15. $7 \times 2 = $?

16. $1 \times 2 = $?

17. $6 \times 2 = $?

18. $4 \times 2 = $?

19. $9 \times 2 = $?

20. $2 \times 2 = $?

21. $\begin{array}{r} 6 \\ \times 2 \\ \hline \end{array}$
22. $\begin{array}{r} 3 \\ \times 2 \\ \hline \end{array}$
23. $\begin{array}{r} 2 \\ \times 2 \\ \hline \end{array}$
24. $\begin{array}{r} 7 \\ \times 2 \\ \hline \end{array}$
25. $\begin{array}{r} 4 \\ \times 2 \\ \hline \end{array}$
26. $\begin{array}{r} 5 \\ \times 2 \\ \hline \end{array}$
27. $\begin{array}{r} 8 \\ \times 2 \\ \hline \end{array}$

28. $\begin{array}{r} 9 \\ \times 2 \\ \hline \end{array}$
29. $\begin{array}{r} 1 \\ \times 2 \\ \hline \end{array}$
30. $\begin{array}{r} 5 \\ \times 2 \\ \hline \end{array}$
31. $\begin{array}{r} 8 \\ \times 2 \\ \hline \end{array}$
32. $\begin{array}{r} 6 \\ \times 2 \\ \hline \end{array}$
33. $\begin{array}{r} 2 \\ \times 2 \\ \hline \end{array}$
34. $\begin{array}{r} 3 \\ \times 2 \\ \hline \end{array}$

Find the missing numbers.

★ 35. ? $\times 2 = 18$ ★ 36. ? $\times 2 = 14$ ★ 37. $2 \times$? $= 16$

Use a practice bar to practice your facts.

38.

1	× 2	=	2
2	× 2	=	4
3	× 2	=	6
4	× 2	=	8
5	× 2	=	10
6	× 2	=	12
7	× 2	=	14
8	× 2	=	16
9	× 2	=	18

Make a card like this.

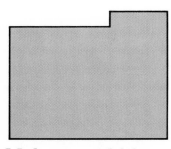

Make a card like this.

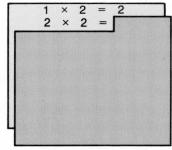

Put them together and practice your facts.

PROBLEM SOLVING ● APPLICATIONS

39. In each bag are 2 socks. There are 5 bags. How many socks are there?

40. Each child has 2 mittens. There are 3 children. How many mittens are there?

★ 41. Each box holds a pair of slippers. There are 7 boxes. How many slippers are there?

★ 42. There is a pair of gloves for each child. There are 6 children. How many gloves are there?

3 as a Factor

How many
peas in all?

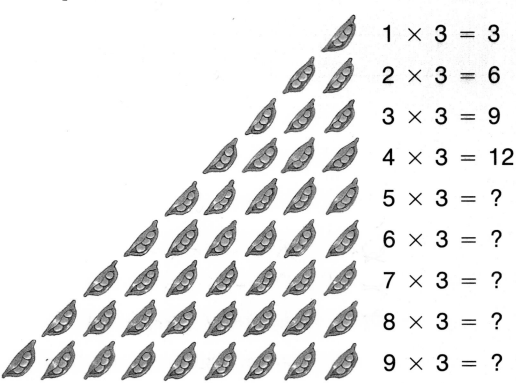

$$3 + 3 + 3 + 3 = 12$$

4 threes = 12
$$4 \times 3 = 12$$

There are 12 peas in all.

$$1 \times 3 = 3$$
$$2 \times 3 = 6$$
$$3 \times 3 = 9$$
$$4 \times 3 = 12$$
$$5 \times 3 = ?$$
$$6 \times 3 = ?$$
$$7 \times 3 = ?$$
$$8 \times 3 = ?$$
$$9 \times 3 = ?$$

Practice • Complete the sentences to show how many in all.

1.

$$3 + 3 + 3 + 3 + 3 = \underline{\quad ? \quad}$$
$$5 \times 3 = \underline{\quad ? \quad}$$

2.

$$3 + 3 = \underline{\quad ? \quad}$$
$$2 \times 3 = \underline{\quad ? \quad}$$

3. $3 \times 3 = \underline{\quad ? \quad}$

4. $6 \times 3 = \underline{\quad ? \quad}$

5. $8 \times 3 = \underline{\quad ? \quad}$

6. $9 \times 3 = \underline{\quad ? \quad}$

7. $1 \times 3 = \underline{\quad ? \quad}$

8. $7 \times 3 = \underline{\quad ? \quad}$

Mixed Practice ● Find the products.

9. $5 \times 3 =$? 10. $8 \times 3 =$? 11. $2 \times 3 =$?

12. $4 \times 3 =$? 13. $1 \times 3 =$? 14. $7 \times 3 =$?

15. $9 \times 3 =$? 16. $6 \times 3 =$? 17. $3 \times 3 =$?

18.	19.	20.	21.	22.	23.	24.
6	4	1	2	5	3	7
$\times 2$	$\times 3$	$\times 3$	$\times 3$	$\times 3$	$\times 2$	$\times 3$

25.	26.	27.	28.	29.	30.	31.
7	8	5	9	6	4	1
$\times 2$	$\times 3$	$\times 2$	$\times 3$	$\times 3$	$\times 2$	$\times 2$

32.	33.	34.	35.	36.	37.	38.
2	7	3	8	4	9	8
$\times 3$	$\times 3$	$\times 3$	$\times 2$	$\times 3$	$\times 2$	$\times 3$

39.	40.	41.	42.	43.	44.	45.
2	3	3	3	2	4	1
$\times 8$	$\times 6$	$\times 7$	$\times 9$	$\times 7$	$\times 2$	$\times 9$

Find the answers.

★ 46.
★ 47.
★ 48.

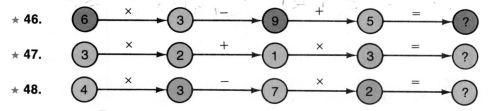

PROBLEM SOLVING ● APPLICATIONS

49. There are 3 carrots in each bag. There are 5 bags on the shelf. How many carrots in all?

50. There are 3 peppers on each plant. There are 7 plants. How many peppers in all?

51. There are 3 tomatoes in each box. We bought 8 boxes. How many tomatoes are there in all?

★ 52. John has 3 rows of lettuce in his garden. Millie has 4 rows of lettuce in her garden. There are 8 heads of lettuce in every row. How many heads of lettuce are there all together?

143

4 as a Factor

How many
tires in all?

$$4 + 4 + 4 = 12$$

3 fours = 12
$$3 \times 4 = 12$$

There are 12 tires in all.

$1 \times 4 = 4$

$2 \times 4 = 8$

$3 \times 4 = 12$

$4 \times 4 = ?$

$5 \times 4 = ?$

$6 \times 4 = ?$

$7 \times 4 = ?$

$8 \times 4 = ?$

$9 \times 4 = ?$

Practice • Complete the sentences to show how many in all.

1.

$2 \times 4 = \underline{\quad?\quad}$

2.

$5 \times 4 = \underline{\quad?\quad}$

3.

$7 \times 4 = \underline{\quad?\quad}$

4. $1 \times 4 = $ ___?___   **5.** $4 \times 4 = $ ___?___   **6.** $4 \times 8 = $ ___?___

7. $4 \times 6 = $ ___?___   **8.** $9 \times 4 = $ ___?___   **9.** $3 \times 4 = $ ___?___

Mixed Practice • Find the products.

10. $3 \times 4 = $ ___?___   **11.** $4 \times 5 = $ ___?___   **12.** $4 \times 1 = $ ___?___

13. $4 \times 3 = $ ___?___   **14.** $6 \times 4 = $ ___?___   **15.** $4 \times 7 = $ ___?___

16. $2 \times 4 = $ ___?___   **17.** $4 \times 6 = $ ___?___   **18.** $1 \times 4 = $ ___?___

19. $5 \times 4 = $ ___?___   **20.** $4 \times 8 = $ ___?___   **21.** $7 \times 4 = $ ___?___

22. $\begin{array}{r} 4 \\ \times 5 \\ \hline \end{array}$	**23.** $\begin{array}{r} 1 \\ \times 4 \\ \hline \end{array}$	**24.** $\begin{array}{r} 4 \\ \times 1 \\ \hline \end{array}$	**25.** $\begin{array}{r} 6 \\ \times 4 \\ \hline \end{array}$	**26.** $\begin{array}{r} 8 \\ \times 4 \\ \hline \end{array}$	**27.** $\begin{array}{r} 4 \\ \times 2 \\ \hline \end{array}$	**28.** $\begin{array}{r} 4 \\ \times 6 \\ \hline \end{array}$
29. $\begin{array}{r} 5 \\ \times 4 \\ \hline \end{array}$	**30.** $\begin{array}{r} 4 \\ \times 4 \\ \hline \end{array}$	**31.** $\begin{array}{r} 2 \\ \times 6 \\ \hline \end{array}$	**32.** $\begin{array}{r} 9 \\ \times 4 \\ \hline \end{array}$	**33.** $\begin{array}{r} 4 \\ \times 9 \\ \hline \end{array}$	**34.** $\begin{array}{r} 3 \\ \times 9 \\ \hline \end{array}$	**35.** $\begin{array}{r} 3 \\ \times 2 \\ \hline \end{array}$
36. $\begin{array}{r} 7 \\ \times 4 \\ \hline \end{array}$	**37.** $\begin{array}{r} 2 \\ \times 3 \\ \hline \end{array}$	**38.** $\begin{array}{r} 4 \\ \times 4 \\ \hline \end{array}$	**39.** $\begin{array}{r} 4 \\ \times 8 \\ \hline \end{array}$	**40.** $\begin{array}{r} 2 \\ \times 5 \\ \hline \end{array}$	**41.** $\begin{array}{r} 7 \\ \times 4 \\ \hline \end{array}$	**42.** $\begin{array}{r} 9 \\ \times 3 \\ \hline \end{array}$
43. $\begin{array}{r} 1 \\ \times 2 \\ \hline \end{array}$	**44.** $\begin{array}{r} 6 \\ \times 4 \\ \hline \end{array}$	**45.** $\begin{array}{r} 4 \\ \times 2 \\ \hline \end{array}$	**46.** $\begin{array}{r} 3 \\ \times 7 \\ \hline \end{array}$	**47.** $\begin{array}{r} 4 \\ \times 8 \\ \hline \end{array}$	**48.** $\begin{array}{r} 2 \\ \times 4 \\ \hline \end{array}$	**49.** $\begin{array}{r} 4 \\ \times 5 \\ \hline \end{array}$

PROBLEM SOLVING • APPLICATIONS

Multiply across and then multiply down.

★ **50.**

★ **51.**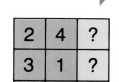

★ **52.**

53. Each car has 4 tires. 8 cars are in the lot. How many tires are there?

54. There are 4 tires on a truck. There are 5 trucks. How many tires are there?

5 as a Factor

How many
buttons in all?

$$5 + 5 + 5 = 15$$

3 fives = 15
$3 \times 5 = 15$

There are 15 buttons in all.

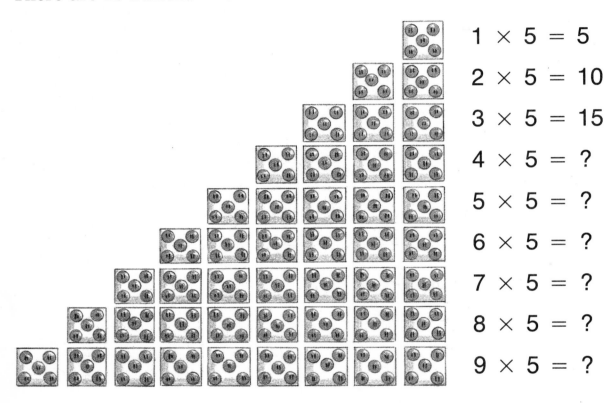

$1 \times 5 = 5$

$2 \times 5 = 10$

$3 \times 5 = 15$

$4 \times 5 = ?$

$5 \times 5 = ?$

$6 \times 5 = ?$

$7 \times 5 = ?$

$8 \times 5 = ?$

$9 \times 5 = ?$

Practice • Complete the sentences to show how many in all.

1.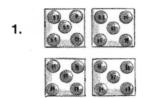

$4 \times 5 = \underline{\ ?\ }$

4. $2 \times 5 = \underline{\ ?\ }$

7. $5 \times 3 = \underline{\ ?\ }$

2.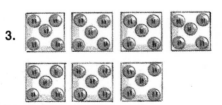

$6 \times 5 = \underline{\ ?\ }$

5. $5 \times 8 = \underline{\ ?\ }$

8. $9 \times 5 = \underline{\ ?\ }$

3.

$7 \times 5 = \underline{\ ?\ }$

6. $1 \times 5 = \underline{\ ?\ }$

9. $5 \times 5 = \underline{\ ?\ }$

Mixed Practice • Find the products.

10. $4 \times 5 =$ ____?____   11. $3 \times 5 =$ ____?____   12. $5 \times 2 =$ ____?____

13. $5 \times 8 =$ ____?____   14. $6 \times 5 =$ ____?____   15. $5 \times 7 =$ ____?____

16. $5 \times 5 =$ ____?____   17. $9 \times 5 =$ ____?____   18. $5 \times 3 =$ ____?____

19. $5 \times 4 =$ ____?____   20. $5 \times 1 =$ ____?____   21. $7 \times 5 =$ ____?____

22. $\begin{array}{r} 5 \\ \times 6 \\ \hline \end{array}$
23. $\begin{array}{r} 5 \\ \times 2 \\ \hline \end{array}$
24. $\begin{array}{r} 4 \\ \times 5 \\ \hline \end{array}$
25. $\begin{array}{r} 8 \\ \times 5 \\ \hline \end{array}$
26. $\begin{array}{r} 5 \\ \times 5 \\ \hline \end{array}$
27. $\begin{array}{r} 5 \\ \times 9 \\ \hline \end{array}$
28. $\begin{array}{r} 1 \\ \times 5 \\ \hline \end{array}$

29. $\begin{array}{r} 3 \\ \times 5 \\ \hline \end{array}$
30. $\begin{array}{r} 4 \\ \times 7 \\ \hline \end{array}$
31. $\begin{array}{r} 5 \\ \times 6 \\ \hline \end{array}$
32. $\begin{array}{r} 5 \\ \times 1 \\ \hline \end{array}$
33. $\begin{array}{r} 7 \\ \times 5 \\ \hline \end{array}$
34. $\begin{array}{r} 2 \\ \times 8 \\ \hline \end{array}$
35. $\begin{array}{r} 5 \\ \times 9 \\ \hline \end{array}$

36. $\begin{array}{r} 5 \\ \times 4 \\ \hline \end{array}$
37. $\begin{array}{r} 9 \\ \times 5 \\ \hline \end{array}$
38. $\begin{array}{r} 3 \\ \times 3 \\ \hline \end{array}$
39. $\begin{array}{r} 5 \\ \times 2 \\ \hline \end{array}$
40. $\begin{array}{r} 4 \\ \times 2 \\ \hline \end{array}$
41. $\begin{array}{r} 8 \\ \times 5 \\ \hline \end{array}$
42. $\begin{array}{r} 5 \\ \times 5 \\ \hline \end{array}$

43. $\begin{array}{r} 4 \\ \times 4 \\ \hline \end{array}$
44. $\begin{array}{r} 5 \\ \times 7 \\ \hline \end{array}$
45. $\begin{array}{r} 5 \\ \times 3 \\ \hline \end{array}$
46. $\begin{array}{r} 4 \\ \times 3 \\ \hline \end{array}$
47. $\begin{array}{r} 6 \\ \times 5 \\ \hline \end{array}$
48. $\begin{array}{r} 2 \\ \times 5 \\ \hline \end{array}$
49. $\begin{array}{r} 3 \\ \times 2 \\ \hline \end{array}$

Find the missing numbers.

★ 50. $5 \times$ ____?____ $= 15$ ★ 51. $5 \times$ ____?____ $= 40$

★ 52. $5 \times$ ____?____ $= 25$ ★ 53. $5 \times$ ____?____ $= 45$

PROBLEM SOLVING • APPLICATIONS

54. I see 5 buttons on each card. I see 6 cards on the hook. How many buttons are there?

★ 55. The sum of two numbers is seven. The product is 12. What are the two numbers?

Skills Maintenance

1. $\begin{array}{r} 467 \\ -177 \\ \hline \end{array}$
2. $\begin{array}{r} 354 \\ -282 \\ \hline \end{array}$
3. $\begin{array}{r} 839 \\ -681 \\ \hline \end{array}$
4. $\begin{array}{r} 766 \\ -390 \\ \hline \end{array}$
5. $\begin{array}{r} 248 \\ -\ 62 \\ \hline \end{array}$

6. $\begin{array}{r} 527 \\ -463 \\ \hline \end{array}$
7. $\begin{array}{r} 473 \\ -192 \\ \hline \end{array}$
8. $\begin{array}{r} 236 \\ -\ 53 \\ \hline \end{array}$
9. $\begin{array}{r} 955 \\ -890 \\ \hline \end{array}$
10. $\begin{array}{r} 612 \\ -281 \\ \hline \end{array}$

0 and 1 as Factors

2 boxes
2 puppies in each
4 puppies in all

2 boxes
1 puppy in each
2 puppies in all

2 boxes
0 puppies in each
0 puppies in all

$2 \times 2 = 4$ $2 \times 1 = 2$ $2 \times 0 = 0$

The product of any number and 1 is that number.
The product of any number and zero is 0.

Practice • Find the products.

1. $4 \times 0 = $ ____   2. $6 \times 1 = $ ____   3. $1 \times 3 = $ ____

4. $0 \times 5 = $ ____   5. $1 \times 9 = $ ____   6. $3 \times 0 = $ ____

7. $\begin{array}{r} 0 \\ \times 7 \\ \hline \end{array}$
8. $\begin{array}{r} 2 \\ \times 1 \\ \hline \end{array}$
9. $\begin{array}{r} 0 \\ \times 1 \\ \hline \end{array}$
10. $\begin{array}{r} 1 \\ \times 4 \\ \hline \end{array}$
11. $\begin{array}{r} 8 \\ \times 1 \\ \hline \end{array}$
12. $\begin{array}{r} 9 \\ \times 0 \\ \hline \end{array}$
13. $\begin{array}{r} 5 \\ \times 1 \\ \hline \end{array}$

14. $\begin{array}{r} 0 \\ \times 6 \\ \hline \end{array}$
15. $\begin{array}{r} 2 \\ \times 0 \\ \hline \end{array}$
16. $\begin{array}{r} 4 \\ \times 1 \\ \hline \end{array}$
17. $\begin{array}{r} 0 \\ \times 4 \\ \hline \end{array}$
18. $\begin{array}{r} 1 \\ \times 7 \\ \hline \end{array}$
19. $\begin{array}{r} 1 \\ \times 8 \\ \hline \end{array}$
20. $\begin{array}{r} 5 \\ \times 0 \\ \hline \end{array}$

Mixed Practice • Find the products.

21. $7 \times 1 = $ ____   22. $0 \times 3 = $ ____   23. $8 \times 0 = $ ____

24. $1 \times 4 = $ ____   25. $0 \times 6 = $ ____   26. $9 \times 1 = $ ____

27. $\begin{array}{r} 0 \\ \times 2 \\ \hline \end{array}$
28. $\begin{array}{r} 7 \\ \times 3 \\ \hline \end{array}$
29. $\begin{array}{r} 3 \\ \times 6 \\ \hline \end{array}$
30. $\begin{array}{r} 1 \\ \times 4 \\ \hline \end{array}$
31. $\begin{array}{r} 0 \\ \times 5 \\ \hline \end{array}$
32. $\begin{array}{r} 5 \\ \times 7 \\ \hline \end{array}$
33. $\begin{array}{r} 1 \\ \times 9 \\ \hline \end{array}$

34. 4
×9

35. 0
×1

36. 9
×3

37. 3
×6

38. 8
×5

39. 0
×3

40. 4
×2

41. 1
×8

42. 6
×5

43. 2
×8

44. 9
×4

45. 8
×4

46. 3
×1

47. 6
×0

48. 4
×0

49. 3
×7

50. 5
×5

51. 1
×6

52. 2
×9

53. 0
×7

54. 3
×5

Write > or <.

⋆ **55.** 5×3 ⬤ 4×2

⋆ **56.** 4×4 ⬤ 0×5

⋆ **57.** 2×8 ⬤ 7×3

⋆ **58.** 3×9 ⬤ 4×7

PROBLEM SOLVING • APPLICATIONS

59. There is 1 dog in each doghouse. There are 5 doghouses. How many dogs are there in all?

⋆ **60.** There are 0 dogs in each pen. There are 4 pens. How many dogs are there in all?

Midchapter Review

Multiply.

1. 5
×2

2. 3
×8

3. 4
×7

4. 2
×9

5. 6
×5

6. 4
×4

7. 9
×3

8. 7
×2

9. 3
×5

10. 6
×4

Multiplication in Any Order

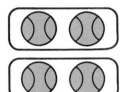 3 twos
$3 \times 2 = 6$

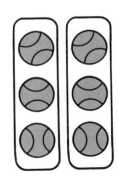 2 threes
$2 \times 3 = 6$

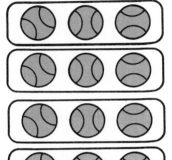 4 threes
$$\begin{array}{r} 4 \\ \times 3 \\ \hline 12 \end{array}$$

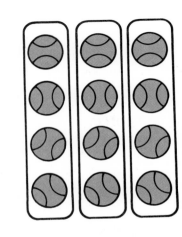 3 fours
$$\begin{array}{r} 3 \\ \times 4 \\ \hline 12 \end{array}$$

You can multiply two numbers in any order. The product is always the same.

Practice • Find the products.

1. $5 \times 2 = $ ____?____

    $2 \times 5 = $ ____?____

2. $1 \times 2 = $ ____?____

    $2 \times 1 = $ ____?____

3. $7 \times 3 = $ ____?____

    $3 \times 7 = $ ____?____

4. $\begin{array}{r} 4 \\ \times 2 \\ \hline \end{array}$ $\begin{array}{r} 2 \\ \times 4 \\ \hline \end{array}$

5. $\begin{array}{r} 1 \\ \times 3 \\ \hline \end{array}$ $\begin{array}{r} 3 \\ \times 1 \\ \hline \end{array}$

6. $\begin{array}{r} 3 \\ \times 4 \\ \hline \end{array}$ $\begin{array}{r} 4 \\ \times 3 \\ \hline \end{array}$

7. $\begin{array}{r} 6 \\ \times 2 \\ \hline \end{array}$ $\begin{array}{r} 2 \\ \times 6 \\ \hline \end{array}$

Mixed Practice • Find the products.

8. $5 \times 3 = $ ____?____

    $3 \times 5 = $ ____?____

9. $6 \times 2 = $ ____?____

    $2 \times 6 = $ ____?____

10. $9 \times 3 = $ ____?____

    $3 \times 9 = $ ____?____

11. $4 \times 2 = \underline{}$ 12. $0 \times 4 = \underline{}$ 13. $4 \times 3 = \underline{}$

$2 \times 4 = \underline{}$ $4 \times 0 = \underline{}$ $3 \times 4 = \underline{}$

14. $\begin{array}{r} 7 \\ \times 2 \\ \hline \end{array}$ $\begin{array}{r} 2 \\ \times 7 \\ \hline \end{array}$ 15. $\begin{array}{r} 1 \\ \times 8 \\ \hline \end{array}$ $\begin{array}{r} 8 \\ \times 1 \\ \hline \end{array}$ 16. $\begin{array}{r} 5 \\ \times 2 \\ \hline \end{array}$ $\begin{array}{r} 2 \\ \times 5 \\ \hline \end{array}$ 17. $\begin{array}{r} 0 \\ \times 6 \\ \hline \end{array}$ $\begin{array}{r} 6 \\ \times 0 \\ \hline \end{array}$

Find the products.

18. $\begin{array}{r} 9 \\ \times 3 \\ \hline \end{array}$ 19. $\begin{array}{r} 7 \\ \times 2 \\ \hline \end{array}$ 20. $\begin{array}{r} 8 \\ \times 2 \\ \hline \end{array}$ 21. $\begin{array}{r} 3 \\ \times 3 \\ \hline \end{array}$ 22. $\begin{array}{r} 9 \\ \times 2 \\ \hline \end{array}$ 23. $\begin{array}{r} 6 \\ \times 3 \\ \hline \end{array}$ 24. $\begin{array}{r} 5 \\ \times 3 \\ \hline \end{array}$

25. $\begin{array}{r} 1 \\ \times 2 \\ \hline \end{array}$ 26. $\begin{array}{r} 7 \\ \times 3 \\ \hline \end{array}$ 27. $\begin{array}{r} 3 \\ \times 6 \\ \hline \end{array}$ 28. $\begin{array}{r} 4 \\ \times 2 \\ \hline \end{array}$ 29. $\begin{array}{r} 2 \\ \times 8 \\ \hline \end{array}$ 30. $\begin{array}{r} 4 \\ \times 3 \\ \hline \end{array}$ 31. $\begin{array}{r} 4 \\ \times 4 \\ \hline \end{array}$

32. $\begin{array}{r} 8 \\ \times 3 \\ \hline \end{array}$ 33. $\begin{array}{r} 1 \\ \times 3 \\ \hline \end{array}$ 34. $\begin{array}{r} 2 \\ \times 9 \\ \hline \end{array}$ 35. $\begin{array}{r} 2 \\ \times 7 \\ \hline \end{array}$ 36. $\begin{array}{r} 3 \\ \times 5 \\ \hline \end{array}$ 37. $\begin{array}{r} 7 \\ \times 2 \\ \hline \end{array}$ 38. $\begin{array}{r} 5 \\ \times 0 \\ \hline \end{array}$

Find the missing factors.

★ 39. $1 \times 6 = 6$ ★ 40. $3 \times 2 = 6$ ★ 41. $9 \times 2 = 18$

$\underline{} \times 1 = 6$ $\underline{} \times 3 = 6$ $\underline{} \times 9 = 18$

PROBLEM SOLVING • APPLICATIONS

42. Daniel plays ball 2 hours a day. How many hours does he play in 6 days?

★ 43. Mindy skates 4 hours each week. How many hours does she skate in 3 weeks? in 5 weeks?

Skills Maintenance

1. $\begin{array}{r} 352 \\ +373 \\ \hline \end{array}$ 2. $\begin{array}{r} 481 \\ +783 \\ \hline \end{array}$ 3. $\begin{array}{r} 865 \\ +694 \\ \hline \end{array}$ 4. $\begin{array}{r} 881 \\ +51 \\ \hline \end{array}$ 5. $\begin{array}{r} 276 \\ +531 \\ \hline \end{array}$

6. $\begin{array}{r} 233 \\ +83 \\ \hline \end{array}$ 7. $\begin{array}{r} 747 \\ +281 \\ \hline \end{array}$ 8. $\begin{array}{r} 342 \\ +572 \\ \hline \end{array}$ 9. $\begin{array}{r} 85 \\ +521 \\ \hline \end{array}$ 10. $\begin{array}{r} 195 \\ +944 \\ \hline \end{array}$

PROBLEM SOLVING • STRATEGIES

Add or Multiply?

Addition and multiplication are operations that are used to join groups of objects to find out how many in all.
To know when to add or multiply, you must read the problem carefully. Look at the pictures, and read the problems below.

 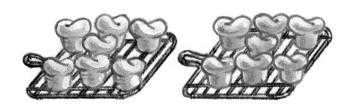

When the addends are different you add. When the addends are the same you can multiply.

One rack has 4 rolls. Another rack has 7 rolls. How many rolls are there in all?

Add to solve.

$$4 + 7 = 11$$

There are 11 rolls in all.

There are 4 racks. Each rack has 7 rolls. How many rolls are there in all?

Multiply to solve.

$$4 \times 7 = 28$$

There are 28 rolls in all.

How would you solve the problem? Write ADD or MULTIPLY.

1. A shelf has 3 loaves of whole wheat bread. Another shelf has 5 loaves. How many loaves are there in all?

Think about what is being asked.

152

2. There are 3 shelves. Each shelf has 5 loaves of bread. How many loaves are there in all?

3. There are 4 shelves of pies in the store. Each shelf has 6 pies. How many pies are there in all?

Solve.

4. There are 6 apple pies on a shelf. There are also 3 cream pies. How many pies are there?

In a multiplication problem, check your answer by adding.

---

5. Phil mixes the batter for 5 minutes. He does this twice. For how many minutes does he mix the batter?

6. Baking begins at 3 A.M. The store opens 6 hours later. When does the store open?

7. It takes 3 hours to make the bread each day. Jenny makes bread for 4 days. How much time does she spend?

8. Greta wraps 5 packages of bran rolls. She wraps 5 times as many corn rolls. How many packages of corn rolls does she wrap?

9. Paco whips cream with a mixer in 3 minutes. Carmen takes 2 times as long to do it by hand. How long does it take Carmen to whip cream?

10. Mr. Eagle bakes 2 pans of dinner rolls. Then he bakes 6 more pans. How many pans does he bake in all?

11. Jody uses 4 eggs in each bowl of muffin batter. She mixes 3 bowls of muffins. How many eggs does she mix?

★ 12. Gan sells 4 bran rolls and 5 wheat rolls. He also sells 5 rye rolls and 4 corn rolls. How many rolls does he sell in all?

★ 13. Ann makes 5 pans of rolls. She uses 1 stick of butter for each pan. How many sticks of butter does she use in all? If she uses 10 sticks of butter, how many pans of rolls does she make?

6 as a Factor

You know these facts.

$$\begin{array}{r} 6 \\ \times 0 \\ \hline 0 \end{array} \quad \begin{array}{r} 6 \\ \times 1 \\ \hline 6 \end{array} \quad \begin{array}{r} 6 \\ \times 2 \\ \hline 12 \end{array} \quad \begin{array}{r} 6 \\ \times 3 \\ \hline 18 \end{array} \quad \begin{array}{r} 6 \\ \times 4 \\ \hline 24 \end{array} \quad \begin{array}{r} 6 \\ \times 5 \\ \hline 30 \end{array}$$

These are new.

$$\begin{array}{r} 6 \\ \times 6 \\ \hline 36 \end{array} \quad \begin{array}{r} 6 \\ \times 7 \\ \hline 42 \end{array} \quad \begin{array}{r} 6 \\ \times 8 \\ \hline 48 \end{array} \quad \begin{array}{r} 6 \\ \times 9 \\ \hline 54 \end{array}$$

Practice ● Multiply.

1. $6 \times 3 =$ ____
2. $6 \times 6 =$ ____
3. $6 \times 1 =$ ____

4. $9 \times 6 =$ ____
5. $6 \times 4 =$ ____
6. $6 \times 5 =$ ____

7. $\begin{array}{r} 6 \\ \times 2 \\ \hline \end{array}$
8. $\begin{array}{r} 8 \\ \times 6 \\ \hline \end{array}$
9. $\begin{array}{r} 6 \\ \times 4 \\ \hline \end{array}$
10. $\begin{array}{r} 2 \\ \times 6 \\ \hline \end{array}$
11. $\begin{array}{r} 6 \\ \times 7 \\ \hline \end{array}$
12. $\begin{array}{r} 0 \\ \times 6 \\ \hline \end{array}$
13. $\begin{array}{r} 6 \\ \times 3 \\ \hline \end{array}$

Mixed Practice ● Multiply.

14. $5 \times 6 =$ ____
15. $6 \times 7 =$ ____
16. $6 \times 9 =$ ____

17. $2 \times 6 = $ _____   **18.** $6 \times 4 = $ _____   **19.** $6 \times 0 = $ _____

20. $6 \times 5 = $ _____   **21.** $0 \times 6 = $ _____   **22.** $5 \times 3 = $ _____

23. $\begin{array}{r} 6 \\ \times 2 \\ \hline \end{array}$
24. $\begin{array}{r} 2 \\ \times 6 \\ \hline \end{array}$
25. $\begin{array}{r} 6 \\ \times 5 \\ \hline \end{array}$
26. $\begin{array}{r} 5 \\ \times 6 \\ \hline \end{array}$
27. $\begin{array}{r} 5 \\ \times 8 \\ \hline \end{array}$
28. $\begin{array}{r} 6 \\ \times 1 \\ \hline \end{array}$
29. $\begin{array}{r} 5 \\ \times 4 \\ \hline \end{array}$

30. $\begin{array}{r} 3 \\ \times 8 \\ \hline \end{array}$
31. $\begin{array}{r} 7 \\ \times 6 \\ \hline \end{array}$
32. $\begin{array}{r} 6 \\ \times 6 \\ \hline \end{array}$
33. $\begin{array}{r} 8 \\ \times 4 \\ \hline \end{array}$
34. $\begin{array}{r} 4 \\ \times 3 \\ \hline \end{array}$
35. $\begin{array}{r} 4 \\ \times 6 \\ \hline \end{array}$
36. $\begin{array}{r} 3 \\ \times 6 \\ \hline \end{array}$

37. $\begin{array}{r} 3 \\ \times 9 \\ \hline \end{array}$
38. $\begin{array}{r} 1 \\ \times 6 \\ \hline \end{array}$
39. $\begin{array}{r} 6 \\ \times 8 \\ \hline \end{array}$
40. $\begin{array}{r} 3 \\ \times 4 \\ \hline \end{array}$
41. $\begin{array}{r} 3 \\ \times 6 \\ \hline \end{array}$
42. $\begin{array}{r} 6 \\ \times 6 \\ \hline \end{array}$
43. $\begin{array}{r} 6 \\ \times 4 \\ \hline \end{array}$

44. $\begin{array}{r} 8 \\ \times 6 \\ \hline \end{array}$
45. $\begin{array}{r} 6 \\ \times 3 \\ \hline \end{array}$
46. $\begin{array}{r} 6 \\ \times 7 \\ \hline \end{array}$
47. $\begin{array}{r} 5 \\ \times 9 \\ \hline \end{array}$
48. $\begin{array}{r} 6 \\ \times 9 \\ \hline \end{array}$
49. $\begin{array}{r} 9 \\ \times 6 \\ \hline \end{array}$
50. $\begin{array}{r} 0 \\ \times 5 \\ \hline \end{array}$

You can group factors in different ways.
The product is always the same.

$$(3 \times 2) \times 4 = ?$$
$$6 \quad \times 4 = 24$$

$$3 \times (2 \times 4) = ?$$
$$3 \times \quad 8 \quad = 24$$

Multiply.

★ **51.** $(2 \times 2) \times 3 = $ _____   ★ **52.** $2 \times (2 \times 3) = $ _____

★ **53.** $(5 \times 1) \times 4 = $ _____   ★ **54.** $5 \times (1 \times 4) = $ _____

PROBLEM SOLVING • APPLICATIONS

55. Mr. Bradshaw buys 4 cartons of juice. 6 cans of juice are in each carton. How many cans of juice does Mr. Bradshaw buy?

56. Mrs. Leonetti buys 7 packages of cheese. Each package has 6 slices. How many slices of cheese does Mrs. Leonetti buy?

★ **57.** What number is 8 times more than 2 times 3?

★ **58.** What number is 6 times more than 4 times 2?

7 as a Factor

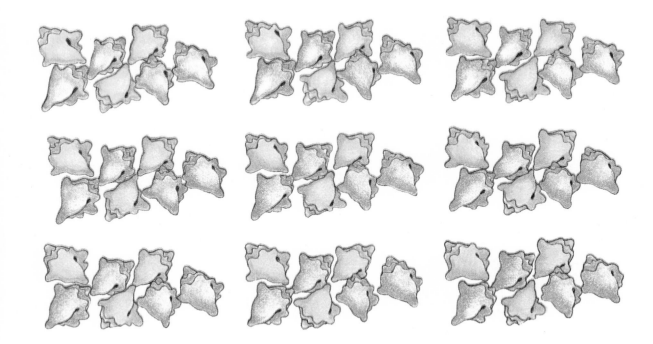

You know these facts.

$$\begin{array}{r}7\\ \times 0\\ \hline 0\end{array}\qquad\begin{array}{r}7\\ \times 1\\ \hline 7\end{array}\qquad\begin{array}{r}7\\ \times 2\\ \hline 14\end{array}\qquad\begin{array}{r}7\\ \times 3\\ \hline 21\end{array}\qquad\begin{array}{r}7\\ \times 4\\ \hline 28\end{array}\qquad\begin{array}{r}7\\ \times 5\\ \hline 35\end{array}\qquad\begin{array}{r}7\\ \times 6\\ \hline 42\end{array}$$

These are new.

$$\begin{array}{r}7\\ \times 7\\ \hline 49\end{array}\qquad\qquad\begin{array}{r}7\\ \times 8\\ \hline 56\end{array}\qquad\qquad\begin{array}{r}7\\ \times 9\\ \hline 63\end{array}$$

Practice ● Multiply.

1. $2 \times 7 = $ ____?____

2. $7 \times 8 = $ ____?____

3. $4 \times 7 = $ ____?____

4. $7 \times 6 = $ ____?____

5. $7 \times 0 = $ ____?____

6. $7 \times 3 = $ ____?____

7. $\begin{array}{r}1\\ \times 7\\ \hline\end{array}$
8. $\begin{array}{r}7\\ \times 3\\ \hline\end{array}$
9. $\begin{array}{r}7\\ \times 9\\ \hline\end{array}$
10. $\begin{array}{r}4\\ \times 7\\ \hline\end{array}$
11. $\begin{array}{r}5\\ \times 7\\ \hline\end{array}$
12. $\begin{array}{r}7\\ \times 6\\ \hline\end{array}$
13. $\begin{array}{r}7\\ \times 7\\ \hline\end{array}$

Mixed Practice • Multiply.

14. $1 \times 7 = $?

15. $5 \times 7 = $?

16. $7 \times 9 = $?

17. $7 \times 4 = $?

18. $6 \times 7 = $?

19. $0 \times 7 = $?

20. $2 \times 7 = $?

21. $7 \times 8 = $?

22. $7 \times 1 = $?

23. $\begin{array}{r} 7 \\ \times 2 \\ \hline \end{array}$
24. $\begin{array}{r} 2 \\ \times 7 \\ \hline \end{array}$
25. $\begin{array}{r} 7 \\ \times 5 \\ \hline \end{array}$
26. $\begin{array}{r} 5 \\ \times 7 \\ \hline \end{array}$
27. $\begin{array}{r} 7 \\ \times 7 \\ \hline \end{array}$
28. $\begin{array}{r} 7 \\ \times 0 \\ \hline \end{array}$
29. $\begin{array}{r} 7 \\ \times 9 \\ \hline \end{array}$

30. $\begin{array}{r} 1 \\ \times 8 \\ \hline \end{array}$
31. $\begin{array}{r} 7 \\ \times 4 \\ \hline \end{array}$
32. $\begin{array}{r} 7 \\ \times 1 \\ \hline \end{array}$
33. $\begin{array}{r} 6 \\ \times 6 \\ \hline \end{array}$
34. $\begin{array}{r} 7 \\ \times 8 \\ \hline \end{array}$
35. $\begin{array}{r} 3 \\ \times 7 \\ \hline \end{array}$
36. $\begin{array}{r} 0 \\ \times 5 \\ \hline \end{array}$

37. $\begin{array}{r} 6 \\ \times 9 \\ \hline \end{array}$
38. $\begin{array}{r} 7 \\ \times 9 \\ \hline \end{array}$
39. $\begin{array}{r} 4 \\ \times 9 \\ \hline \end{array}$
40. $\begin{array}{r} 6 \\ \times 7 \\ \hline \end{array}$
41. $\begin{array}{r} 1 \\ \times 7 \\ \hline \end{array}$
42. $\begin{array}{r} 3 \\ \times 3 \\ \hline \end{array}$
43. $\begin{array}{r} 3 \\ \times 8 \\ \hline \end{array}$

44. $\begin{array}{r} 7 \\ \times 3 \\ \hline \end{array}$
45. $\begin{array}{r} 6 \\ \times 8 \\ \hline \end{array}$
46. $\begin{array}{r} 8 \\ \times 7 \\ \hline \end{array}$
47. $\begin{array}{r} 4 \\ \times 7 \\ \hline \end{array}$
48. $\begin{array}{r} 1 \\ \times 9 \\ \hline \end{array}$
49. $\begin{array}{r} 0 \\ \times 9 \\ \hline \end{array}$
50. $\begin{array}{r} 7 \\ \times 6 \\ \hline \end{array}$

PROBLEM SOLVING • APPLICATIONS

★ 51. The puzzle has been done. Write the exercises.

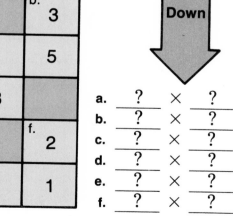

Across

a. 9×7

c. $? \times ?$

d. $? \times ?$

e. $? \times ?$

g. $? \times ?$

Down

a. $? \times ?$

b. $? \times ?$

c. $? \times ?$

d. $? \times ?$

e. $? \times ?$

f. $? \times ?$

52. There are 3 children. Each child finds 7 shells. How many shells are found in all?

53. Brian looked for starfish for 5 days. He found 7 starfish each day. How many starfish did he find in all?

8 and 9 as Factors

You know these facts.

8	8	8	8	8	8	8	8
×0	×1	×2	×3	×4	×5	×6	×7
0	8	16	24	32	40	48	56

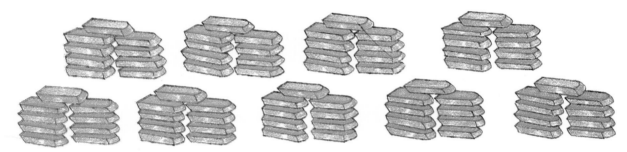

You know these facts also.

9	9	9	9	9	9	9	9
×0	×1	×2	×3	×4	×5	×6	×7
0	9	18	27	36	45	54	63

These are new.

$$\begin{array}{r} 8 \\ \times 8 \\ \hline 64 \end{array} \qquad \begin{array}{r} 8 \\ \times 9 \\ \hline 72 \end{array} \qquad \begin{array}{r} 9 \\ \times 9 \\ \hline 81 \end{array}$$

Practice • Multiply.

1. $8 \times 8 =$ ___?___

2. $8 \times 9 =$ ___?___

3. $9 \times 8 =$ ___?___

4. $8 \times 0 =$ ___?___

5. $0 \times 9 =$ ___?___

6. $2 \times 8 =$ ___?___

Mixed Practice • Multiply.

7. $0 \times 8 =$ ___?___

8. $1 \times 9 =$ ___?___

9. $4 \times 8 =$ ___?___

10. $9 \times 3 =$ ___?___   11. $1 \times 8 =$ ___?___   12. $7 \times 9 =$ ___?___

13. $4 \times 9 =$ ___?___   14. $6 \times 7 =$ ___?___   15. $8 \times 3 =$ ___?___

16. $7 \times 8 =$ ___?___   17. $2 \times 9 =$ ___?___   18. $9 \times 0 =$ ___?___

19. $\begin{array}{r} 8 \\ \times 8 \\ \hline \end{array}$	20. $\begin{array}{r} 9 \\ \times 2 \\ \hline \end{array}$	21. $\begin{array}{r} 8 \\ \times 3 \\ \hline \end{array}$	22. $\begin{array}{r} 9 \\ \times 8 \\ \hline \end{array}$	23. $\begin{array}{r} 8 \\ \times 7 \\ \hline \end{array}$	24. $\begin{array}{r} 7 \\ \times 7 \\ \hline \end{array}$	25. $\begin{array}{r} 8 \\ \times 6 \\ \hline \end{array}$
26. $\begin{array}{r} 5 \\ \times 7 \\ \hline \end{array}$	27. $\begin{array}{r} 8 \\ \times 5 \\ \hline \end{array}$	28. $\begin{array}{r} 9 \\ \times 9 \\ \hline \end{array}$	29. $\begin{array}{r} 8 \\ \times 1 \\ \hline \end{array}$	30. $\begin{array}{r} 7 \\ \times 4 \\ \hline \end{array}$	31. $\begin{array}{r} 9 \\ \times 3 \\ \hline \end{array}$	32. $\begin{array}{r} 6 \\ \times 9 \\ \hline \end{array}$
33. $\begin{array}{r} 5 \\ \times 9 \\ \hline \end{array}$	34. $\begin{array}{r} 9 \\ \times 1 \\ \hline \end{array}$	35. $\begin{array}{r} 6 \\ \times 3 \\ \hline \end{array}$	36. $\begin{array}{r} 5 \\ \times 8 \\ \hline \end{array}$	37. $\begin{array}{r} 4 \\ \times 9 \\ \hline \end{array}$	38. $\begin{array}{r} 5 \\ \times 0 \\ \hline \end{array}$	39. $\begin{array}{r} 3 \\ \times 4 \\ \hline \end{array}$
40. $\begin{array}{r} 9 \\ \times 6 \\ \hline \end{array}$	41. $\begin{array}{r} 7 \\ \times 6 \\ \hline \end{array}$	42. $\begin{array}{r} 4 \\ \times 8 \\ \hline \end{array}$	43. $\begin{array}{r} 7 \\ \times 8 \\ \hline \end{array}$	44. $\begin{array}{r} 2 \\ \times 8 \\ \hline \end{array}$	45. $\begin{array}{r} 4 \\ \times 9 \\ \hline \end{array}$	46. $\begin{array}{r} 6 \\ \times 8 \\ \hline \end{array}$

Find the missing factors.

⋆ 47. ___?___ $\times 9 = 63$ ⋆ 48. ___?___ $\times 8 = 48$

⋆ 49. $8 \times$ ___?___ $= 56$ ⋆ 50. $9 \times$ ___?___ $= 54$

PROBLEM SOLVING • APPLICATIONS

⋆ 51. Multiply.

The first product has 1 digit. All the rest have 2 digits each. Add the 2 digits in each product. What do you notice?

$\begin{array}{r} 9 \\ \times 1 \\ \hline \end{array}$	$\begin{array}{r} 9 \\ \times 2 \\ \hline \end{array}$	$\begin{array}{r} 9 \\ \times 3 \\ \hline \end{array}$	$\begin{array}{r} 9 \\ \times 4 \\ \hline \end{array}$	$\begin{array}{r} 9 \\ \times 5 \\ \hline \end{array}$	$\begin{array}{r} 9 \\ \times 6 \\ \hline \end{array}$	$\begin{array}{r} 9 \\ \times 7 \\ \hline \end{array}$	$\begin{array}{r} 9 \\ \times 8 \\ \hline \end{array}$	$\begin{array}{r} 9 \\ \times 9 \\ \hline \end{array}$

52. Laura has 6 packages of pencils. There are 8 pencils in each package. How many pencils does Laura have?

53. There are 4 packages of erasers. 9 erasers are in each package. How many erasers are there in all?

Multiplication Table

The factors are across the top and down the left side.
The table shows that 3 × 2 = 6.
It also shows that 6 × 7 = 42.

×	0	1	2	3	4	5	6	7	8	9
0										
1										
2										
3			6							
4										
5										
6								42		
7										
8										
9										

Practice ● Make your own multiplication chart.

Fill in all the products.

Mixed Practice ● Multiply.

1. $4 \times 8 =$ ___?___   2. $3 \times 8 =$ ___?___   3. $6 \times 2 =$ ___?___

4. $8 \times 7 =$ ___?___   5. $4 \times 3 =$ ___?___   6. $9 \times 4 =$ ___?___

7. $0 \times 7 =$ ___?___   8. $1 \times 3 =$ ___?___   9. $2 \times 7 =$ ___?___

10. $4 \times 9 =$ ___?___   11. $9 \times 8 =$ ___?___   12. $8 \times 6 =$ ___?___

13. $\begin{array}{r} 4 \\ \times 6 \\ \hline \end{array}$ 14. $\begin{array}{r} 0 \\ \times 8 \\ \hline \end{array}$ 15. $\begin{array}{r} 3 \\ \times 6 \\ \hline \end{array}$ 16. $\begin{array}{r} 4 \\ \times 4 \\ \hline \end{array}$ 17. $\begin{array}{r} 7 \\ \times 5 \\ \hline \end{array}$ 18. $\begin{array}{r} 2 \\ \times 2 \\ \hline \end{array}$ 19. $\begin{array}{r} 5 \\ \times 9 \\ \hline \end{array}$

20. $\begin{array}{r} 6 \\ \times 6 \\ \hline \end{array}$ 21. $\begin{array}{r} 6 \\ \times 4 \\ \hline \end{array}$ 22. $\begin{array}{r} 2 \\ \times 5 \\ \hline \end{array}$ 23. $\begin{array}{r} 4 \\ \times 8 \\ \hline \end{array}$ 24. $\begin{array}{r} 9 \\ \times 9 \\ \hline \end{array}$ 25. $\begin{array}{r} 4 \\ \times 5 \\ \hline \end{array}$ 26. $\begin{array}{r} 6 \\ \times 7 \\ \hline \end{array}$

27. $\begin{array}{r} 8 \\ \times 4 \\ \hline \end{array}$ 28. $\begin{array}{r} 7 \\ \times 6 \\ \hline \end{array}$ 29. $\begin{array}{r} 1 \\ \times 0 \\ \hline \end{array}$ 30. $\begin{array}{r} 3 \\ \times 3 \\ \hline \end{array}$ 31. $\begin{array}{r} 5 \\ \times 4 \\ \hline \end{array}$ 32. $\begin{array}{r} 7 \\ \times 8 \\ \hline \end{array}$ 33. $\begin{array}{r} 2 \\ \times 3 \\ \hline \end{array}$

34. $\begin{array}{r} 9 \\ \times 7 \\ \hline \end{array}$ 35. $\begin{array}{r} 2 \\ \times 8 \\ \hline \end{array}$ 36. $\begin{array}{r} 5 \\ \times 3 \\ \hline \end{array}$ 37. $\begin{array}{r} 6 \\ \times 9 \\ \hline \end{array}$ 38. $\begin{array}{r} 5 \\ \times 5 \\ \hline \end{array}$ 39. $\begin{array}{r} 7 \\ \times 4 \\ \hline \end{array}$ 40. $\begin{array}{r} 8 \\ \times 8 \\ \hline \end{array}$

PROBLEM SOLVING ● APPLICATIONS

Use your multiplication table.
Write as many facts as you can for each product.

41. 36 42. 20 43. 72 44. 16 45. 12 46. 24

Complete the sentences.

★ 47. $5 \times$ ___?___ $= 40$ ★ 48. $3 \times$ ___?___ $= 21$ ★ 49. $7 \times$ ___?___ $= 63$

★ 50. ___?___ $\times 2 = 8$ ★ 51. ___?___ $\times 1 = 6$ ★ 52. ___?___ $\times 6 = 36$

Multiplication Facts Drill

Multiply.

1. $\begin{array}{r} 2 \\ \times 2 \\ \hline \end{array}$
2. $\begin{array}{r} 7 \\ \times 5 \\ \hline \end{array}$
3. $\begin{array}{r} 0 \\ \times 1 \\ \hline \end{array}$
4. $\begin{array}{r} 5 \\ \times 9 \\ \hline \end{array}$
5. $\begin{array}{r} 1 \\ \times 6 \\ \hline \end{array}$
6. $\begin{array}{r} 3 \\ \times 2 \\ \hline \end{array}$

7. $\begin{array}{r} 1 \\ \times 8 \\ \hline \end{array}$
8. $\begin{array}{r} 9 \\ \times 5 \\ \hline \end{array}$
9. $\begin{array}{r} 6 \\ \times 6 \\ \hline \end{array}$
10. $\begin{array}{r} 1 \\ \times 2 \\ \hline \end{array}$
11. $\begin{array}{r} 6 \\ \times 4 \\ \hline \end{array}$
12. $\begin{array}{r} 2 \\ \times 5 \\ \hline \end{array}$

13. $\begin{array}{r} 4 \\ \times 1 \\ \hline \end{array}$
14. $\begin{array}{r} 4 \\ \times 8 \\ \hline \end{array}$
15. $\begin{array}{r} 9 \\ \times 1 \\ \hline \end{array}$
16. $\begin{array}{r} 5 \\ \times 7 \\ \hline \end{array}$
17. $\begin{array}{r} 0 \\ \times 4 \\ \hline \end{array}$
18. $\begin{array}{r} 9 \\ \times 9 \\ \hline \end{array}$

19. $\begin{array}{r} 4 \\ \times 5 \\ \hline \end{array}$
20. $\begin{array}{r} 2 \\ \times 0 \\ \hline \end{array}$
21. $\begin{array}{r} 6 \\ \times 7 \\ \hline \end{array}$
22. $\begin{array}{r} 8 \\ \times 4 \\ \hline \end{array}$
23. $\begin{array}{r} 1 \\ \times 4 \\ \hline \end{array}$
24. $\begin{array}{r} 7 \\ \times 6 \\ \hline \end{array}$

25. $\begin{array}{r} 1 \\ \times 0 \\ \hline \end{array}$
26. $\begin{array}{r} 3 \\ \times 3 \\ \hline \end{array}$
27. $\begin{array}{r} 5 \\ \times 2 \\ \hline \end{array}$
28. $\begin{array}{r} 3 \\ \times 9 \\ \hline \end{array}$
29. $\begin{array}{r} 7 \\ \times 3 \\ \hline \end{array}$
30. $\begin{array}{r} 7 \\ \times 8 \\ \hline \end{array}$

31. $\begin{array}{r} 2 \\ \times 3 \\ \hline \end{array}$
32. $\begin{array}{r} 8 \\ \times 0 \\ \hline \end{array}$
33. $\begin{array}{r} 7 \\ \times 7 \\ \hline \end{array}$
34. $\begin{array}{r} 0 \\ \times 3 \\ \hline \end{array}$
35. $\begin{array}{r} 9 \\ \times 6 \\ \hline \end{array}$
36. $\begin{array}{r} 5 \\ \times 4 \\ \hline \end{array}$

37. $\begin{array}{r} 1 \\ \times 1 \\ \hline \end{array}$
38. $\begin{array}{r} 9 \\ \times 0 \\ \hline \end{array}$
39. $\begin{array}{r} 2 \\ \times 1 \\ \hline \end{array}$
40. $\begin{array}{r} 6 \\ \times 5 \\ \hline \end{array}$
41. $\begin{array}{r} 9 \\ \times 7 \\ \hline \end{array}$
42. $\begin{array}{r} 2 \\ \times 8 \\ \hline \end{array}$

43. $\begin{array}{r} 5 \\ \times 0 \\ \hline \end{array}$
44. $\begin{array}{r} 3 \\ \times 5 \\ \hline \end{array}$
45. $\begin{array}{r} 8 \\ \times 1 \\ \hline \end{array}$
46. $\begin{array}{r} 0 \\ \times 2 \\ \hline \end{array}$
47. $\begin{array}{r} 6 \\ \times 9 \\ \hline \end{array}$
48. $\begin{array}{r} 2 \\ \times 6 \\ \hline \end{array}$

49. $\begin{array}{r} 0 \\ \times 9 \\ \hline \end{array}$
50. $\begin{array}{r} 3 \\ \times 0 \\ \hline \end{array}$
51. $\begin{array}{r} 7 \\ \times 2 \\ \hline \end{array}$
52. $\begin{array}{r} 4 \\ \times 3 \\ \hline \end{array}$
53. $\begin{array}{r} 0 \\ \times 6 \\ \hline \end{array}$
54. $\begin{array}{r} 4 \\ \times 7 \\ \hline \end{array}$

55. $\begin{array}{r} 8 \\ \times 2 \\ \hline \end{array}$
56. $\begin{array}{r} 5 \\ \times 8 \\ \hline \end{array}$
57. $\begin{array}{r} 5 \\ \times 5 \\ \hline \end{array}$
58. $\begin{array}{r} 7 \\ \times 4 \\ \hline \end{array}$
59. $\begin{array}{r} 3 \\ \times 1 \\ \hline \end{array}$
60. $\begin{array}{r} 7 \\ \times 9 \\ \hline \end{array}$

61. $\begin{array}{r} 8 \\ \times 6 \\ \hline \end{array}$
62. $\begin{array}{r} 5 \\ \times 3 \\ \hline \end{array}$
63. $\begin{array}{r} 4 \\ \times 0 \\ \hline \end{array}$
64. $\begin{array}{r} 1 \\ \times 9 \\ \hline \end{array}$
65. $\begin{array}{r} 4 \\ \times 2 \\ \hline \end{array}$
66. $\begin{array}{r} 8 \\ \times 8 \\ \hline \end{array}$

67. 8 ×5	68. 2 ×4	69. 1 ×7	70. 5 ×1	71. 9 ×3	72. 5 ×6
73. 4 ×8	74. 8 ×7	75. 0 ×7	76. 4 ×9	77. 8 ×3	78. 3 ×4
79. 1 ×3	80. 6 ×1	81. 9 ×8	82. 3 ×7	83. 6 ×2	84. 0 ×5
85. 7 ×0	86. 9 ×4	87. 2 ×7	88. 6 ×8	89. 4 ×6	90. 0 ×8
91. 2 ×9	92. 7 ×1	93. 3 ×6	94. 1 ×5	95. 6 ×3	96. 9 ×2
97. 3 ×8	98. 6 ×0	99. 4 ×4	100. 8 ×9		

PROBLEM SOLVING • APPLICATIONS

Each product stands for a letter. Find the products. Then solve the riddles.

9 ×9	6 ×2	7 ×9	9 2	9 ×8	8 ×5	4 ×2
A	B	C	D	E	F	G
6 ×8	8 ×2	7 ×5	6 ×6	9 ×5	1 ×1	5 ×4
H	I	J	K	L	M	N
8 ×8	9 ×6	6 ×4	8 ×7	7 ×2	6 ×7	9 ×1
O	P	Q	R	S	T	U
3 ×5	6 ×5	7 ×1	7 ×7	6 ×0		
V	W	X	Y	Z		

★101. How do you keep a rhinoceros from charging?

42–81–36–72   81–30–81–49

48–16–14   63–56–72–18–16–42

63–81–56–18

★102. What day of the year is an order to go forward?

1–81–56–63–48

40–64–9–56–42–48

★103. A night has a thousand eyes. What has a thousand ears?

81

63–64–56–20–40–16–72–45–18

163

PROBLEM SOLVING • STRATEGIES

Problems Without Numbers

You must read a problem carefully to know whether to add, subtract, or multiply. You can usually tell which operation to use by the question that is being asked.

Read the problems below. Which operation would you use to solve each problem?

Glen works in a shop. He helps some people. Then he helps more people. How many people does he help?

You can add.

Amy has some money. She buys a bird with part of the money. How much does she have left?

You can subtract.

Each cage has the same number of birds. There are many cages. How many birds are there in the pet shop?

You can multiply.

How would you solve? Write ADD, SUBTRACT, or MULTIPLY.

1. Katie has some money. She gets some more money. How much money does she have now?

Try each problem with numbers to check your answer.

2. The pet shop has some boxes of fish food on sale. All boxes cost the same. How much do all the boxes cost?

3. José bought a book. He gave the salesperson some money. How much change does he get?

Solve.

4. Rick spends $.89 for bird seed. He gives the salesperson $1.00. How much change does he get?

Decide which operation to use before you do the problem.

---

5. Pam buys a turtle for $.75 and a bowl for $.98. How much more did she pay for the bowl?

6. Leon sees 4 cages of birds. Each cage has 7 birds in it. How many birds does he see?

7. Dora buys a bell for $.15 and a toy bone for $.18. How much does she spend?

8. The pet shop has 6 dogs and 9 cats. How many pets in all?

9. 9 rabbit treats cost the same as 6 cat treats. How many more rabbit treats could you get?

10. Mrs. Choy wants a food dish that costs $3.98. She has $2.75. How much more money does she need?

★ 11. There are 3 tanks of goldfish and 2 tanks of angelfish. Each tank has 9 fish. How many fish are there in all?

★ 12. Lou buys 6 packages of dog treats and 4 packages of cat treats. Each package has 5 treats. How many treats does he buy in all?

REVIEW

Multiply. (pages 138–151, 154–159)

1. $4 \times 2 = $ ___?___   2. $7 \times 4 = $ ___?___   3. $7 \times 1 = $ ___?___

4. $4 \times 6 = $ ___?___   5. $5 \times 5 = $ ___?___   6. $8 \times 2 = $ ___?___

7. $3 \times 4 = $ ___?___   8. $9 \times 9 = $ ___?___   9. $6 \times 0 = $ ___?___

10. $7 \times 8 = $ ___?___   11. $3 \times 3 = $ ___?___   12. $5 \times 8 = $ ___?___

13. $2 \atop \underline{\times 6}$	14. $4 \atop \underline{\times 8}$	15. $4 \atop \underline{\times 4}$	16. $6 \atop \underline{\times 1}$	17. $0 \atop \underline{\times 8}$	18. $5 \atop \underline{\times 7}$
19. $3 \atop \underline{\times 4}$	20. $5 \atop \underline{\times 3}$	21. $0 \atop \underline{\times 1}$	22. $7 \atop \underline{\times 7}$	23. $6 \atop \underline{\times 5}$	24. $1 \atop \underline{\times 3}$
25. $2 \atop \underline{\times 2}$	26. $6 \atop \underline{\times 6}$	27. $6 \atop \underline{\times 7}$	28. $1 \atop \underline{\times 9}$	29. $9 \atop \underline{\times 3}$	30. $7 \atop \underline{\times 3}$
31. $8 \atop \underline{\times 6}$	32. $9 \atop \underline{\times 7}$	33. $3 \atop \underline{\times 8}$	34. $5 \atop \underline{\times 2}$	35. $4 \atop \underline{\times 5}$	36. $8 \atop \underline{\times 8}$

Solve.

37. Harry works 3 hours a day at the fair. How many hours does he work in 6 days? (p. 142)

38. Susan plays 4 games. She wins 2 prizes at each game. How many prizes does she win in all? (p. 144)

39. There are 5 booths at the fair. Each booth has 2 ticket sellers. How many ticket sellers are there in all? (p. 146)

40. There are 2 shelves. Each shelf has 7 prizes. How many prizes are there in all? (p. 156)

Pictographs

Pat's class made a **pictograph.**
It tells about books read in the class library last week.
It shows how many books of each kind were read.

More science books than mystery books were read.
Did the class read more mystery books or more adventure books?

Each ▢ stands for 2 books.
You count by twos to find out how many science books were read.
Six science books were read.
Ask 15 friends to tell you what kind of book they like the best.
Make a pictograph.
Let each ▢ stand for 1 book.

TEST

Multiply.

1. $5 \times 2 = \underline{}$ 2. $3 \times 2 = \underline{}$ 3. $8 \times 2 = \underline{}$

4. $7 \times 6 = \underline{}$ 5. $9 \times 6 = \underline{}$ 6. $7 \times 8 = \underline{}$

7. $9 \times 4 = \underline{}$ 8. $8 \times 9 = \underline{}$ 9. $4 \times 3 = \underline{}$

10. $8 \times 5 = \underline{}$ 11. $7 \times 7 = \underline{}$ 12. $5 \times 4 = \underline{}$

13. $\begin{array}{r} 6 \\ \times 3 \\ \hline \end{array}$ 14. $\begin{array}{r} 7 \\ \times 4 \\ \hline \end{array}$ 15. $\begin{array}{r} 2 \\ \times 6 \\ \hline \end{array}$ 16. $\begin{array}{r} 8 \\ \times 3 \\ \hline \end{array}$ 17. $\begin{array}{r} 5 \\ \times 7 \\ \hline \end{array}$ 18. $\begin{array}{r} 8 \\ \times 8 \\ \hline \end{array}$

19. $\begin{array}{r} 5 \\ \times 5 \\ \hline \end{array}$ 20. $\begin{array}{r} 1 \\ \times 0 \\ \hline \end{array}$ 21. $\begin{array}{r} 7 \\ \times 6 \\ \hline \end{array}$ 22. $\begin{array}{r} 4 \\ \times 2 \\ \hline \end{array}$ 23. $\begin{array}{r} 5 \\ \times 9 \\ \hline \end{array}$ 24. $\begin{array}{r} 2 \\ \times 9 \\ \hline \end{array}$

25. $\begin{array}{r} 4 \\ \times 9 \\ \hline \end{array}$ 26. $\begin{array}{r} 9 \\ \times 9 \\ \hline \end{array}$ 27. $\begin{array}{r} 0 \\ \times 3 \\ \hline \end{array}$ 28. $\begin{array}{r} 4 \\ \times 6 \\ \hline \end{array}$ 29. $\begin{array}{r} 1 \\ \times 1 \\ \hline \end{array}$ 30. $\begin{array}{r} 8 \\ \times 5 \\ \hline \end{array}$

31. $\begin{array}{r} 7 \\ \times 3 \\ \hline \end{array}$ 32. $\begin{array}{r} 8 \\ \times 6 \\ \hline \end{array}$ 33. $\begin{array}{r} 6 \\ \times 6 \\ \hline \end{array}$ 34. $\begin{array}{r} 1 \\ \times 7 \\ \hline \end{array}$ 35. $\begin{array}{r} 6 \\ \times 5 \\ \hline \end{array}$ 36. $\begin{array}{r} 4 \\ \times 8 \\ \hline \end{array}$

Solve.

37. Juanita plays ball 2 hours a day. How many hours does she play in 7 days?

38. There are 3 desks. Each desk has 4 books. How many books are there in all?

39. Dara fills 6 boxes with books. She puts 8 books in each box. How many books are there in all?

40. Larry has 7 packages of stamps. There are 9 stamps in each package. How many stamps does Larry have in all?

Intersections

In one town, 7 streets run north and south.
6 streets run east and west.
They cross at points called intersections.
How many intersections are there?

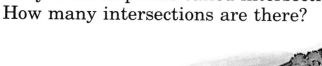

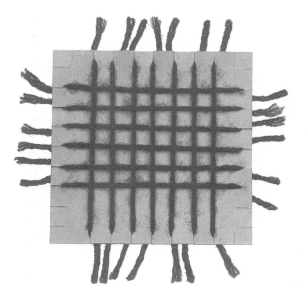

Make a model.

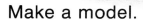

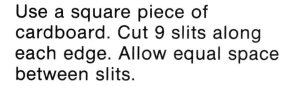

Use a square piece of cardboard. Cut 9 slits along each edge. Allow equal space between slits.

Fit yarn into the slits:
7 pieces one way for the streets that run north and south.
6 pieces the other way for the streets that run east and west.
There are 42 intersections.

Solve the problems. Use your model if you wish.

1. In Cartersburg, 9 streets run north and south.
   Only 8 streets run east and west.
   How many intersections does Cartersburg have?
   (Hint: Fit 9 pieces of yarn one way; 8 pieces the other way.)

2. In Maryville, they want one traffic light at each intersection.
   There are 5 streets that run north and south.
   Only 3 streets run east and west.
   How many traffic lights do they need?

3. Amityville wants 2 stop signs at each intersection.
   There are 3 streets that run north and south.
   There are 3 streets that run east and west.
   How many stop signs should they buy?

4. Jamestown wants a litter basket on each corner.
   There are 4 corners at each intersection.
   There are 3 streets that run north and south.
   There are 2 streets that run east and west.
   How many litter baskets should they buy?

CALCULATOR

Multiplication on a Calculator

You push the ⊗ command button to multiply on a calculator.

To multiply 5 × 4, push ⑤ ⊗ ④ ⊜ . Screen: *20.*

Use your calculator to multiply.

1. 8 × 5 = ___?___
2. 0 × 4 = ___?___
3. 3 × 8 = ___?___
4. 1 × 9 = ___?___
5. 7 × 2 = ___?___
6. 6 × 6 = ___?___

You can multiply more than two numbers.
Eileen has 4 wristwatches on each wrist. Each watch has an hour hand, a minute hand, and a second hand. How many watch hands does Eileen have?

4 wristwatches × 2 wrists = 8 wristwatches in all
8 wristwatches × 3 hands = 24 watch hands in all

On a calculator, push ④ ⊗ ② ⊗ ③ ⊜ . Screen: *24.*

Use your calculator to multiply.

7. 5 × 2 × 4 = ___?___
8. 3 × 4 × 5 = ___?___
9. 9 × 1 × 8 × 1 = ___?___
10. 6 × 0 × 9 × 2 = ___?___
11. 5 × 3 × 3 × 2 = ___?___
12. 8 × 2 × 2 × 3 = ___?___

13. A cat had 3 kittens. Each kitten had 4 paws. Each paw had 5 claws. How many claws were there?

14. Emma had 4 dolls. Each doll had 5 dresses. Each dress had 2 buttons. How many buttons were there?

15. As I was thinking up some tricks, I saw a hen with 7 chicks. And every chick had 7 sticks, and every stick had 7 nicks. Tricks, chicks, sticks, nicks, how many were thinking up some tricks?

16. Frank had 2 train sets. Each train had 4 cars. Each car carried 5 tigers. Each tiger had 4 paws. Each paw had no claws. How many claws were there?

Remember to turn the calculator off.

Choose the correct answers.

1. 8 + ___?___ = 15

A. 2
B. 7
C. 8
D. not here

2. Compare.

6,205 6,025

A. >
B. <
C. =
D. not here

3. Round 67 to the nearest ten.

A. 60
B. 70
C. 100
D. not here

4.
```
  41
+ 36
```

A. 5
B. 16
C. 77
D. not here

5.
```
  863
+ 289
```

A. 626
B. 1,052
C. 1,146
D. not here

6. $.48 + $.56 = ___?___

A. $.08
B. $1.04
C. $.94
D. not here

7.
```
  187
-  43
```

A. 44
B. 144
C. 121
D. not here

8.
```
  600
- 246
```

A. 264
B. 846
C. 354
D. not here

9.
```
   7
× 8
```

A. 63
B. 81
C. 64
D. not here

10. Bill has $2.75. He buys paints for $2.69. How much money does he have left?

A. $5.44
B. $3.15
C. $.06
D. not here

11. Carlos buys 8 packages of brushes. There are 3 brushes in each package. How many brushes does he buy in all?

A. 27
B. 24
C. 21
D. not here

Division Facts

Meaning of Division

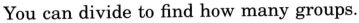

There are 12 bananas.
Put 3 in each group.
How many groups are there?

You can divide to find how many groups.

$$12 \div 3 = 4$$

divisor

quotient

dividend

Read. ⟶ 12 divided by 3 equals 4.

There are 4 groups of 3 in 12.

Practice ● Complete the sentences.

1.

How many groups of 2 are in 8?

$$8 \div 2 = \underline{\quad ? \quad}$$

2.

How many groups of 3 are in 9?

$$9 \div 3 = \underline{\quad ? \quad}$$

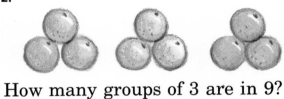

3.

How many groups of 5 are in 10?

$$10 \div 5 = \underline{\quad ? \quad}$$

4.

How many groups of 4 are in 12?

$$12 \div 4 = \underline{\quad ? \quad}$$

More Practice ● Complete the sentences.

5.

$$8 \div 4 = \underline{\quad ? \quad}$$

6.
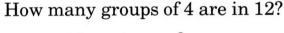 

$$12 \div 2 = \underline{\quad ? \quad}$$

7.

10 ÷ 2 = ___?___

8.

6 ÷ 3 = ___?___

9.

18 ÷ 3 = ___?___

10.

15 ÷ 5 = ___?___

PROBLEM SOLVING • APPLICATIONS

Write a division fact for each picture.

11.

12.

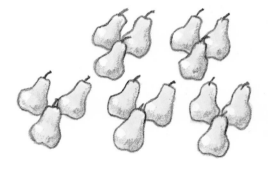

13.

14.

★ **15.** Draw 15 .

Show how many groups of 3 are in 15.

★ **16.** Draw 16 .

Show how many groups of 4 are in 16.

175

Dividing by 2

Mrs. Schwartz makes 12 muffins.
She puts 2 muffins in each bag.
How many bags are there?

You can divide to find how many
groups.

$$12 \div 2 = 6 \longleftarrow \text{Number of bags}$$

↑ Muffins
in all

↑ Muffins
in each bag

There are 6 bags.

You can use a multiplication
fact to find the quotient.

$$12 \div 2 = ?$$

Think: $? \times 2 = 12.$
Since $6 \times 2 = 12,$
then $12 \div 2 = 6.$

Practice • Find the quotients.

1.

$$14 \div 2 = \underline{\quad?\quad}$$

2.

$$8 \div 2 = \underline{\quad?\quad}$$

3. $6 \div 2 = \underline{\quad?\quad}$

4. $16 \div 2 = \underline{\quad?\quad}$

5. $2 \div 2 = \underline{\quad?\quad}$

6. $10 \div 2 = \underline{\quad?\quad}$

7. $4 \div 2 = \underline{\quad?\quad}$

8. $18 \div 2 = \underline{\quad?\quad}$

Mixed Practice ● Find the quotients.

9.

$10 \div 2 = \underline{\quad ? \quad}$

10.

$6 \div 2 = \underline{\quad ? \quad}$

11. $14 \div 2 = \underline{\quad ? \quad}$ **12.** $12 \div 2 = \underline{\quad ? \quad}$ **13.** $16 \div 2 = \underline{\quad ? \quad}$

14. $18 \div 2 = \underline{\quad ? \quad}$ **15.** $4 \div 2 = \underline{\quad ? \quad}$ **16.** $8 \div 2 = \underline{\quad ? \quad}$

17. $8 \div 2 = \underline{\quad ? \quad}$ **18.** $2 \div 2 = \underline{\quad ? \quad}$ **19.** $6 \div 2 = \underline{\quad ? \quad}$

How fast can you go?

★ **20.** Start at the left. Divide each number by 2.

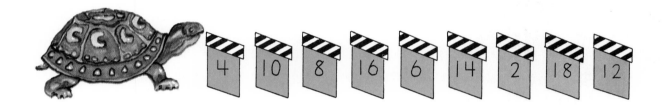

PROBLEM SOLVING ● APPLICATIONS

21. There are 16 slices of bread. We use 2 slices for each sandwich. How many sandwiches are there?

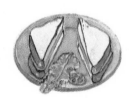

22. There are 18 pieces of fruit. Each child will get 2 pieces. How many children are there?

★ **23.** There are 8 red apples and 4 yellow apples. There are 2 apples in each bag. How many bags are there?

177

Dividing by 3

There are 12 rolls of wallpaper.
3 rolls are in each box.
How many boxes are there?

$12 \div 3 = ?$

$$12 \div 3 = ?$$

You can use a multiplication fact to find the quotient.

Think: $? \times 3 = 12.$
Since $4 \times 3 = 12,$
then $12 \div 3 = 4.$

There are 4 boxes.

Practice ● Find the quotients.

1.

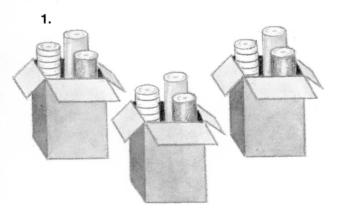

$$9 \div 3 = \underline{\ ?\ }$$

2.

$$18 \div 3 = \underline{\ ?\ }$$

3. $15 \div 3 = \underline{\ ?\ }$ **4.** $3 \div 3 = \underline{\ ?\ }$ **5.** $6 \div 3 = \underline{\ ?\ }$

6. $24 \div 3 = \underline{\ ?\ }$ **7.** $12 \div 3 = \underline{\ ?\ }$ **8.** $21 \div 3 = \underline{\ ?\ }$

Mixed Practice • Find the quotients.

9.

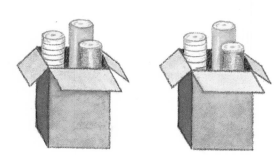

10.

$$6 \div 3 = \underline{\ ?\ }$$

$$15 \div 3 = \underline{\ ?\ }$$

11. $3 \div 3 = \underline{\ ?\ }$ **12.** $21 \div 3 = \underline{\ ?\ }$ **13.** $6 \div 2 = \underline{\ ?\ }$

14. $12 \div 2 = \underline{\ ?\ }$ **15.** $18 \div 3 = \underline{\ ?\ }$ **16.** $12 \div 3 = \underline{\ ?\ }$

17. $27 \div 3 = \underline{\ ?\ }$ **18.** $9 \div 3 = \underline{\ ?\ }$ **19.** $14 \div 2 = \underline{\ ?\ }$

20. $18 \div 2 = \underline{\ ?\ }$ **21.** $21 \div 3 = \underline{\ ?\ }$ **22.** $8 \div 2 = \underline{\ ?\ }$

23. $16 \div 2 = \underline{\ ?\ }$ **24.** $24 \div 3 = \underline{\ ?\ }$ **25.** $15 \div 3 = \underline{\ ?\ }$

Find the missing numbers.

★**26.** $27 \div 3 = \underline{\ ?\ } \div 3 = \underline{\ ?\ }$

★**27.** $12 \div 2 = \underline{\ ?\ } \div 3 = \underline{\ ?\ }$

PROBLEM SOLVING • APPLICATIONS

28. There are 18 rolls of wallpaper. There are 3 rolls in each box. How many boxes are there?

29. Miguel has 24 bags of paste. He puts 3 bags in each carton. How many cartons does he fill?

★**30.** Pauline has 10 rolls of blue wallpaper and 4 rolls of pink wallpaper. There are 2 rolls in each box. How many boxes are there?

★**31.** Wes has 18 rolls of yellow wallpaper, 3 rolls of red, and 6 rolls of orange wallpaper. He puts 3 rolls in each box. How many boxes are there?

Dividing by 4

Lita helps her father make
picnic tables and benches.
They have 20 table legs.
Each table needs 4 legs.
How many tables can they make?

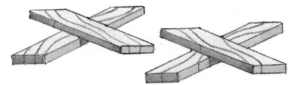
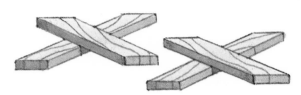

$20 \div 4 = ?$

You can use a multiplication
fact to find the quotient.

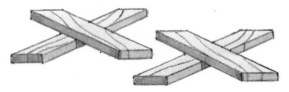

$$20 \div 4 = ?$$

Think: $? \times 4 = 20.$
Since $5 \times 4 = 20,$
then $20 \div 4 = 5.$

They can make 5 tables.

Practice • Find the quotients.

1.

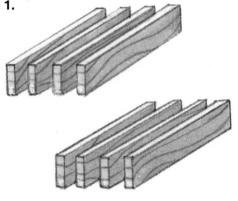

$8 \div 4 = \underline{\quad ? \quad}$

2.

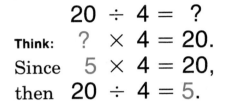

$24 \div 4 = \underline{\quad ? \quad}$

3. $16 \div 4 = \underline{\quad ? \quad}$ **4.** $32 \div 4 = \underline{\quad ? \quad}$ **5.** $20 \div 4 = \underline{\quad ? \quad}$

6. $4 \div 4 = \underline{\quad ? \quad}$ **7.** $36 \div 4 = \underline{\quad ? \quad}$ **8.** $12 \div 4 = \underline{\quad ? \quad}$

180

Mixed Practice ● Find the quotients.

9.

$$32 \div 4 = \underline{\quad ? \quad}$$

10.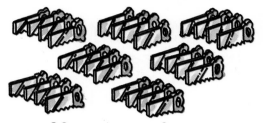

$$28 \div 4 = \underline{\quad ? \quad}$$

11. $36 \div 4 = \underline{\quad ? \quad}$ 12. $4 \div 4 = \underline{\quad ? \quad}$ 13. $20 \div 4 = \underline{\quad ? \quad}$

14. $12 \div 4 = \underline{\quad ? \quad}$ 15. $24 \div 4 = \underline{\quad ? \quad}$ 16. $32 \div 4 = \underline{\quad ? \quad}$

17. $8 \div 4 = \underline{\quad ? \quad}$ 18. $28 \div 4 = \underline{\quad ? \quad}$ 19. $16 \div 4 = \underline{\quad ? \quad}$

20. $18 \div 3 = \underline{\quad ? \quad}$ 21. $12 \div 4 = \underline{\quad ? \quad}$ 22. $24 \div 4 = \underline{\quad ? \quad}$

23. $16 \div 4 = \underline{\quad ? \quad}$ 24. $10 \div 2 = \underline{\quad ? \quad}$ 25. $4 \div 4 = \underline{\quad ? \quad}$

26. $18 \div 2 = \underline{\quad ? \quad}$ 27. $8 \div 4 = \underline{\quad ? \quad}$ 28. $12 \div 3 = \underline{\quad ? \quad}$

29. $20 \div 4 = \underline{\quad ? \quad}$ 30. $27 \div 3 = \underline{\quad ? \quad}$ 31. $28 \div 4 = \underline{\quad ? \quad}$

32. $36 \div 4 = \underline{\quad ? \quad}$ 33. $32 \div 4 = \underline{\quad ? \quad}$ 34. $16 \div 2 = \underline{\quad ? \quad}$

Make a practice bar.

| $4 \div 4 = 1$ |
| $8 \div 4 = 2$ |
| $12 \div 4 = 3$ |
| $16 \div 4 = 4$ |
| $20 \div 4 = 5$ |
| $24 \div 4 = 6$ |
| $28 \div 4 = 7$ |
| $32 \div 4 = 8$ |
| $36 \div 4 = 9$ |

Make a card like this.

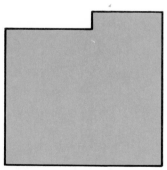

Make a card like this.

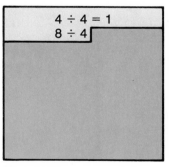

$4 \div 4 = 1$
$8 \div 4$

Put them together. Practice your facts.

PROBLEM SOLVING ● APPLICATIONS

35. I see 12 people sitting on benches. There are 4 people on each bench. How many benches are there?

★ 36. Divide a number by 4. Add 3 to get 9. What is the number?

Dividing by 5

There are 15 children
playing basketball.
5 children are on each team.
How many teams are there?

$15 \div 5 = ?$

You can use a multiplication
fact to find the quotient.

$$15 \div 5 = ?$$

Think: $\quad ? \times 5 = 15.$

Since $\quad 3 \times 5 = 15,$

There are 3 teams. $\qquad$ then $\quad 15 \div 5 = 3.$

Practice • Find the quotients.

1.

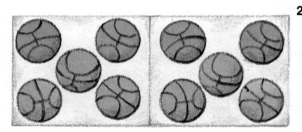

$10 \div 5 = \underline{\quad?\quad}$

2.

$25 \div 5 = \underline{\quad?\quad}$

3. $35 \div 5 = \underline{\quad?\quad}$ **4.** $30 \div 5 = \underline{\quad?\quad}$ **5.** $45 \div 5 = \underline{\quad?\quad}$

6. $20 \div 5 = \underline{\quad?\quad}$ **7.** $5 \div 5 = \underline{\quad?\quad}$ **8.** $40 \div 5 = \underline{\quad?\quad}$

Mixed Practice • Find the quotients.

9.

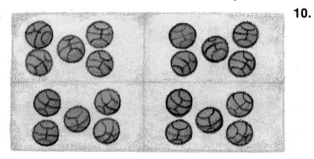

$20 \div 5 = \underline{\quad?\quad}$

10.

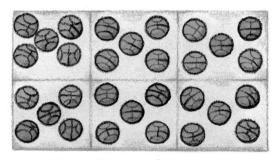

$30 \div 5 = \underline{\quad?\quad}$

11. $35 \div 5 =$ ___?___   12. $5 \div 5 =$ ___?___   13. $40 \div 5 =$ ___?___

14. $15 \div 5 =$ ___?___   15. $45 \div 5 =$ ___?___   16. $20 \div 5 =$ ___?___

17. $25 \div 5 =$ ___?___   18. $10 \div 5 =$ ___?___   19. $30 \div 5 =$ ___?___

20. $40 \div 5 =$ ___?___   21. $16 \div 4 =$ ___?___   22. $25 \div 5 =$ ___?___

23. $5 \div 5 =$ ___?___   24. $12 \div 2 =$ ___?___   25. $45 \div 5 =$ ___?___

26. $15 \div 3 =$ ___?___   27. $20 \div 5 =$ ___?___   28. $32 \div 4 =$ ___?___

Find the missing numbers.

★ 29.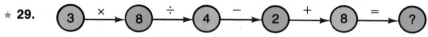

★ 30.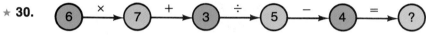

PROBLEM SOLVING • APPLICATIONS

31. There are 30 children playing basketball. 5 children are on each team. How many teams are there?

★ 32. Room A has 20 children. Room B has 20 children. They are all playing basketball. If there are 5 on a team, how many teams are there?

Skills Maintenance

1. $\begin{array}{r} 5 \\ \times 3 \\ \hline \end{array}$ 2. $\begin{array}{r} 8 \\ \times 2 \\ \hline \end{array}$ 3. $\begin{array}{r} 2 \\ \times 7 \\ \hline \end{array}$ 4. $\begin{array}{r} 9 \\ \times 3 \\ \hline \end{array}$ 5. $\begin{array}{r} 4 \\ \times 8 \\ \hline \end{array}$ 6. $\begin{array}{r} 5 \\ \times 5 \\ \hline \end{array}$

7. $\begin{array}{r} 0 \\ \times 4 \\ \hline \end{array}$ 8. $\begin{array}{r} 6 \\ \times 3 \\ \hline \end{array}$ 9. $\begin{array}{r} 5 \\ \times 8 \\ \hline \end{array}$ 10. $\begin{array}{r} 9 \\ \times 1 \\ \hline \end{array}$ 11. $\begin{array}{r} 7 \\ \times 5 \\ \hline \end{array}$ 12. $\begin{array}{r} 3 \\ \times 4 \\ \hline \end{array}$

PROBLEM SOLVING • STRATEGIES

Two Uses of Division

Two uses of division are $\begin{cases} \text{to find how many groups there are.} \\ \text{to find how many are in each group.} \end{cases}$

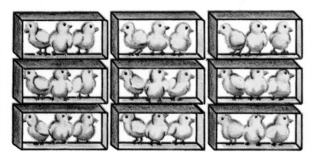

Read each problem.

There are 27 birds at the zoo. 3 birds are in each cage. How many cages are there?

Divide to find how many groups.

$$27 \div 3 = \quad ?$$
$$27 \div 3 = \quad 9$$

There are 9 cages.

Al sees 27 snakes at the zoo. The snakes are in 3 cages. Each cage has the same number of snakes. How many snakes are in each cage?

Divide to find how many are in each group.

$$27 \div 3 = \quad ?$$
$$27 \div 3 = \quad 9$$

There are 9 snakes in each cage.

Can you use division to solve the problem? Write YES or NO.

1. Rex watches 12 lions. There are 4 lions in each den. How many dens of lions are there?

Read the problem carefully.

2. Freda sees 4 bears. Each bear has 2 cubs. How many bears are there in all?

3. Helen sees 9 tigers. The tigers are in 3 cages. Each cage has the same number of tigers. How many tigers are in each cage?

Solve.

4. Mike sees 20 ponies at the pony ride. The ponies are in 5 equal groups. How many ponies are in each group?

Use multiplication to check your answers.

---

5. Yani counts 16 deer. The deer are in 4 groups, with the same number in each group. How many deer are in each group?

6. There are 6 elephants in the zoo. Together they eat 18 bales of hay a day. How many bales of hay does each elephant get?

7. A zoo keeper feeds 10 fish to 2 sea lions. Each sea lion gets the same number. How many fish does each sea lion get?

8. Ramon sees 30 monkeys. There are 5 monkeys in each cage. How many cages of monkeys are there?

9. The zoo sells packages of crackers to feed the animals. There are 25 crackers in a box. The crackers are divided equally into 5 packages. How many crackers are in each package?

10. The zoo has 15 camels. There are 3 camels in each pen. How many pens are there?

★ 11. Fernando has 8 crackers in one bag and 6 crackers in another bag. He feeds the same number of crackers to each of 2 lambs. How many crackers does each lamb get?

★ 12. On Monday 11 snakes were born. On Tuesday 10 more snakes were born. The snake keeper put 3 snakes in each nursery pen. How many pens are there in all?

Another Way to Show Division

Roy is building model planes.
He has 20 buttons to use for wheels.
He uses 4 buttons for each plane.
How many planes can he build?

Division can be shown in two ways.

$$20 \div 4 = 5$$

quotient — divisor — dividend

$$4)\overline{20} \quad 5$$

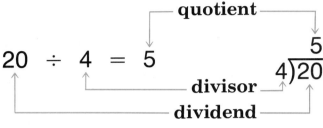

Roy can build 5 planes.

More Examples

$$28 \div 4 = 7 \qquad 27 \div 3 = 9 \qquad 40 \div 5 = 8$$

$$4)\overline{28} \quad 7 \qquad 3)\overline{27} \quad 9 \qquad 5)\overline{40} \quad 8$$

Practice • Find the quotients.

1. $3)\overline{24}$ 2. $5)\overline{10}$ 3. $4)\overline{12}$ 4. $3)\overline{18}$ 5. $2)\overline{16}$ 6. $5)\overline{40}$

7. $2)\overline{10}$ 8. $4)\overline{32}$ 9. $3)\overline{15}$ 10. $5)\overline{15}$ 11. $2)\overline{6}$ 12. $4)\overline{16}$

More Practice • Find the quotients.

13. $3)\overline{21}$ 14. $5)\overline{30}$ 15. $4)\overline{20}$ 16. $3)\overline{27}$ 17. $5)\overline{20}$ 18. $4)\overline{4}$

19. $3)\overline{3}$ 20. $4)\overline{12}$ 21. $3)\overline{27}$ 22. $3)\overline{6}$ 23. $4)\overline{16}$ 24. $2)\overline{14}$

25. $4\overline{)8}$ 26. $4\overline{)28}$ 27. $5\overline{)5}$ 28. $3\overline{)12}$ 29. $3\overline{)24}$ 30. $5\overline{)35}$

31. $4\overline{)36}$ 32. $2\overline{)18}$ 33. $4\overline{)4}$ 34. $3\overline{)15}$ 35. $4\overline{)20}$ 36. $5\overline{)25}$

37. $5\overline{)45}$ 38. $4\overline{)28}$ 39. $3\overline{)27}$ 40. $3\overline{)3}$ 41. $4\overline{)24}$ 42. $3\overline{)9}$

43. $4\overline{)24}$ 44. $3\overline{)18}$ 45. $3\overline{)21}$ 46. $5\overline{)40}$ 47. $4\overline{)32}$ 48. $2\overline{)12}$

★ 49. Find the missing numbers.

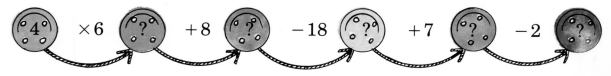

4 ×6 ? +8 ? −18 ? +7 ? −2 ?

PROBLEM SOLVING • APPLICATIONS

50. Kathy has 40 corks. She uses 5 corks to make each cork bird. How many cork birds can she make?

★ 51. You need 5 spools to make a spool doll. How many spool dolls can be made with 35 spools? with 40 spools?

Midchapter Review

Find the quotients.

1. $16 \div 2 = \underline{\quad?\quad}$ 2. $12 \div 4 = \underline{\quad?\quad}$ 3. $18 \div 3 = \underline{\quad?\quad}$

4. $20 \div 5 = \underline{\quad?\quad}$ 5. $24 \div 3 = \underline{\quad?\quad}$ 6. $25 \div 5 = \underline{\quad?\quad}$

7. $4\overline{)28}$ 8. $5\overline{)45}$ 9. $2\overline{)10}$ 10. $5\overline{)35}$ 11. $4\overline{)36}$ 12. $3\overline{)27}$

Dividing by 6

There are 42 people riding the Tilt-and-Turn. 6 people are in each car. How many cars are there?

$42 \div 6 = ?$

You can use a multiplication fact to find the quotient.

$$42 \div 6 = ? \quad\longrightarrow\quad 6\overline{)42}^{\,?}$$

Think: $? \times 6 = 42.$

Since $7 \times 6 = 42,$

then $42 \div 6 = 7. \quad\longrightarrow\quad 6\overline{)42}^{\,7}$

There are 7 cars.

Practice • Complete.

1. $12 \div 6 = \underline{\ ?\ }$
   Think: $\underline{\ ?\ } \times 6 = 12$

2. $30 \div 6 = \underline{\ ?\ }$
   Think: $\underline{\ ?\ } \times 6 = 30$

3. $42 \div 6 = \underline{\ ?\ }$
   Think: $\underline{\ ?\ } \times 6 = 42$

4. $36 \div 6 = \underline{\ ?\ }$
   Think: $\underline{\ ?\ } \times 6 = 36$

5. $18 \div 6 = \underline{\ ?\ }$
   Think: $\underline{\ ?\ } \times 6 = 18$

6. $24 \div 6 = \underline{\ ?\ }$
   Think: $\underline{\ ?\ } \times 6 = 24$

Divide.

7. $6\overline{)18}$ 8. $6\overline{)36}$ 9. $6\overline{)48}$ 10. $6\overline{)24}$ 11. $6\overline{)54}$ 12. $6\overline{)6}$

Mixed Practice ● Divide.

13. $18 \div 6 = $ __?__   14. $36 \div 6 = $ __?__   15. $48 \div 6 = $ __?__

16. $42 \div 6 = $ __?__   17. $6 \div 6 = $ __?__   18. $24 \div 6 = $ __?__

19. $12 \div 6 = $ __?__   20. $54 \div 6 = $ __?__   21. $30 \div 6 = $ __?__

22. $6\overline{)24}$ 23. $6\overline{)54}$ 24. $6\overline{)48}$ 25. $6\overline{)36}$ 26. $6\overline{)12}$ 27. $6\overline{)42}$

28. $6\overline{)6}$ 29. $6\overline{)30}$ 30. $4\overline{)16}$ 31. $4\overline{)24}$ 32. $5\overline{)35}$ 33. $6\overline{)18}$

34. $4\overline{)36}$ 35. $6\overline{)54}$ 36. $6\overline{)12}$ 37. $6\overline{)30}$ 38. $6\overline{)42}$ 39. $3\overline{)12}$

40. $6\overline{)18}$ 41. $5\overline{)30}$ 42. $4\overline{)20}$ 43. $6\overline{)36}$ 44. $6\overline{)6}$ 45. $6\overline{)24}$

PROBLEM SOLVING ● APPLICATIONS

Use the numbers in the INPUT column. Follow the rule.
List the OUTPUTS.

★ 46. Divide by 6.

INPUT	OUTPUT
18	3
42	?
6	?
24	?

★ 47. Divide by 5.

INPUT	OUTPUT
20	4
45	?
25	?
30	?

★ 48. Divide by 6.

INPUT	OUTPUT
48	8
30	?
12	?
54	?

49. Max has 36 balloons. He ties them into bunches of 6. How many bunches of balloons does he have?

50. At the park are 30 members of the Youth Club. Each car brought 6 people. How many cars are there?

Dividing by 7

Steve is making a clown costume.
He needs 35 bells.
There are 7 bells on a card.
How many cards of bells does he need?

$$35 \div 7 = ?$$

You can use a multiplication fact
to find the quotient.

$$35 \div 7 = ? \longrightarrow 7\overline{)35}^{?}$$

Think: $? \times 7 = 35.$

Since $5 \times 7 = 35,$

then $35 \div 7 = 5. \longrightarrow 7\overline{)35}^{5}$

Steve needs 5 cards of bells.

Practice ● Complete.

1. $56 \div 7 = \underline{\quad?\quad}$
   Think: $\underline{\quad?\quad} \times 7 = 56$

2. $21 \div 7 = \underline{\quad?\quad}$
   Think: $\underline{\quad?\quad} \times 7 = 21$

3. $42 \div 7 = \underline{\quad?\quad}$
   Think: $\underline{\quad?\quad} \times 7 = 42$

4. $28 \div 7 = \underline{\quad?\quad}$
   Think: $\underline{\quad?\quad} \times 7 = 28$

5. $49 \div 7 = \underline{\quad?\quad}$
   Think: $\underline{\quad?\quad} \times 7 = 49$

6. $14 \div 7 = \underline{\quad?\quad}$
   Think: $\underline{\quad?\quad} \times 7 = 14$

Divide.

7. $7\overline{)42}$ 8. $7\overline{)56}$ 9. $7\overline{)7}$ 10. $7\overline{)35}$ 11. $7\overline{)63}$ 12. $7\overline{)21}$

Mixed Practice ● Divide.

13. $21 \div 7 = \underline{\quad?\quad}$ 14. $14 \div 7 = \underline{\quad?\quad}$ 15. $28 \div 7 = \underline{\quad?\quad}$

16. $35 \div 7 = \underline{\quad?\quad}$ 17. $56 \div 7 = \underline{\quad?\quad}$ 18. $42 \div 7 = \underline{\quad?\quad}$

19. $63 \div 7 = \underline{\quad?\quad}$ 20. $7 \div 7 = \underline{\quad?\quad}$ 21. $49 \div 7 = \underline{\quad?\quad}$

22. $7\overline{)28}$ 23. $7\overline{)49}$ 24. $7\overline{)63}$ 25. $7\overline{)21}$ 26. $7\overline{)42}$ 27. $7\overline{)14}$

28. $7\overline{)7}$ **29.** $3\overline{)27}$ **30.** $7\overline{)35}$ **31.** $6\overline{)48}$ **32.** $7\overline{)56}$ **33.** $7\overline{)28}$

34. $7\overline{)14}$ **35.** $7\overline{)49}$ **36.** $5\overline{)45}$ **37.** $7\overline{)56}$ **38.** $4\overline{)36}$ **39.** $7\overline{)63}$

40. $7\overline{)21}$ **41.** $3\overline{)21}$ **42.** $7\overline{)42}$ **43.** $7\overline{)7}$ **44.** $6\overline{)54}$ **45.** $7\overline{)35}$

When any number is divided by 1, the quotient is that number.

$$1\overline{)6}^{6}$$

46. $1\overline{)8}$ **47.** $1\overline{)4}$ **48.** $1\overline{)7}$ **49.** $1\overline{)3}$ **50.** $1\overline{)5}$ **51.** $1\overline{)9}$

52. $2 \div 1 = \underline{}$ **53.** $6 \div 1 = \underline{}$ **54.** $5 \div 1 = \underline{}$

PROBLEM SOLVING • APPLICATIONS

55. Steve makes a paper-bag mask. He uses 42 paper curls for hair. He uses a different color for every 7 curls. How many colors does he use?

56. There are 56 people at Steve's backyard circus. 7 people sit on each bench. How many benches are there?

★57. Divide a number by 7. Add 5 to get 14. What is the number?

★58. Divide a number by 6. Add 7 to get 15. What is the number?

Dividing by 8

Mr. Jones has 24 bricks.
He uses 8 bricks to make each
pattern block.
How many pattern blocks
can Mr. Jones make?

$24 \div 8 = ?$

You can use a multiplication
fact to find the quotient.

$$24 \div 8 = ? \longrightarrow 8\overline{)24}^{?}$$

Think:
Since
then

$$? \times 8 = 24.$$
$$3 \times 8 = 24,$$
$$24 \div 8 = 3. \longrightarrow 8\overline{)24}^{3}$$

Mr. Jones can make 3 pattern blocks.

Practice • Complete.

1. $40 \div 8 = \underline{\quad?\quad}$
Think: $\underline{\quad?\quad} \times 8 = 40$

2. $64 \div 8 = \underline{\quad?\quad}$
Think: $\underline{\quad?\quad} \times 8 = 64$

3. $24 \div 8 = \underline{\quad?\quad}$
Think: $\underline{\quad?\quad} \times 8 = 24$

4. $16 \div 8 = \underline{\quad?\quad}$
Think: $\underline{\quad?\quad} \times 8 = 16$

5. $32 \div 8 = \underline{\quad?\quad}$
Think: $\underline{\quad?\quad} \times 8 = 32$

6. $48 \div 8 = \underline{\quad?\quad}$
Think: $\underline{\quad?\quad} \times 8 = 48$

Divide.

7. $8\overline{)24}$
8. $8\overline{)56}$
9. $8\overline{)72}$
10. $8\overline{)40}$
11. $8\overline{)8}$
12. $8\overline{)64}$

Mixed Practice • Divide.

13. $48 \div 8 = \underline{\quad?\quad}$
14. $24 \div 8 = \underline{\quad?\quad}$
15. $72 \div 8 = \underline{\quad?\quad}$

16. $8 \div 8 = \underline{\quad?\quad}$
17. $32 \div 8 = \underline{\quad?\quad}$
18. $56 \div 8 = \underline{\quad?\quad}$

19. $64 \div 8 = \underline{\quad?\quad}$
20. $16 \div 8 = \underline{\quad?\quad}$
21. $40 \div 8 = \underline{\quad?\quad}$

22. $8\overline{)16}$ **23.** $8\overline{)64}$ **24.** $8\overline{)32}$ **25.** $8\overline{)56}$ **26.** $8\overline{)72}$ **27.** $8\overline{)24}$

28. $8\overline{)8}$ **29.** $3\overline{)24}$ **30.** $8\overline{)16}$ **31.** $8\overline{)64}$ **32.** $6\overline{)54}$ **33.** $8\overline{)40}$

34. $6\overline{)36}$ **35.** $8\overline{)48}$ **36.** $7\overline{)42}$ **37.** $8\overline{)56}$ **38.** $8\overline{)32}$ **39.** $8\overline{)72}$

40. $8\overline{)40}$ **41.** $4\overline{)32}$ **42.** $8\overline{)8}$ **43.** $8\overline{)24}$ **44.** $6\overline{)18}$ **45.** $8\overline{)48}$

PROBLEM SOLVING • APPLICATIONS

★ **46.** Solve the puzzle. Find the missing dividends.

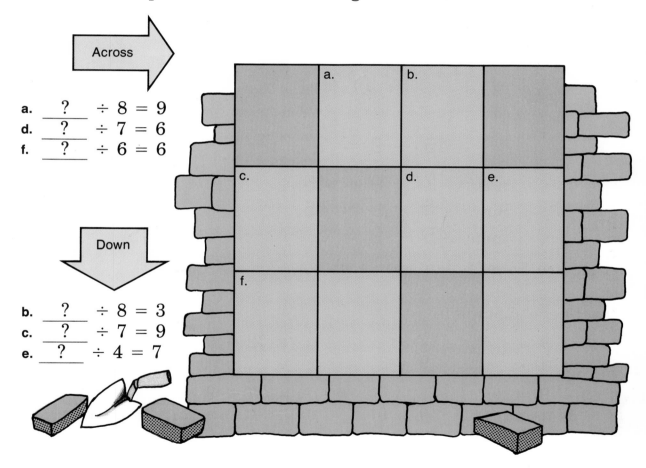

Across

a. $\underline{\quad ? \quad} \div 8 = 9$
d. $\underline{\quad ? \quad} \div 7 = 6$
f. $\underline{\quad ? \quad} \div 6 = 6$

Down

b. $\underline{\quad ? \quad} \div 8 = 3$
c. $\underline{\quad ? \quad} \div 7 = 9$
e. $\underline{\quad ? \quad} \div 4 = 7$

47. There are 56 bricks. 8 bricks are in each pile. How many piles are there?

48. Deacon has 40 bricks to take to his father. He takes 8 bricks at a time in his wagon. How many trips does he make?

Dividing by 9

The students in Mrs. Sherman's room plant 45 bean seeds. They plant 9 rows of seeds. Each row has the same number of seeds. How many seeds are planted in each row?

$45 \div 9 = ?$

You can use a multiplication fact to find the quotient.

$$45 \div 9 = ? \longrightarrow 9\overline{)45}^{?}$$

Think: $? \times 9 = 45.$
Since $5 \times 9 = 45,$
then $45 \div 9 = 5.$ $\longrightarrow 9\overline{)45}^{5}$

There are 5 seeds planted in each row.

Practice • Complete.

1. $36 \div 9 = \underline{}$
   Think: $\underline{} \times 9 = 36$

2. $72 \div 9 = \underline{}$
   Think: $\underline{} \times 9 = 72$

3. $9 \div 9 = \underline{}$
   Think: $\underline{} \times 9 = 9$

4. $27 \div 9 = \underline{}$
   Think: $\underline{} \times 9 = 27$

5. $45 \div 9 = \underline{}$
   Think: $\underline{} \times 9 = 45$

6. $54 \div 9 = \underline{}$
   Think: $\underline{} \times 9 = 54$

Divide.

7. $9\overline{)18}$ 8. $9\overline{)63}$ 9. $9\overline{)81}$ 10. $9\overline{)9}$ 11. $9\overline{)36}$ 12. $9\overline{)27}$

Mixed Practice • Divide.

13. $18 \div 9 =$ ___?___   14. $45 \div 9 =$ ___?___   15. $81 \div 9 =$ ___?___

16. $27 \div 9 =$ ___?___   17. $9 \div 9 =$ ___?___   18. $63 \div 9 =$ ___?___

19. $72 \div 9 =$ ___?___   20. $54 \div 9 =$ ___?___   21. $36 \div 9 =$ ___?___

22. $9\overline{)72}$ 23. $9\overline{)18}$ 24. $9\overline{)45}$ 25. $7\overline{)56}$ 26. $9\overline{)63}$ 27. $8\overline{)40}$

28. $9\overline{)54}$ 29. $5\overline{)25}$ 30. $9\overline{)81}$ 31. $9\overline{)27}$ 32. $6\overline{)12}$ 33. $9\overline{)72}$

34. $7\overline{)63}$ 35. $5\overline{)40}$ 36. $9\overline{)36}$ 37. $9\overline{)9}$ 38. $9\overline{)81}$ 39. $8\overline{)56}$

40. $9\overline{)45}$ 41. $9\overline{)54}$ 42. $7\overline{)49}$ 43. $9\overline{)63}$ 44. $9\overline{)27}$ 45. $9\overline{)36}$

Find the missing numbers.

★ 46. ___?___ $\overline{)42}^{\,7}$ ★ 47. ___?___ $\overline{)45}^{\,5}$ ★ 48. ___?___ $\overline{)64}^{\,8}$ ★ 49. ___?___ $\overline{)56}^{\,8}$ ★ 50. ___?___ $\overline{)27}^{\,3}$

PROBLEM SOLVING • APPLICATIONS

51. Mrs. Sherman puts 36 clay pots in 9 stacks. Each stack has the same number of clay pots. How many clay pots are in each stack?

52. The children planted 27 tomato seeds in 9 boxes. Each box had the same number of seeds. How many seeds were planted in each box?

Skills Maintenance

Write > or <.

1. 2,365 ⬤ 2,645   2. 1,428 ⬤ 1,429   3. 2,098 ⬤ 2,100

4. 1,576 ⬤ 1,558   5. 2,965 ⬤ 2,865   6. 7,200 ⬤ 7,201

7. 9,428 ⬤ 9,422   8. 6,703 ⬤ 6,801   9. 2,345 ⬤ 3,245

10. 3,721 ⬤ 3,275   11. 8,146 ⬤ 8,150   12. 6,666 ⬤ 6,660

Division Facts Drill

Divide.

1. $8\overline{)24}$ 2. $7\overline{)14}$ 3. $3\overline{)9}$ 4. $9\overline{)0}$ 5. $1\overline{)4}$

6. $2\overline{)4}$ 7. $1\overline{)3}$ 8. $8\overline{)48}$ 9. $5\overline{)10}$ 10. $6\overline{)18}$

11. $9\overline{)81}$ 12. $6\overline{)24}$ 13. $2\overline{)16}$ 14. $8\overline{)40}$ 15. $3\overline{)24}$

16. $5\overline{)25}$ 17. $3\overline{)0}$ 18. $1\overline{)5}$ 19. $8\overline{)56}$ 20. $6\overline{)6}$

21. $7\overline{)56}$ 22. $8\overline{)16}$ 23. $2\overline{)2}$ 24. $4\overline{)20}$ 25. $4\overline{)28}$

26. $1\overline{)3}$ 27. $5\overline{)35}$ 28. $9\overline{)18}$ 29. $8\overline{)32}$ 30. $1\overline{)9}$

31. $9\overline{)36}$ 32. $7\overline{)21}$ 33. $9\overline{)45}$ 34. $1\overline{)2}$ 35. $3\overline{)12}$

36. $7\overline{)7}$ 37. $4\overline{)12}$ 38. $6\overline{)12}$ 39. $7\overline{)28}$ 40. $3\overline{)18}$

41. $4\overline{)4}$ 42. $4\overline{)36}$ 43. $1\overline{)1}$ 44. $2\overline{)0}$ 45. $1\overline{)8}$

46. $6\overline{)0}$ 47. $5\overline{)30}$ 48. $3\overline{)6}$ 49. $9\overline{)9}$ 50. $2\overline{)14}$

51. $5\overline{)0}$ 52. $6\overline{)36}$ 53. $3\overline{)21}$ 54. $8\overline{)72}$ 55. $4\overline{)24}$

56. $1\overline{)7}$ **57.** $9\overline{)54}$ **58.** $7\overline{)49}$ **59.** $2\overline{)6}$ **60.** $1\overline{)0}$

61. $6\overline{)48}$ **62.** $5\overline{)20}$ **63.** $8\overline{)0}$ **64.** $9\overline{)72}$ **65.** $2\overline{)10}$

66. $7\overline{)63}$ **67.** $2\overline{)18}$ **68.** $4\overline{)0}$ **69.** $6\overline{)54}$ **70.** $9\overline{)27}$

71. $5\overline{)5}$ **72.** $4\overline{)32}$ **73.** $2\overline{)8}$ **74.** $5\overline{)45}$ **75.** $1\overline{)6}$

76. $5\overline{)15}$ **77.** $7\overline{)35}$ **78.** $6\overline{)42}$ **79.** $8\overline{)64}$ **80.** $5\overline{)40}$

81. $4\overline{)8}$ **82.** $6\overline{)30}$ **83.** $7\overline{)42}$ **84.** $4\overline{)16}$ **85.** $9\overline{)63}$

86. $3\overline{)15}$ **87.** $8\overline{)8}$ **88.** $3\overline{)27}$ **89.** $2\overline{)12}$ **90.** $7\overline{)0}$

Divide across and then divide down.

91.

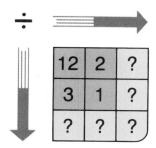

92.

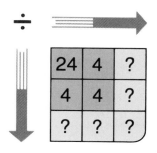

93.

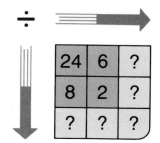

94.

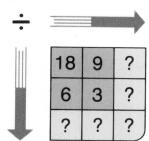

95.

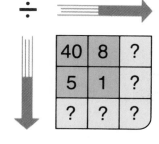

96.

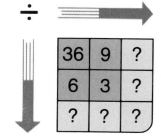

PROBLEM SOLVING · STRATEGIES

Multiply or Divide?

Make sure you read the problem carefully before you
decide to multiply or divide.

Cleo saw 4 rows of paint jars.
She counted 5 jars in each row.
How many jars did Cleo count?

Multiply to solve.

$$4 \times 5 = \underline{\quad ? \quad}$$
$$4 \times 5 = \underline{\quad 20 \quad} \longrightarrow \begin{array}{r} 5 \\ \times 4 \\ \hline 20 \end{array}$$

Cleo counted 20 jars.

Justin saw 24 jars of paint.
Each row had 6 jars. How
many rows did he see?

Divide to solve.

$$24 \div 6 = \underline{\quad ? \quad}$$
$$24 \div 6 = \underline{\quad 4 \quad} \longrightarrow 6\overline{)24}^{\,4}$$

Justin saw 4 rows.

How would you solve the problem? Write MULTIPLY or DIVIDE.

1. Each class needs 3 packs of
   clay. There are 6 classes. How
   many packs are needed?

**You can check a
multiplication problem by
dividing.**

2. Mr. Scott ordered 24 bottles
   of glue. They were shared
   equally by 4 classes. How
   many bottles did each class
   get?

3. A box holds 30 packs of clay.
   On each table are 6 packs.
   How many tables are there?

4. Marie put 8 colored pencils
   in each box. She used 4
   boxes. How many colored
   pencils did she have?

5. A box holds 4 paintbrushes.
   There are 5 boxes. How
   many paintbrushes are
   there?

Solve.

6. There are 8 jars of paint in a box. How many jars are in 8 boxes?

You can check a division problem by multiplying.

7. Becky saved 48 ice-cream sticks. She uses 6 sticks for each flower. How many flowers did she make?

8. A sheet of heavy paper costs 9¢. How much do 9 sheets cost?

9. Miss Crow teaches 3 art classes. There are 8 students in each class. How many students does Mrs. Crow teach?

10. Today 18 desks need to be cleaned. There were 3 students to share the work equally. How many desks does each student clean?

★ 11. A box holds 36 packs of paper. Another box holds 27 packs. There were 7 classes to share the paper equally. How many packs does each class get?

★ 12. Mr. Crane has 5 jars of red paint. He has 7 times as many jars of blue paint. How much paint does he have in all?

Division with Remainders

There are 23 marbles.
You give 5 to each friend.
How many friends get 5 marbles?

$23 \div 5 = ?$

Think: How many fives are in 23?

$1 \times 5 = 5$
$2 \times 5 = 10$
$3 \times 5 = 15$
$\boxed{4 \times 5 = 20}$
$5 \times 5 = 25$

Since 5 fives > 23,
there must be 4
fives in 23.
The quotient is 4.
There are 3 marbles
left over.

4 friends get 5 marbles.

Use the multiplication fact to find the quotient and the remainder.

Step 1	**Step 2**	**Step 3**	**Step 4**
Write 4 above 23.	Multiply. $4 \times 5 = 20$	Subtract.	Show the remainder in the answer.

Step 1:
$$\begin{array}{r} 4 \\ 5\overline{)23} \end{array}$$

Step 2:
$$\begin{array}{r} 4 \\ 5\overline{)23} \\ 20 \end{array}$$

Step 3:
$$\begin{array}{r} 4 \\ 5\overline{)23} \\ -20 \\ \hline 3 \end{array}$$

Step 4:
$$\begin{array}{r} 4 \text{ r } 3 \\ 5\overline{)23} \\ -20 \\ \hline 3 \end{array}$$

Practice • Find the quotients and remainders.

1. $3\overline{)25}$ 2. $4\overline{)18}$ 3. $2\overline{)11}$ 4. $6\overline{)28}$ 5. $8\overline{)50}$ 6. $5\overline{)32}$

7. $3\overline{)10}$ 8. $9\overline{)30}$ 9. $4\overline{)22}$ 10. $5\overline{)17}$ 11. $2\overline{)17}$ 12. $6\overline{)26}$

Mixed Practice • Find the quotients and remainders.

13. $7\overline{)17}$ 14. $3\overline{)29}$ 15. $5\overline{)16}$ 16. $2\overline{)13}$ 17. $4\overline{)10}$ 18. $3\overline{)22}$

19. $5\overline{)47}$ 20. $4\overline{)27}$ 21. $5\overline{)33}$ 22. $3\overline{)19}$ 23. $2\overline{)5}$ 24. $5\overline{)12}$

25. $9\overline{)11}$ 26. $2\overline{)15}$ 27. $8\overline{)42}$ 28. $6\overline{)34}$ 29. $4\overline{)26}$ 30. $7\overline{)16}$

31. $6\overline{)39}$ 32. $7\overline{)24}$ 33. $8\overline{)36}$ 34. $3\overline{)17}$ 35. $9\overline{)49}$ 36. $2\overline{)19}$

37. $9\overline{)40}$ 38. $4\overline{)39}$ 39. $5\overline{)44}$ 40. $8\overline{)46}$ 41. $3\overline{)26}$ 42. $7\overline{)45}$

43. $43 \div 6 = $ ____   44. $59 \div 6 = $ ____   45. $24 \div 9 = $ ____

46. $66 \div 7 = $ ____   47. $28 \div 5 = $ ____   48. $30 \div 8 = $ ____

PROBLEM SOLVING • APPLICATIONS

49. Linda has 22 marbles. She puts 5 marbles in each bag. How many bags are there? How many marbles are left over?

50. There are 52 jacks. In each box are 9 jacks. How many boxes are there? How many jacks are left over?

51. The boys have 41 marbles. Each boy needs 6 marbles to play the game. How many boys can play? How many marbles are left over?

52. There are 74 jacks in the box. We need 8 jacks for each person. How many people can play jacks? How many jacks are left over?

★ 53. Divide a number by 2. The quotient is 7, and the remainder is 1. What is the number?

★ 54. Divide a number by 8. The quotient is 8, and the remainder is 7. What is the number?

REVIEW

Find the quotients. (pages 176–183, 188–195)

1. $18 \div 3 =$ ___?___
2. $10 \div 2 =$ ___?___
3. $48 \div 6 =$ ___?___
4. $16 \div 4 =$ ___?___
5. $42 \div 7 =$ ___?___
6. $20 \div 5 =$ ___?___
7. $63 \div 9 =$ ___?___
8. $72 \div 8 =$ ___?___
9. $36 \div 4 =$ ___?___
10. $24 \div 6 =$ ___?___
11. $21 \div 3 =$ ___?___
12. $32 \div 8 =$ ___?___

Divide. (pages 186–197)

13. $2\overline{)16}$
14. $4\overline{)28}$
15. $6\overline{)42}$
16. $3\overline{)27}$
17. $5\overline{)35}$

18. $7\overline{)49}$
19. $6\overline{)30}$
20. $8\overline{)48}$
21. $5\overline{)25}$
22. $9\overline{)18}$

23. $8\overline{)56}$
24. $4\overline{)32}$
25. $7\overline{)21}$
26. $9\overline{)54}$
27. $6\overline{)36}$

28. $5\overline{)45}$
29. $7\overline{)63}$
30. $8\overline{)64}$
31. $9\overline{)36}$
32. $2\overline{)18}$

Find the quotients and remainders. (pages 200–201)

33. $7\overline{)25}$
34. $5\overline{)32}$
35. $4\overline{)27}$
36. $2\overline{)11}$
37. $6\overline{)41}$

38. $8\overline{)60}$
39. $9\overline{)80}$
40. $3\overline{)29}$
41. $8\overline{)62}$
42. $7\overline{)45}$

Solve.

43. You have 36 biscuits. You have 9 friends. How many biscuits can you give each friend and have no biscuits left over? (p. 194)

44. You need 2 slices of bread for a sandwich. A loaf of bread has 17 slices. How many sandwiches can you make? How many slices are left over? (p. 200)

PROJECT

Dividing by Two and Five

When one number is divided evenly by another number, there is no remainder.

$$\begin{array}{r} 6 \\ 3\overline{)18} \end{array}$$

$$\begin{array}{r} 5\ \text{r}\ 1 \\ 3\overline{)\ 16} \\ -15 \\ \hline 1 \end{array}$$

18 can be divided evenly by 3.

16 cannot be divided by 3 evenly. There is 1 left over.

Try to divide each number evenly by 2.

Try to divide each number evenly by 5.

Make a table like this one. Fill in the numbers.

Numbers that can be divided evenly by 2	Numbers that can be divided evenly by 5

Look at the table.

How can you tell if a number can be divided evenly by 2?

How can you tell if a number can be divided evenly by 5?

Find the quotients.

1. $18 \div 2 = $ ___?___

2. $4 \div 4 = $ ___?___

3. $35 \div 7 = $ ___?___

4. $32 \div 4 = $ ___?___

5. $81 \div 9 = $ ___?___

6. $45 \div 5 = $ ___?___

7. $30 \div 5 = $ ___?___

8. $36 \div 4 = $ ___?___

9. $64 \div 8 = $ ___?___

10. $56 \div 7 = $ ___?___

11. $63 \div 9 = $ ___?___

12. $12 \div 4 = $ ___?___

Divide.

13. $5\overline{)10}$

14. $7\overline{)63}$

15. $6\overline{)42}$

16. $2\overline{)14}$

17. $3\overline{)3}$

18. $4\overline{)24}$

19. $9\overline{)72}$

20. $4\overline{)28}$

21. $3\overline{)24}$

22. $6\overline{)18}$

23. $3\overline{)6}$

24. $8\overline{)48}$

25. $5\overline{)15}$

26. $7\overline{)14}$

27. $3\overline{)27}$

28. $5\overline{)40}$

29. $9\overline{)27}$

30. $8\overline{)56}$

31. $9\overline{)54}$

32. $7\overline{)28}$

Find the quotients and remainders.

33. $5\overline{)16}$

34. $2\overline{)9}$

35. $3\overline{)25}$

36. $8\overline{)75}$

37. $4\overline{)21}$

38. $9\overline{)14}$

39. $8\overline{)30}$

40. $6\overline{)41}$

41. $2\overline{)5}$

42. $3\overline{)14}$

Solve.

43. There are 36 pieces of carrot cake. 9 pieces are in each pan. How many pans are there?

44. Sally made 29 muffins. She put 3 muffins in each bag. How many bags did she fill? How many muffins were left over?

Modular Arithmetic

Who are these mice visiting?

Five mice live on a wheel.
Each mouse has a house.
Each house has a number.

The mice like to visit each other.
They run around the wheel.
They used to bump into each other.
Now they all run in the same direction.

If the mouse in house 0 runs 3 spaces,
it visits the mouse in house 3.

If the mouse in house 3 runs 3 spaces,
it visits the mouse in house 1.

Copy and complete
the table.

Mouse starts in this house.	It runs this many spaces.	Mouse visits in this house.
0	3	3
3	3	1
4	3	?
1	2	?
4	2	?
3	4	?
2	4	?
0	6	?
1	6	?
4	6	?
3	7	?
2	7	?
1	8	?
0	8	?
2	9	?

CALCULATOR

Division on a Calculator

You push the ⊕ command button to divide on a calculator.
First turn the calculator on.
To calculate 18 ÷ 9, push ① ⑧ ⊕ ⑨ ⊜. Screen: 2.
Write the answer, 2.

Use your calculator to divide.

1. 25 ÷ 5 = ___?___   2. 16 ÷ 8 = ___?___   3. 12 ÷ 4 = ___?___

Remember that 6)‾24‾ is the same as 24 ÷ 6.
To calculate 7)‾35‾, push ③ ⑤ ⊕ ⑦ ⊜. Screen: 5.

Divide.   4. 8)‾32‾   5. 9)‾45‾   6. 5)‾15‾

If the division problem has a remainder, do the problem in steps.
To calculate 6)‾55‾, follow the steps for finding remainders.

Step 1: Divide: Push ⑤ ⑤ ⊕ ⑥ ⊜ . Screen: 9.1666666
    The quotient is 9, with a remainder.

Step 2: Multiply: 6 × 9 gives the product on the screen. 54.

Step 3: Subtract: 55 − 54 gives the remainder
    on the screen. 1.

$$\overset{9r1}{6)\overline{55}}$$

Step 4: Write the answer the way you learned before: 6)‾55‾.

Calculate 8)‾62‾. **Step 1:** 62 ÷ 8. Screen: 7.75

    Step 2: 8 × 7. Screen: 56.

    Step 3: 62 − 56. Screen: 6.

$$\overset{7r6}{8)\overline{62}}$$

    Step 4: Write the answer. 8)‾62‾

Find the quotients and the remainders.

7. 7)‾51‾   8. 6)‾39‾   9. 2)‾13‾   10. 5)‾29‾

You can check *division* on a calculator by using *multiplication*. If you think that $32 \div 4 = 9$, you can multiply 4 and 9 to check. But $4 \times 9 = 36$, and so $32 \div 4$ cannot be 9. If you think that $32 \div 4 = 8$, you can use multiplication to check. $4 \times 8 = 32$, so now you know which quotient is correct.

On a separate sheet of paper, put a check (✔) next to the division problems that are correct. If the division problem is wrong, write the correct quotient.

11. $36 \div 4 = 8$ 12. $18 \div 9 = 2$ 13. $14 \div 7 = 3$

14. $72 \div 9 = 9$ 15. $15 \div 3 = 4$ 16. $16 \div 4 = 4$

Practice all these commands with the same numbers.

17. $9 + 3 = $ _?_   18. $9 - 3 = $ _?_   19. $9 \times 3 = $ _?_

20. $9 \div 3 = $ _?_   21. $6 + 2 = $ _?_   22. $6 - 2 = $ _?_

23. $6 \times 2 = $ _?_   24. $6 \div 2 = $ _?_

The answers go *up* in value when commands are put in this order.

25. $8 \div 4 = $ _?_   26. $8 - 4 = $ _?_   27. $8 + 4 = $ _?_

28. $8 \times 4 = $ _?_   29. $6 \div 3 = $ _?_   30. $6 - 3 = $ _?_

31. $6 + 3 = $ _?_   32. $6 \times 3 = $ _?_

Try some more. Be sure to push the correct command button.

33. $7 + 9 = $ _?_   34. $5 \times 6 = $ _?_   35. $9 - 6 = $ _?_

36. $2 + 7 = $ _?_   37. $81 \div 9 = $ _?_   38. $8 - 4 = $ _?_

Solve.

39. Inez has 4 apples. Jerry gives her 3 more. Stella eats one of them. Two spoil and are thrown away. Ramon gives her three more. How many apples does Inez have left?

40. Mary buys 40 favors for guests. She will not give herself a favor. 4 guests arrive early. 2 guests arrive on time. 2 guests arrive late. How many favors does each guest get?

Remember to turn the calculator off.

Choose the correct answers.

1. 23 + 8 + 39 = ___?___

- **A.** 60
- **B.** 70
- **C.** 59
- **D.** not here

2. $54.98
   + 12.69

- **A.** $42.39
- **B.** $77.77
- **C.** $67.67
- **D.** not here

3. Round 352 to the nearest hundred.

- **A.** 300
- **B.** 400
- **C.** 350
- **D.** not here

4. 350
    − 296

- **A.** 145
- **B.** 646
- **C.** 54
- **D.** not here

5. $15.25 − 4.89 = ___?___

- **A.** $18.24
- **B.** $10.36
- **C.** $11.36
- **D.** not here

6. 9 × 6 = ___?___

- **A.** 63
- **B.** 54
- **C.** 45
- **D.** not here

7. 9
   ×0

- **A.** 9
- **B.** 90
- **C.** 1
- **D.** not here

8. 1 × 8 = ___?___

- **A.** 1
- **B.** 8
- **C.** 9
- **D.** not here

9. 7)63

- **A.** 8
- **B.** 6
- **C.** 9
- **D.** not here

10. Mia buys 6 packages of tags. There are 8 tags in each package. How many tags does Mia have in all?

- **A.** 48
- **B.** 64
- **C.** 56
- **D.** not here

11. Jay has 83 beads. He puts 9 beads on each bracelet. How many bracelets can Jay make? How many beads are left over?

- **A.** 8 r 7
- **B.** 9 r 2
- **C.** 11 r 1
- **D.** not here

Measurement

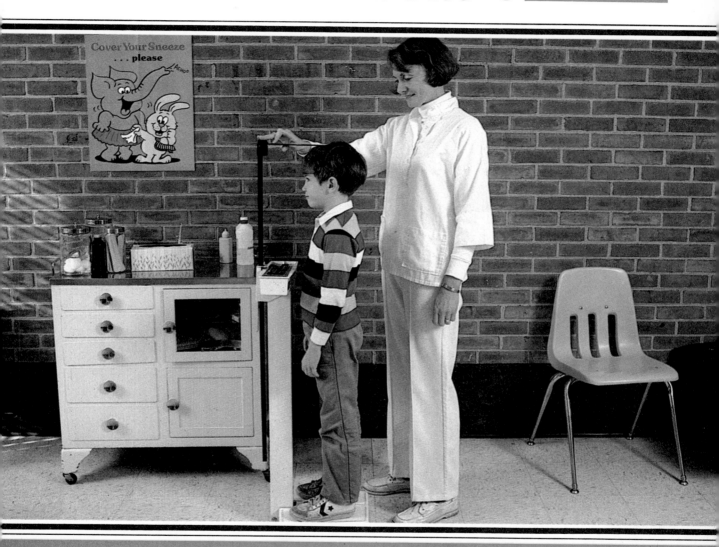

Centimeter

You can measure length by using small units.

The yarn is 5 paper clips long.

A **centimeter (cm)** is a metric unit used to measure length.

You can use a centimeter ruler to measure length.
Line up the end of the ruler with the end of the object.

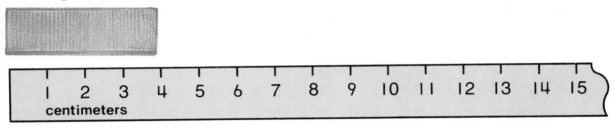

The ribbon is 4 centimeters long.

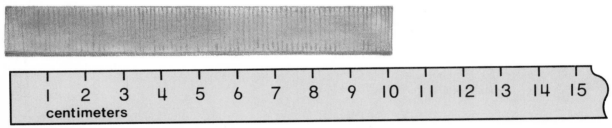

The length of this ribbon is between 10 and 11
centimeters. It is nearer to 10 centimeters.
The length is 10 centimeters to the **nearest
centimeter.**

Practice • Measure the length to the nearest centimeter.

1.
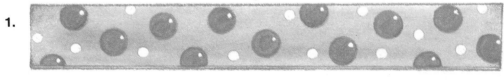

2.

3.

More Practice • Measure the length to the nearest centimeter.

4.

5.

6.

7.

8.

9.

10.

Draw the line segments. Use your ruler.

11. 5 cm

12. 8 cm

13. 11 cm

14. 3 cm

15. 14 cm

16. 6 cm

17. 9 cm

18. 12 cm

PROBLEM SOLVING • APPLICATIONS

Guess how long it is. Then measure to find out.

	Guess	Length
⋆ 19. Chalkboard eraser		
⋆ 20. Your pencil		
⋆ 21. Piece of chalk		
⋆ 22. Your shoe		

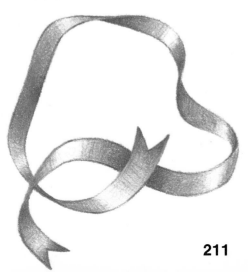

Meter and Kilometer

A **meter (m)** is another metric unit used to measure length.
There are 100 centimeters in a meter.

A baseball bat is about 1 meter long.

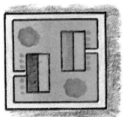

A **kilometer (km)** is a metric unit used to measure long distances.
There are 1,000 meters in a kilometer.

$$1,000 \text{ meters (m)} = 1 \text{ kilometer (km)}$$

There are about 12 city blocks in 1 kilometer.

Practice • Is it more than a meter? Write YES or NO.

1. the length of a pencil

2. the length of a room

3. the length of your arm

4. the height of your classroom door

Which unit of measure would you use?
Write CENTIMETER, METER, or KILOMETER.

5. the height of a tree

6. the length of a shoe box

7. the length of your hair

8. the length of a river

Mixed Practice • Is it more than a meter? Write YES or NO.

9. your height

10. the length of a bicycle

11. the length of your shoe

12. the length of a city block

13. the length of a kitten

14. the length of a car

Which unit of measure would you use?
Write CENTIMETER, METER, or KILOMETER.

15. the height of a building

16. the distance from Chicago to St. Louis

17. the width of notebook paper

18. the height of a drinking glass

19. the distance across an ocean

20. the length of a city block

21. the length of a paintbrush

22. the distance from earth to the moon

23. the length of a ship

24. the length of a necklace

Complete.

★25. 1 m = _?_ cm   ★26. _?_ km = 6,000 m   ★27. 6 m = _?_ cm

★28. _?_ m = 300 cm   ★29. _?_ km = 9,000 m   ★30. _?_ m = 400 cm

★31. 1 km = _?_ m   ★32. 8 km = _?_ m   ★33. 3 km = _?_ m

★34. _?_ km = 2,000 m   ★35. _?_ m = 500 cm   ★36. 7 m = _?_ cm

PROBLEM SOLVING • APPLICATIONS

37. Clark travels from home to school. Then he travels to the stadium. How many kilometers does Clark travel?

★38. In the morning, Clark travels from home to the stadium and back home again. After lunch, he travels from home to school. He leaves school, stops off at home, and goes to the stadium. Does Clark travel more in the morning or afternoon? How much more?

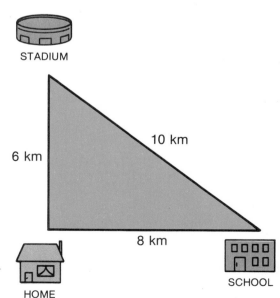

STADIUM

10 km

6 km

8 km

HOME

SCHOOL

213

Perimeter

John and Karen are making a
rug for the dollhouse. They want
to put fringe around the rug.
How much fringe do they need?

The distance around a figure
is its **perimeter.**

To find the perimeter, John
places string around the rug.
Then he measures the length of
the string.
The perimeter is 14 centimeters.

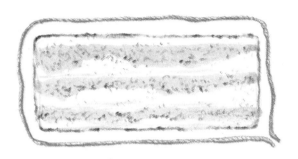

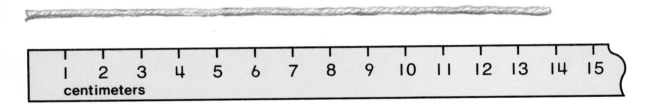

Karen finds the perimeter another way.
She measures each side. Then she adds the measures.

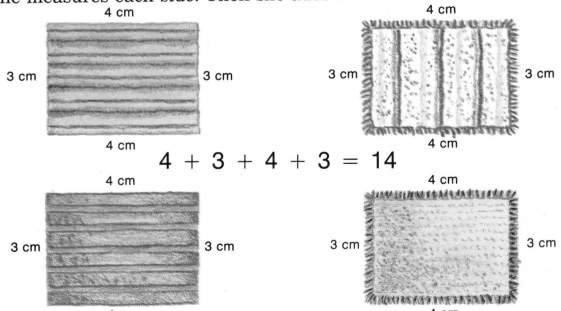

4 cm

3 cm   3 cm

4 cm

4 cm

3 cm   3 cm

4 cm

$$4 + 3 + 4 + 3 = 14$$

4 cm

3 cm   3 cm

4 cm

4 cm

3 cm   3 cm

4 cm

The perimeter is 14 centimeters.

Practice ● Find the perimeter in centimeters.

1.

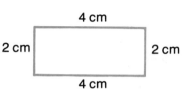

4 cm
2 cm   2 cm
4 cm

2.

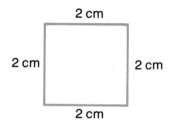

2 cm
2 cm   2 cm
2 cm

3.

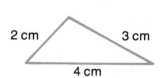

2 cm   3 cm
4 cm

Mixed Practice ● Find the perimeter in centimeters.

4.

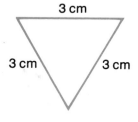

3 cm
3 cm   3 cm

5.

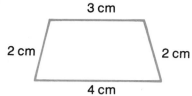

3 cm
2 cm   2 cm
4 cm

6.

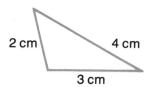

2 cm   4 cm
3 cm

7.

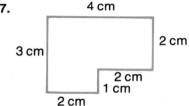

4 cm
3 cm   2 cm
2 cm
1 cm
2 cm

8.

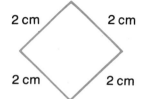

2 cm   2 cm
2 cm   2 cm

9.

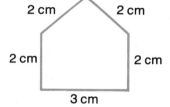

2 cm   2 cm
2 cm   2 cm
3 cm

Measure each side to the nearest centimeter.
Find the perimeter.

10.

11.

12.

PROBLEM SOLVING ● APPLICATIONS

13. A rug in the dollhouse has two sides that are each 12 centimeters long. The other two sides are each 9 centimeters long. What is the perimeter of the rug?

★ **14.** The perimeter of the kitchen floor in the dollhouse is 36 centimeters. Each of the four sides is the same length. How long is each side?

215

Area

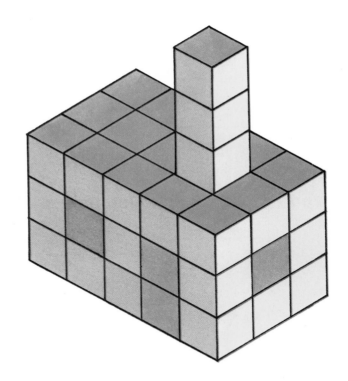

The number of square units that cover a surface is the **area** of a surface.

1 square centimeter

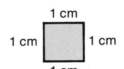

Count to find the area. The area is 6 square centimeters.

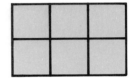

A **square centimeter (sq cm)** is a unit of area.

Practice • Find the area in square centimeters.

1.
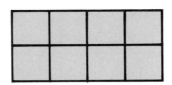

2.
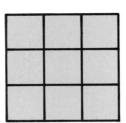

3.
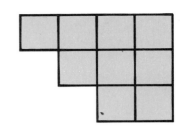

4.
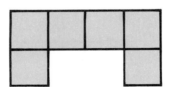

5.
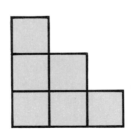

6.
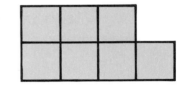

More Practice ● Find the area in square centimeters.

7.

8.

9.

10.

11.

12.

13.

14.

15.

PROBLEM SOLVING ● APPLICATIONS

Use a piece of centimeter graph paper.
Draw a figure to show the area.

16. 9 square centimeters

17. 7 square centimeters

18. 10 square centimeters

19. 8 square centimeters

★ 20. How many tiles were used
to cover all 6 sides of the
box?

Volume

The number of cubic units that will fit inside the box is the **volume** of the box.

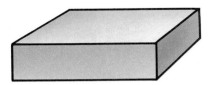

1 cubic centimeter

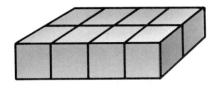

Count to find the volume. The volume of the box is 8 cubic centimeters.

A **cubic centimeter (cubic cm)** is a unit of volume.

Practice • Find the volume in cubic centimeters.

1.

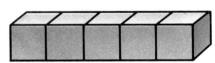

2.

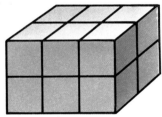

More Practice • Find the volume in cubic centimeters.

3.

4.

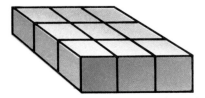

5.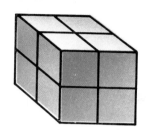

6.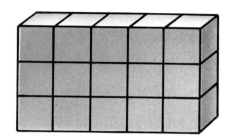

★7.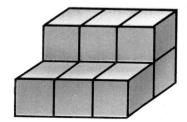

★8.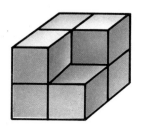

PROBLEM SOLVING • APPLICATIONS

9. Marion fills a box with blocks. Each block is 1 cubic centimeter. What is the volume of the box?

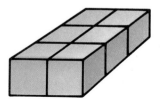

10. Mr. Secord fills a box with blocks. Each block is 1 cubic centimeter. What is the volume of the box?

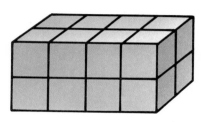

PROBLEM SOLVING · STRATEGIES

Draw a Picture

Sometimes drawing a picture can help you solve a problem.
Anna wanted to put a fence around 3 sides of her garden.
The sides measured 4 meters, 5 meters, and 6 meters.
How much fencing did Anna need?

Anna drew a picture.

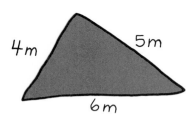

Anna could see from the
picture that she needed to
find the perimeter.

$$4 + 5 + 6 = 15$$

The perimeter is 15 meters.

Anna needed 15 meters of fencing.

Draw a picture that will help you solve each problem.

1. Dino walked around 4 sides
   of his garden. He measured
   the sides as 3 m, 6 m, 3 m,
   and 6 m long. How far did
   Dino walk in all?

   **Remember to add all the
   sides to find the perimeter.**

2. Wanda built a wall around
   the 4 sides of her garden.
   Each side measured 2 m.
   How long was the wall?

3. The Acme Garden Center
   sells garden soil in boxes
   that measure 1 meter on
   each side. They made a
   stack with 6 boxes in a row
   and 3 rows. What was the
   volume of the stack?

4. Mr. Walter made his garden
   in square units. Each unit
   had 4 sides that measured 1
   meter each. Each row was 4
   units long. The garden had
   3 rows. What was the area
   of the garden in square
   meters?

Solve.

5. Gene dug a ditch around the 4 sides of his garden. The sides measured 2 m, 6 m, 3 m, and 6 m. What was the perimeter of his garden?

Be sure your answer has the right unit of measure.

6. Carmen planted seeds in a seed box. The sides of the box were 1 m, 2 m, 1 m, 2 m. What was the perimeter of the seed box?

7. Miko used a piece of string to mark the sides of her garden. The sides measured 3 m, 4 m, and 5 m. How much string did Miko use?

8. Wendell wanted to fence the 5 sides of his garden. Each side measured 2 m. How much fence did he need?

9. Sam measured the sides of his garden. The sides were 2 m, 4 m, 5 m, and 4 m long. What was the perimeter of Sam's garden?

10. The garden center gets plants in boxes that measure 1 meter along each edge. A truck can hold a stack that is 3 boxes wide, 5 boxes deep, and 4 boxes high. What is the volume of the truck?

★ 11. Bill's flower garden measures 6 m on each side. The garden has 6 sides. What is the perimeter?

★ 12. Ethel measured the sides of her garden. The sides were 3 m, 5 m, 3 m, and 5 m long. What was the perimeter of her garden? What was the area?

221

Milliliter and Liter

The **milliliter (mL)** and the **liter (L)** are metric units used to measure liquids.

One cubic centimeter holds 1 milliliter.

1,000 cubic centimeters hold 1,000 milliliters.

There are 1,000 milliliters in 1 liter.

1,000 milliliters (mL) = 1 liter (L)

250 milliliters

700 milliliters

5 milliliters

10 liters

3 liters

4 liters

Practice • Which unit of measure would you use? Write MILLILITER or LITER.

1. water in a bathtub

2. soup in a bowl

3. shampoo in a bottle

4. lemonade in a pitcher

5. gasoline in a car

6. milk in a cup

222

Mixed Practice • Which unit of measure would you use?

7. paint in a bucket

8. medicine in a spoon

9. juice in a glass

10. water in an aquarium

11. medicine in a bottle

12. water in a wading pool

13. water in a washing machine

14. milk in a baby's bottle

Choose the correct measures.

15.

250 milliliters or 250 liters

16.

1 milliliter or 1 liter

17.

5 milliliters or 5 liters

18.

1 milliliter or 1 liter

19.

475 milliliters or 475 liters

20.

15 milliliters or 15 liters

PROBLEM SOLVING • **APPLICATIONS**

21. Amy pours herself a glass of apple juice. Does she pour 200 milliliters or 200 liters of juice?

★ 22. Michael has 2 cartons of milk. One carton contains 467 milliliters. The other has 513 milliliters. Does Michael have enough milk to fill a liter container?

Skills Maintenance

1. 366 +156	2. 475 +235	3. 198 +118	4. 549 +793	5. 673 + 48
6. 346 +374	7. 858 +675	8. 534 +266	9. 469 + 72	10. 575 +259

Gram and Kilogram

The **gram (g)** and the **kilogram (kg)** are metric units of mass.

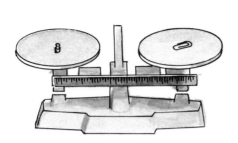

A paper clip is about 1 gram.

A pair of shoes is about 1 kilogram.

There are 1,000 grams in 1 kilogram.

1,000 grams (g) = 1 kilogram (kg)

50 grams

5 grams

180 grams

2 kilograms

7 kilograms

70 kilograms

Practice ● Which unit of measure would you use?
Write GRAM or KILOGRAM.

1. a pencil   2. a leaf   3. a bicycle   4. a penny

5. a cup   6. a bear   7. a golf ball   8. a bowling ball

Mixed Practice ● Choose the correct measures.

9.
5 grams or
5 kilograms

10.
1 gram or
1 kilogram

11.
50 grams or
50 kilograms

12.
1 gram or
1 kilogram

13.
720 grams or
720 kilograms

14.
500 grams or
500 kilograms

PROBLEM SOLVING ● APPLICATIONS

The mass of a milliliter of water is 1 gram.
A liter of water is 1 kilogram.

Write the measures.

★ 15. 4 milliliters of water
_____?_____ grams

★ 16. 94 milliliters of water
_____?_____ grams

★ 17. 12 liters of water
_____?_____ kilograms

★ 18. 260 liters of water
_____?_____ kilograms

Midchapter Review

Which unit of measure would you use? Write CENTIMETER,
METER, or KILOMETER.

1. the length of your classroom

2. the length of a pencil

3. the length of a paper clip

4. the distance from Miami to
   Dallas

5. Find the perimeter
   in centimeters.

6. Find the area in
   square centimeters.

7. Find the volume
   in cubic centimeters.

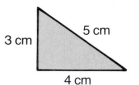

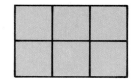

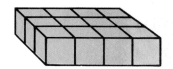

Degrees Celsius

A **degree Celsius** (°C) is a metric unit
used to measure temperature.

This is a Celsius thermometer.
Each mark on this thermometer stands
for 2 degrees Celsius.

The red liquid is at 20. The temperature
is **20 degrees Celsius (20°C).**

Suppose the liquid were at A.
This is below the zero mark.
We say it is **20 degrees Celsius
below zero.**

Practice • What is the temperature?

Use the thermometer.

1. hot day   2. water freezes

3. hot soup   4. room temperature

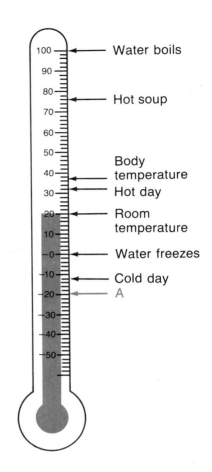

Water boils

Hot soup

Body
temperature

Hot day

Room
temperature

Water freezes

Cold day

A

Choose the correct temperature.

5.

18°C or 12°C below zero

6.

22°C or 60°C

226

Mixed Practice ● What is the temperature?
Use the thermometer on page 226.

7. water boils   8. cold day   9. body temperature

Choose the correct temperature.

10.

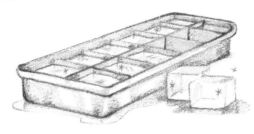

15°C or 0°C

11.

30°C or 10°C

12.

18°C or 2°C below zero

13.

5°C or 40°C

PROBLEM SOLVING ● APPLICATIONS

Use a Celsius thermometer.
Measure the temperature at the same time every day for one week.

Write the temperature for each day on a table.

Day 1	Day 2	Day 3	Day 4	Day 5	Day 6	Day 7

★ 14. Which day had the highest temperature?

★ 15. Which day had the lowest temperature?

Inch

An **inch (in.)** is a customary unit used to measure length.

This nail is one inch long.

You can use an inch ruler to measure length.

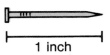

1 inch

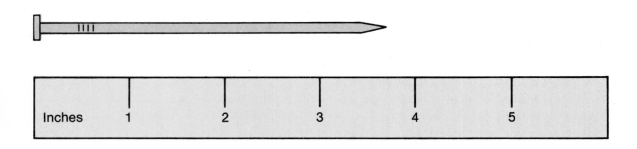

| Inches | 1 | 2 | 3 | 4 | 5 |

The length of the nail is between 3 and 4 inches.

It is nearer to 4 inches.

The length is 4 inches to the **nearest inch.**

Practice ● Measure the length to the nearest inch.

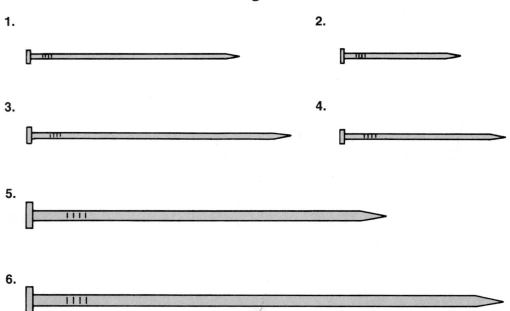

1.

2.

3.

4.

5.

6.

228

Mixed Practice • Measure the length to the nearest inch.

7.

8.

9.

10.   11.

Draw the line segment. Use your inch ruler.

12. 4 inches   **13.** 1 inch   **14.** 5 inches   **15.** 3 inches

16. 6 inches   **17.** 2 inches   ★**18.** 7 inches   ★**19.** 8 inches

PROBLEM SOLVING • APPLICATIONS

This ruler is marked in half inches.

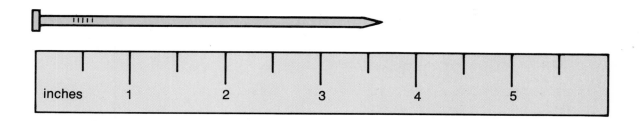

The length of the nail is $3\frac{1}{2}$ inches to the nearest **half inch.**

Estimate and then measure to the nearest half inch.

★**20.** the length of your pencil   ★**21.** the length of your thumb

★**22.** the width of your paper   ★**23.** the length of your shoe

229

Foot, Yard, and Mile

The **foot (ft)**, **yard (yd)**, and **mile (mi)** are other customary units used to measure length.

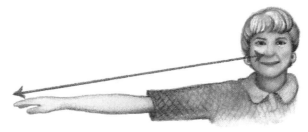

The distance from your elbow to your fingertips is about 1 foot.
There are 12 inches in a foot.

The distance from an adult's nose to fingertips is about 1 yard. There are 3 feet in a yard.

12 inches (in.) = 1 foot (ft)   3 feet (ft) = 1 yard (yd)
36 inches (in.) = 1 yard (yd)

The length of a train with 120 boxcars is about 1 mile.
There are 5,280 feet in a mile.

5,280 feet (ft) = 1 mile (mi)

Practice • Is the measure more than a foot? Write YES or NO.

1. the length of a finger

2. the length of a couch

3. the length of your arm

4. the length of a pen

Is the measure more than a yard? Write YES or NO.

5. the height of a house

6. the length of a kitten

7. the length of a hammer

8. the length of a car

230

Mixed Practice ● Is the measure more than a foot?
Write YES or NO.

9. the height of a soup can

10. the length of a baseball bat

11. the length of a toothbrush

12. the height of your desk

Is the measure more than a yard? Write YES or NO.

13. your height

14. the length of your arm

15. the length of a bicycle

16. the height of the classroom door

17. the height of a flagpole

18. the height of your desk

Choose the correct measures.

19. the length of a room
    15 inches or 15 feet

20. the height of a person
    6 feet or 6 yards

21. the length of a pencil
    8 inches or 8 feet

22. the distance between
    Boston and Tampa
    1,420 yards or 1,420 miles

23. the length of a river
    320 inches or 320 miles

24. the height of a bookcase
    48 inches or 48 feet

25. the length of a bridge
    20 inches or 20 yards

26. the length of a swimming pool
    8 yards or 8 miles

Since 1 foot = 12 inches, then
2 feet = 2 × 12 inches, or 24
inches.

PROBLEM SOLVING ● APPLICATIONS

Write how many inches in each.

27. 7 feet

28. 9 feet

29. 7 yards

30. 9 yards

★ 31. 2 feet and 3 inches

★ 32. 4 yards and 5 inches

Perimeter and Area

Matthew wants to find the perimeter and the area of the figure. To find the perimeter, he measures each side in inches. Then he adds the measures.

$$2 + 3 + 2 + 3 = 10$$

The perimeter is 10 inches.

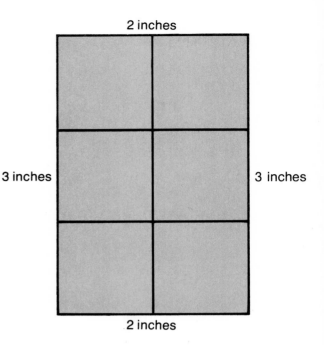

To find the area, he counts the number of **square inches (sq in.)** that cover the surface.

The area is 6 square inches.

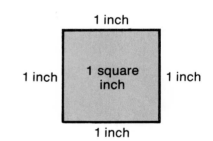

Practice • Find the perimeter in inches. Find the area in square inches.

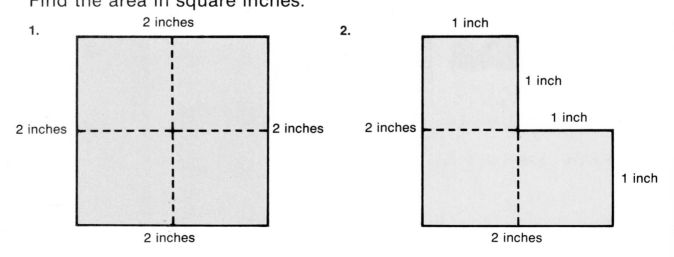

More Practice • Find the perimeter in inches.
Find the area in square inches.

Each —— stands for 1 inch. Each stands for 1 square inch.

3.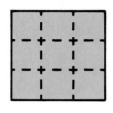

4.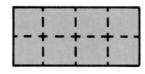

5.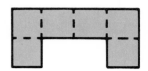

6.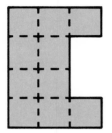

7.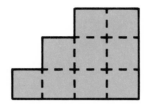

8.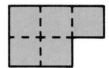

9.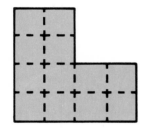

10.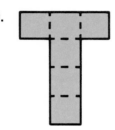

11.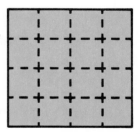

PROBLEM SOLVING • APPLICATIONS

Two halves of a square inch make one square inch.

make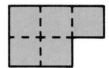

Find the area in square inches.

★ 12.

★ 13.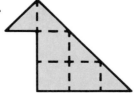

★ 14.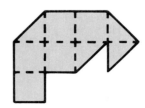

Volume

The **cubic inch (cubic in.)** is a unit of volume.

You can find the volume of a box by counting the number of cubic inches that fit inside the box.

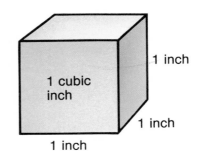

1 inch

1 cubic inch

1 inch

1 inch

Practice • Each 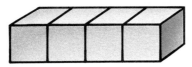 stands for 1 cubic inch. Find the volume in cubic inches.

1.

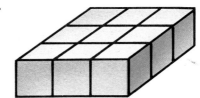

2.

3.

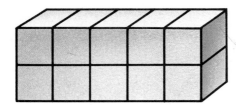

4.

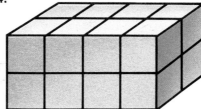

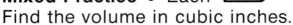

Mixed Practice • Each 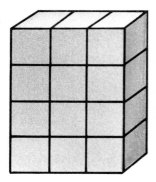 stands for 1 cubic inch. Find the volume in cubic inches.

5.

6.

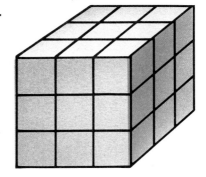

7.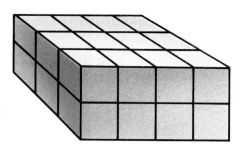

8.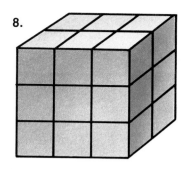

★ 9.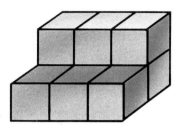

★ 10.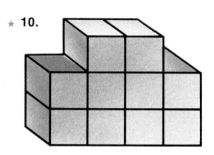

PROBLEM SOLVING ● APPLICATIONS

Draw a picture if you need help solving the problems.

★ 11. Lauren fills a box with blocks. Each block is one cubic inch. In one layer she puts 3 rows of blocks with 5 blocks in each row. It takes 4 layers to fill the box. What is the volume of the box?

★ 12. Morris fills a crate with boxes. Each box is one cubic inch. In one layer he puts 4 rows of boxes with 6 boxes in each row. It takes 5 layers to fill the crate. What is the volume of the crate?

Cup, Pint, Quart, and Gallon

The **cup (c)**, the **pint (pt)**, the **quart (qt)**, and the **gallon (gal)** are customary units used to measure liquids.

1 cup

There are 2 cups in 1 pint.

2 cups (c) = 1 pint (pt)

There are 2 pints in 1 quart.
2 pints (pt) = 1 quart (qt)

There are 4 quarts in 1 gallon.
4 quarts (qt) = 1 gallon (gal)

Practice ● Complete.

	1.	2.	3.	4.	5.	6.	7.
Quarts	1	2	3	4	5	6	7	8
Pints	2	4	?	?	?	?	?	?
Cups	4	?	?	?	?	?	?	?

8. 6 pt = ___?___ c

9. 4 qt = ___?___ pt

10. 3 pt = ___?___ c

11. 6 pt = ___?___ qt

12. 10 pt = ___?___ qt

13. 4 c = ___?___ pt

236

Mixed Practice • Complete.

14. 2 pt = ___?___ c   15. 4 pt = ___?___ qt   16. 6 c = ___?___ pt

17. 3 qt = ___?___ pt   18. 4 qt = ___?___ gal   19. 10 pt = ___?___ qt

20. 2 c = ___?___ pt   21. 4 pt = ___?___ c   22. 2 gal = ___?___ qt

★ 23. 1 qt = ___?___ c   ★ 24. 1 gal = ___?___ pt   ★ 25. 12 c = ___?___ qt

Which is the greater amount?

26. 4 qt or 4 pt   27. 4 pt or 7 c   28. 3 pt or 2 qt

29. 5 c or 2 pt   30. 1 pt or 1 qt   31. 3 c or 1 pt

32. 7 qt or 2 gal   33. 3 pt or 1 qt   34. 6 qt or 1 gal

Choose the correct measures.

35.

1 c or 1 qt

36.

2 qt or 2 gal

37.

1 c or 1 gal

PROBLEM SOLVING • APPLICATIONS

38. Doward bought 2 gallons of milk on Wednesday. How many quarts of milk did he buy on Wednesday?

39. Jody bought 2 quarts of milk on Monday and a gallon of milk on Tuesday. How many quarts did he buy?

Skills Maintenance

1.	863 −489	2.	452 −297	3.	764 −575	4.	562 −495	5.	340 − 82
6.	257 −159	7.	734 −148	8.	341 − 78	9.	851 −789	10.	830 −463

Ounce and Pound

The **ounce (oz)** and the **pound (lb)** are customary units used to measure how much things weigh.

A slice of bread weighs about 1 ounce.
There are 16 ounces in 1 pound.

A carton of butter weighs 1 pound.

16 oz = 1 lb

12 ounces

3 ounces

8 pounds

40 pounds

Practice • Which unit of measure would you use?
Write OUNCE or POUND.

1. a lion   2. an egg   3. a woman   4. a pencil

5. a mouse   6. a sock   7. a typewriter   8. a desk

238

Mixed Practice • Which unit of measure would you use?
Write OUNCE or POUND.

9. a sled   **10.** a muffin   **11.** a goldfish   **12.** a pig

13. a carrot   **14.** a tire   **15.** a mitten   **16.** a monkey

Choose the correct measures.

17.

4 ounces or
4 pounds

18.

5 ounces or
5 pounds

19.

1 ounce or
1 pound

20.

12 ounces or
12 pounds

21.

3 ounces or
3 pounds

22.

9 ounces or
9 pounds

PROBLEM SOLVING • APPLICATIONS

The box of cereal weighs 1 pound 4 ounces.
How much does the box of cereal weigh in
ounces?

1 lb 4 oz = 16 oz + 4 oz   Remember:
          = 20 oz   1 lb = 16 oz

The box of cereal weighs 20 ounces.

How many ounces?

★ **23.** 1 pound 2 ounces ★ **24.** 1 pound 10 ounces ★ **25.** 1 pound 14 ounces

★ **26.** 2 pounds 2 ounces ★ **27.** 4 pounds 7 ounces ★ **28.** 5 pounds 12 ounces

PROBLEM SOLVING • STRATEGIES

Making and Using Tables

Tables can help solve problems.
Here is an example.

The students in Mrs. Lind's room
are making masks.
Tim is in charge of making the paste.
To make the paste, he uses
1 cup of water for every 2 cups of
flour. How much flour does he need
for 2 cups of water? For 6 cups?
Tim makes a table.

Water (cups)	1	2	3	4	5	6	7	8	9
Flour (cups)	2	4	6	8	10	12	14	16	18

To read the table

Step 1: find the number of cups of water across the top.
Step 2: find the number of cups of flour across the bottom.

Tim needs 4 cups of flour for 2 cups of water.
He needs 12 cups of flour for 6 cups of water.
To make the table, Tim

Step 1: wrote 1 through 9 for the cups of water.
Step 2: counted on from 2 to fill in the number of cups of flour.

Copy and complete the table. Use it to answer the questions.
Rosa cuts string to tie the masks. Each string is 6 inches long.

1. How much string does she
   need for 2 ties?

2. How many ties can she
   make from 36 inches of
   string?

Ties	1	2	3	4	5	?
String (inches)	6	?	18	?	?	36

240

Copy and complete the table. Use the table to answer the questions.

Suki and Jack make clay beads for the masks. They use 1 ounce of clay to make 7 beads.

Clay (ounces)	1	2	3	4	?	?	?	8	?
Beads	7	14	?	?	35	42	?	56	?

3. How many beads can they make with 2 ounces of clay?

4. How many beads can they make with 7 ounces of clay?

5. How much clay will they need to make 35 beads?

6. How much clay will they need to make 63 beads?

7. How much clay will they need to make 42 beads?

Chris and Sandy mix paint for the masks. They mix 2 ounces of paint powder with 6 cups of water.

Paint powder (ounces)	2	4	6	8	?	?	?	?	?
Water (cups)	6	12	18	?	30	?	?	48	?

8. How much paint powder is needed for 18 cups of water?

9. How much water is needed for 10 ounces of paint powder?

10. How much water is needed for 16 ounces of paint powder?

Make sure you read the correct column when using a table.

★ 11. How much paint powder is needed for 60 cups of water?

★ 12. How much water is needed for 20 ounces of paint powder?

REVIEW

Measure the length to the nearest centimeter. (pages 210–211)

1.

2.

3. Find the perimeter in centimeters. (pages 214–215)

Find the area in square centimeters. (pages 216–217)

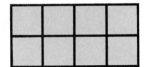

4. Find the volume in cubic centimeters. (pages 218–219)

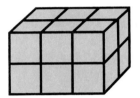

Choose the correct measures. (pages 222–227)

5.

250 milliliters or 250 liters

6.

20 grams or 20 kilograms

7.

0°C or 30°C

Measure the length to the nearest inch. (pages 228–229)

8.

9.

Choose the correct measures. (pages 230–231, 236–239)

10.

2 yards or 2 feet

11.

2 cups or 2 quarts

12.

5 ounces or 5 pounds

PROJECT

Degrees Fahrenheit

A **degree Fahrenheit** (°F) is a customary unit used to measure temperature.

This is a Fahrenheit thermometer. Each mark on this thermometer stands for 2 degrees Fahrenheit.

The red liquid is at 70. The temperature is **70 degrees Fahrenheit (70°F).**

Find the temperature for each of the following.

1. your classroom
2. outdoors
3. a glass of cold water
4. a glass of warm water

Now copy the table and list your results.

	°F
classroom	
outdoors	
cold water	
warm water	

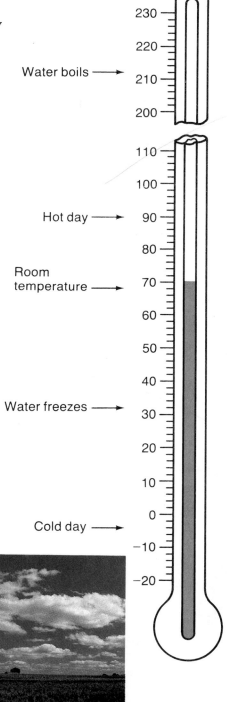

Water boils → 210

Hot day → 90

Room temperature → 70

Water freezes → 30

Cold day → 0

TEST

Measure the length to the nearest centimeter.

1.

2.

3. Find the perimeter in centimeters.
Find the area in square centimeters.

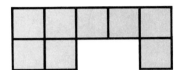

4. Find the volume in cubic centimeters.

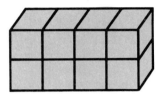

Choose the correct measures.

5.

1 milliliter or
1 liter

6.

100 grams or
100 kilograms

7.

32°C or 0°C

Measure the length to the nearest inch.

8.

9.

Choose the correct measures.

10.

1 cup or 1 gallon

11.

5 cups or
5 gallons

12.

4 ounces or
4 pounds

Below Zero

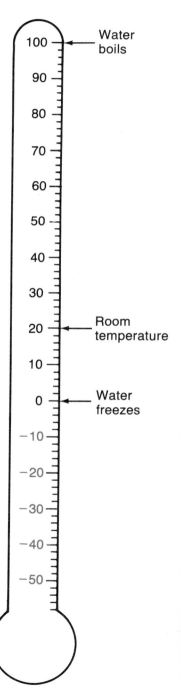

Look near the bottom of the thermometer. Do you see the numerals in red? They are for temperatures **below zero**.

Suppose the temperature is 10 degrees Celsius above zero. Overnight, the temperature falls 20 degrees. In the morning, it is 10 degrees Celsius below zero. That's cold!

Copy and complete this chart.

Evening temperature (degrees Celsius)	Overnight change (degrees Celsius)	Morning temperature (degrees Celsius)
20 above 0	rises 8	28 above 0
5 above 0	falls 8	3 below 0
36 above 0	rises 4	?
24 above 0	falls 4	?
12 below 0	rises 10	?
3 below 0	rises 9	?
8 above 0	falls 10	?
20 below 0	falls 12	?
32 below 0	rises 22	?
4 below 0	falls 14	?

COMPUTER

Computer Hardware

Decimal numbers are made up of decimal digits.
There are 10 decimal digits:
0, 1, 2, 3, 4, 5, 6, 7, 8, and 9.
The word *digit* comes from an old word
    that means "fingers" or "toes."
We have 10 fingers and 10 toes.

8 is a 1–digit decimal number.

74 is a 2–digit decimal number.

Binary numbers are made up of binary digits.
There are 2 binary digits: 0 and 1.
The term *binary digits* has been
    shortened to bits.

101 is a 3–bit binary number.

Bits produce very long numbers.
The decimal number 100,000 in binary
    is 110000110100000
It takes a 17-bit number to represent
    the smallest 6-digit decimal number.

100010001000 is a 12–bit binary number.

The machinery of the computer is called hardware.
Hardware is made of metal or plastic in
    the form of electronic devices.
Computers are really groupings of thousands
    of electronic devices.
Like a calculator, electronic devices can be off or on.
    If an electronic device is *off,* it holds the binary digit 0.
    If an electronic device is *on,* it holds the binary digit 1.
A number in a computer is a series of electronic devices.
Some of the devices are on and some are off.
The 3-bit number 101 is "Three devices are *on, off, on.*"
1010 is a 4-bit number. Four devices are *on, off, on, off.*

Copy and complete. Write the missing numbers and words.

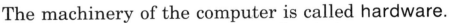

1. 0110 is a __?__ -bit number. __?__ devices are __?__ .

2. 10010 is a __?__ -bit number. __?__ devices are __?__ .

3. 110111 is a __?__ -bit number. __?__ devices are __?__ .

Choose the correct answers.

1. $17 - \underline{\ ?\ } = 9$

A. 12
B. 8
C. 26
D. not here

2. Round 847 to the nearest hundred.

A. 700
B. 800
C. 900
D. not here

3. Name 1,000 more.

5,065

A. 5,165
B. 6,000
C. 6,065
D. not here

4. $286 + 79 = \underline{\ ?\ }$

A. 365
B. 1,076
C. 374
D. not here

5. $\begin{aligned} \$\ .74 \\ +\ 6.95 \end{aligned}$

A. $7.69
B. $5.81
C. $6.69
D. not here

6. $402 - 67 = \underline{\ ?\ }$

A. 355
B. 469
C. 333
D. not here

7. $\begin{aligned} 923 \\ -687 \end{aligned}$

A. 364
B. 216
C. 236
D. not here

8. $8 \times 9 = \underline{\ ?\ }$

A. 72
B. 54
C. 63
D. not here

9. $42 \div 6 = \underline{\ ?\ }$

A. 6
B. 7
C. 5
D. not here

10. $6\overline{)28}$

A. 4 r 4   B. 4 r 3
C. 3 r 3   D. not here

11. The length of a car is about _____.

A. 5 cm   B. 5 m
C. 5 km   D. not here

12. 1 gallon = $\underline{\ ?\ }$ quarts

A. 2   B. 4
C. 6   D. not here

Skills Maintenance *continued*

Choose the correct answers.

13. Wally has 8 pepper plants. He buys 6 more. How many pepper plants does he have in all?

A. 2 B. 48
C. 14 D. not here

14. Stillwater Hills has 16 fire fighters. Now 9 are at a fire. How many fire fighters are left?

A. 7 B. 8
C. 25 D. not here

15. Deborah has 146 baseball cards. Wayne has 29 baseball cards. How many more cards does Deborah have?

A. 175 B. 117
C. 127 D. not here

16. Elsie has 5 dollars, 2 quarters, 4 dimes and 1 nickel. How much money does she have in all?

A. $5.49 B. $5.54
C. $5.59 D. not here

17. Marty goes fishing at 11:00. He fishes for 3 hours. What time is it when Marty stops fishing?

A. 8:00 B. 3:00
C. 2:00 D. not here

18. Mrs. Kane has 8 bundles of magazines. There are 6 magazines in each bundle. How many magazines does Mrs. Kane have?

A. 54 B. 48
C. 72 D. not here

19. A garden has two sides that are each 6 meters long. The other two sides are each 3 meters long. What is the perimeter of the garden?

A. 18 m B. 9 m
C. 36 m D. not here

20. There are 54 watering cans. There are 6 cans in each carton. How many cartons are there?

A. 48 B. 9
C. 8 D. not here

Multiplying by One-Digit Numbers

Multiplying Tens and Hundreds

If you can count by tens, you can multiply tens.

10	10	10	10	10	10	10	10	10
× 1	× 2	× 3	× 4	× 5	× 6	× 7	× 8	× 9
10	20	30	40	50	60	70	80	90

If you can count by hundreds, you can multiply hundreds.

100	100	100	100	100	100	100	100	100
× 1	× 2	× 3	× 4	× 5	× 6	× 7	× 8	× 9
100	200	300	400	500	600	700	800	900

If you can multiply ones, then you can multiply tens and hundreds.

$$\begin{array}{r} 3 \\ \times 2 \\ \hline 6 \end{array} \qquad \begin{array}{r} 30 \\ \times 2 \\ \hline 60 \end{array} \qquad \begin{array}{r} 300 \\ \times 2 \\ \hline 600 \end{array}$$

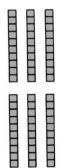 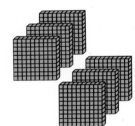

$3 \times 5 \ = 15$

$3 \times 50 \ = 150$

$3 \times 500 = 1500$

Practice • Find the products.

1. $\begin{array}{r} 20 \\ \times 3 \\ \hline \end{array}$
2. $\begin{array}{r} 40 \\ \times 2 \\ \hline \end{array}$
3. $\begin{array}{r} 30 \\ \times 5 \\ \hline \end{array}$
4. $\begin{array}{r} 50 \\ \times 6 \\ \hline \end{array}$
5. $\begin{array}{r} 30 \\ \times 2 \\ \hline \end{array}$
6. $\begin{array}{r} 20 \\ \times 4 \\ \hline \end{array}$

7. $\begin{array}{r} 300 \\ \times 2 \\ \hline \end{array}$
8. $\begin{array}{r} 200 \\ \times 4 \\ \hline \end{array}$
9. $\begin{array}{r} 800 \\ \times 7 \\ \hline \end{array}$
10. $\begin{array}{r} 700 \\ \times 3 \\ \hline \end{array}$
11. $\begin{array}{r} 500 \\ \times 7 \\ \hline \end{array}$
12. $\begin{array}{r} 700 \\ \times 6 \\ \hline \end{array}$

Mixed Practice • Multiply.

13. 30
    × 3

14. 20
    × 3

15. 40
    × 3

16. 30
    × 6

17. 50
    × 4

18. 70
    × 2

19. 30
    × 4

20. 40
    × 5

21. 80
    × 2

22. 60
    × 3

23. 90
    × 2

24. 60
    × 6

25. 300
    × 3

26. 400
    × 2

27. 500
    × 5

28. 900
    × 5

29. 800
    × 6

30. 900
    × 3

31. 800
    × 3

32. 700
    × 7

33. 900
    × 2

34. 700
    × 3

35. 700
    × 6

36. 600
    × 7

37. $7 \times 20 = $ ___?___

38. $5 \times 80 = $ ___?___

39. $5 \times 60 = $ ___?___

40. $4 \times 800 = $ ___?___

41. $5 \times 300 = $ ___?___

42. $7 \times 700 = $ ___?___

43. $5 \times 500 = $ ___?___

★ 44. $8 \times 900 = $ ___?___

★ 45. $9 \times 900 = $ ___?___

PROBLEM SOLVING • APPLICATIONS

46. There are 30 teams in the free-skating contest. There are 4 people on each team. How many people are in the contest?

47. Skaters from 8 teams have new skates. Each team has 10 skaters. How many skaters have new skates?

48. The roller-skating contest is held on 3 Saturdays. Each Saturday 400 people watch the contest. How many people in all watch the contest?

★ 49. There are 10 people on a roller-skating team. Each week 6 different teams skate. The skating contest is held for 3 weeks. How many people skate in all?

251

Multiplying Two-Digit Numbers

In each picnic basket are 34 sandwiches.
There are 2 picnic baskets.
How many sandwiches are there in all?

$2 \times 34 = ?$

Step 1
Multiply the ones by 2.

Step 2
Multiply the tens by 2.

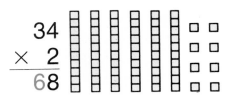

$$\begin{array}{r} 34 \\ \times\ 2 \\ \hline 8 \end{array}$$

$$\begin{array}{r} 34 \\ \times\ 2 \\ \hline 68 \end{array}$$

There are 68 sandwiches in all.

Practice ● Multiply.

1. $\begin{array}{r} 23 \\ \times\ 3 \\ \hline \end{array}$
2. $\begin{array}{r} 12 \\ \times\ 4 \\ \hline \end{array}$
3. $\begin{array}{r} 43 \\ \times\ 2 \\ \hline \end{array}$
4. $\begin{array}{r} 32 \\ \times\ 3 \\ \hline \end{array}$
5. $\begin{array}{r} 24 \\ \times\ 2 \\ \hline \end{array}$
6. $\begin{array}{r} 13 \\ \times\ 3 \\ \hline \end{array}$

7. $\begin{array}{r} 34 \\ \times\ 2 \\ \hline \end{array}$
8. $\begin{array}{r} 22 \\ \times\ 2 \\ \hline \end{array}$
9. $\begin{array}{r} 44 \\ \times\ 2 \\ \hline \end{array}$
10. $\begin{array}{r} 11 \\ \times\ 9 \\ \hline \end{array}$
11. $\begin{array}{r} 14 \\ \times\ 2 \\ \hline \end{array}$
12. $\begin{array}{r} 12 \\ \times\ 3 \\ \hline \end{array}$

Mixed Practice ● Multiply.

13. $\begin{array}{r} 22 \\ \times\ 3 \\ \hline \end{array}$
14. $\begin{array}{r} 11 \\ \times\ 6 \\ \hline \end{array}$
15. $\begin{array}{r} 12 \\ \times\ 2 \\ \hline \end{array}$
16. $\begin{array}{r} 13 \\ \times\ 2 \\ \hline \end{array}$
17. $\begin{array}{r} 23 \\ \times\ 2 \\ \hline \end{array}$
18. $\begin{array}{r} 21 \\ \times\ 3 \\ \hline \end{array}$

19. $\begin{array}{r} 11 \\ \times\ 5 \\ \hline \end{array}$	20. $\begin{array}{r} 67 \\ \times\ 0 \\ \hline \end{array}$	21. $\begin{array}{r} 34 \\ \times\ 2 \\ \hline \end{array}$	22. $\begin{array}{r} 33 \\ \times\ 2 \\ \hline \end{array}$	23. $\begin{array}{r} 20 \\ \times\ 4 \\ \hline \end{array}$	24. $\begin{array}{r} 21 \\ \times\ 2 \\ \hline \end{array}$
25. $\begin{array}{r} 30 \\ \times\ 3 \\ \hline \end{array}$	26. $\begin{array}{r} 41 \\ \times\ 2 \\ \hline \end{array}$	27. $\begin{array}{r} 57 \\ \times\ 1 \\ \hline \end{array}$	28. $\begin{array}{r} 11 \\ \times\ 8 \\ \hline \end{array}$	29. $\begin{array}{r} 22 \\ \times\ 4 \\ \hline \end{array}$	30. $\begin{array}{r} 10 \\ \times\ 4 \\ \hline \end{array}$

31. $1 \times 86 =$ __?__   32. $2 \times 31 =$ __?__   33. $7 \times 11 =$ __?__

34. $0 \times 52 =$ __?__   35. $2 \times 40 =$ __?__   36. $3 \times 20 =$ __?__

Complete the sentences.
Multiply inside the parentheses first.

37. $(3 \times 7) + 4 =$ __?__   38. $(2 \times 3) + 1 =$ __?__

39. $(4 \times 5) + 3 =$ __?__   40. $(8 \times 4) + 3 =$ __?__

41. $(3 \times 6) + 2 =$ __?__   42. $(7 \times 2) + 6 =$ __?__

Find the answers.

★ 43.

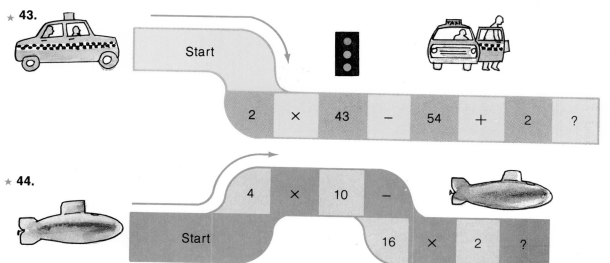

★ 44.

PROBLEM SOLVING • APPLICATIONS

45. There are 12 cars going to the picnic. There are 4 students in each car. How many students are there in all?

46. There are 31 cups in each bag. There are 3 bags of cups. How many cups are there in all?

Regrouping Ones

Claire can take 24 pictures with one roll of film. She has 3 rolls of film. How many pictures can she take?

$3 \times 24 = ?$

Step 1
Multiply the ones by 3.
Regroup 12 as 1 ten 2 ones.

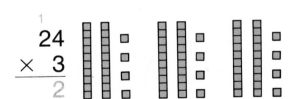

$$\begin{array}{r} 1 \\ 24 \\ \times\ 3 \\ \hline 2 \end{array}$$

Step 2
Multiply the tens by 3.
Add the 1 ten.

$$\begin{array}{r} 1 \\ 24 \\ \times\ 3 \\ \hline 72 \end{array}$$

Claire can take 72 pictures.

Practice • Multiply.

1. $\begin{array}{r} 19 \\ \times\ 4 \\ \hline \end{array}$	2. $\begin{array}{r} 13 \\ \times\ 6 \\ \hline \end{array}$	3. $\begin{array}{r} 37 \\ \times\ 2 \\ \hline \end{array}$	4. $\begin{array}{r} 27 \\ \times\ 3 \\ \hline \end{array}$	5. $\begin{array}{r} 14 \\ \times\ 5 \\ \hline \end{array}$	6. $\begin{array}{r} 48 \\ \times\ 2 \\ \hline \end{array}$
7. $\begin{array}{r} 12 \\ \times\ 5 \\ \hline \end{array}$	8. $\begin{array}{r} 25 \\ \times\ 3 \\ \hline \end{array}$	9. $\begin{array}{r} 36 \\ \times\ 2 \\ \hline \end{array}$	10. $\begin{array}{r} 13 \\ \times\ 7 \\ \hline \end{array}$	11. $\begin{array}{r} 16 \\ \times\ 4 \\ \hline \end{array}$	12. $\begin{array}{r} 29 \\ \times\ 2 \\ \hline \end{array}$

Mixed Practice • Multiply.

13. $\begin{array}{r} 15 \\ \times\ 6 \\ \hline \end{array}$	14. $\begin{array}{r} 23 \\ \times\ 4 \\ \hline \end{array}$	15. $\begin{array}{r} 12 \\ \times\ 8 \\ \hline \end{array}$	16. $\begin{array}{r} 17 \\ \times\ 4 \\ \hline \end{array}$	17. $\begin{array}{r} 24 \\ \times\ 3 \\ \hline \end{array}$	18. $\begin{array}{r} 16 \\ \times\ 6 \\ \hline \end{array}$

19. $\begin{array}{r} 35 \\ \times\ 2 \\ \hline \end{array}$
20. $\begin{array}{r} 18 \\ \times\ 3 \\ \hline \end{array}$
21. $\begin{array}{r} 12 \\ \times\ 7 \\ \hline \end{array}$
22. $\begin{array}{r} 23 \\ \times\ 3 \\ \hline \end{array}$
23. $\begin{array}{r} 18 \\ \times\ 5 \\ \hline \end{array}$
24. $\begin{array}{r} 25 \\ \times\ 2 \\ \hline \end{array}$

25. $\begin{array}{r} 15 \\ \times\ 3 \\ \hline \end{array}$
26. $\begin{array}{r} 47 \\ \times\ 2 \\ \hline \end{array}$
27. $\begin{array}{r} 15 \\ \times\ 4 \\ \hline \end{array}$
28. $\begin{array}{r} 14 \\ \times\ 6 \\ \hline \end{array}$
29. $\begin{array}{r} 17 \\ \times\ 5 \\ \hline \end{array}$
30. $\begin{array}{r} 45 \\ \times\ 2 \\ \hline \end{array}$

31. $2 \times 13 = \underline{\ ?\ }$
32. $4 \times 22 = \underline{\ ?\ }$
33. $3 \times 26 = \underline{\ ?\ }$

34. $7 \times 14 = \underline{\ ?\ }$
35. $5 \times 19 = \underline{\ ?\ }$
36. $6 \times 12 = \underline{\ ?\ }$

37. $3 \times 28 = \underline{\ ?\ }$
38. $2 \times 39 = \underline{\ ?\ }$
39. $4 \times 18 = \underline{\ ?\ }$

PROBLEM SOLVING • APPLICATIONS

40. Arlo can take 36 pictures with one roll of film. He has 2 rolls of film. How many pictures can he take?

41. Melvin puts 6 pictures on each page of an album. He fills 15 pages. How many pictures does he put in the album?

Study the table. Who takes more pictures?

⋆ 42. Jay has 5 rolls of film. Mike has 4 rolls of film.

⋆ 43. Jay has 7 rolls of film. Betsy has 3 rolls of film.

Pictures on a Roll

Jay	12
Mike	20
Betsy	24

Midchapter Review

Multiply.

1. $\begin{array}{r} 40 \\ \times\ 7 \\ \hline \end{array}$
2. $\begin{array}{r} 500 \\ \times\ 6 \\ \hline \end{array}$
3. $\begin{array}{r} 13 \\ \times\ 3 \\ \hline \end{array}$
4. $\begin{array}{r} 21 \\ \times\ 4 \\ \hline \end{array}$
5. $\begin{array}{r} 24 \\ \times\ 2 \\ \hline \end{array}$

6. $\begin{array}{r} 17 \\ \times\ 5 \\ \hline \end{array}$
7. $\begin{array}{r} 29 \\ \times\ 3 \\ \hline \end{array}$
8. $\begin{array}{r} 38 \\ \times\ 2 \\ \hline \end{array}$
9. $\begin{array}{r} 14 \\ \times\ 4 \\ \hline \end{array}$
10. $\begin{array}{r} 23 \\ \times\ 4 \\ \hline \end{array}$

Regrouping Ones and Tens

Ms. Brown makes 87 stops on her route each day.
She worked 4 days this week.
How many stops did she make?

$4 \times 87 = ?$

Step 1
Multiply the ones by 4. Regroup 28 as 2 tens 8 ones.

$$
\begin{array}{r}
2 \\
87 \\
\times\ 4 \\
\hline
8
\end{array}
$$

Step 2
Multiply the tens by 4. Add the 2 tens. Regroup 34 tens as 3 hundreds 4 tens.

$$
\begin{array}{r}
2 \\
87 \\
\times\ 4 \\
\hline
348
\end{array}
$$

Ms. Brown made 348 stops.

More Examples

$$
\begin{array}{r} 21 \\ \times\ 6 \\ \hline 126 \end{array}
\qquad
\begin{array}{r} 62 \\ \times\ 4 \\ \hline 248 \end{array}
\qquad
\begin{array}{r} 74 \\ \times\ 3 \\ \hline 222 \end{array}
\qquad
\begin{array}{r} 39 \\ \times\ 3 \\ \hline 117 \end{array}
\qquad
\begin{array}{r} 96 \\ \times\ 4 \\ \hline 384 \end{array}
$$

Practice • Multiply.

1. $\begin{array}{r} 32 \\ \times\ 6 \\ \hline \end{array}$
2. $\begin{array}{r} 47 \\ \times\ 5 \\ \hline \end{array}$
3. $\begin{array}{r} 68 \\ \times\ 3 \\ \hline \end{array}$
4. $\begin{array}{r} 94 \\ \times\ 7 \\ \hline \end{array}$
5. $\begin{array}{r} 53 \\ \times\ 8 \\ \hline \end{array}$
6. $\begin{array}{r} 29 \\ \times\ 4 \\ \hline \end{array}$

7. $\begin{array}{r} 49 \\ \times\ 5 \\ \hline \end{array}$
8. $\begin{array}{r} 16 \\ \times\ 9 \\ \hline \end{array}$
9. $\begin{array}{r} 71 \\ \times\ 2 \\ \hline \end{array}$
10. $\begin{array}{r} 32 \\ \times\ 4 \\ \hline \end{array}$
11. $\begin{array}{r} 65 \\ \times\ 3 \\ \hline \end{array}$
12. $\begin{array}{r} 34 \\ \times\ 8 \\ \hline \end{array}$

Mixed Practice • Multiply.

13. $\begin{array}{r} 37 \\ \times\ 6 \\ \hline \end{array}$
14. $\begin{array}{r} 56 \\ \times\ 2 \\ \hline \end{array}$
15. $\begin{array}{r} 67 \\ \times\ 7 \\ \hline \end{array}$
16. $\begin{array}{r} 62 \\ \times\ 6 \\ \hline \end{array}$
17. $\begin{array}{r} 78 \\ \times\ 5 \\ \hline \end{array}$
18. $\begin{array}{r} 54 \\ \times\ 7 \\ \hline \end{array}$

19. $\begin{array}{r} 51 \\ \times\ 8 \\ \hline \end{array}$	20. $\begin{array}{r} 83 \\ \times\ 2 \\ \hline \end{array}$	21. $\begin{array}{r} 95 \\ \times\ 5 \\ \hline \end{array}$	22. $\begin{array}{r} 64 \\ \times\ 3 \\ \hline \end{array}$	23. $\begin{array}{r} 79 \\ \times\ 6 \\ \hline \end{array}$	24. $\begin{array}{r} 20 \\ \times\ 9 \\ \hline \end{array}$
25. $\begin{array}{r} 68 \\ \times\ 6 \\ \hline \end{array}$	26. $\begin{array}{r} 64 \\ \times\ 8 \\ \hline \end{array}$	27. $\begin{array}{r} 18 \\ \times\ 4 \\ \hline \end{array}$	28. $\begin{array}{r} 82 \\ \times\ 4 \\ \hline \end{array}$	29. $\begin{array}{r} 29 \\ \times\ 7 \\ \hline \end{array}$	30. $\begin{array}{r} 27 \\ \times\ 3 \\ \hline \end{array}$
31. $\begin{array}{r} 68 \\ \times\ 5 \\ \hline \end{array}$	32. $\begin{array}{r} 43 \\ \times\ 3 \\ \hline \end{array}$	33. $\begin{array}{r} 67 \\ \times\ 4 \\ \hline \end{array}$	34. $\begin{array}{r} 68 \\ \times\ 2 \\ \hline \end{array}$	35. $\begin{array}{r} 11 \\ \times\ 8 \\ \hline \end{array}$	36. $\begin{array}{r} 97 \\ \times\ 3 \\ \hline \end{array}$

37. $7 \times 34 =$ ____?____   38. $2 \times 38 =$ ____?____   39. $7 \times 45 =$ ____?____

40. $5 \times 66 =$ ____?____   ★41. $9 \times 63 =$ ____?____   ★42. $9 \times 83 =$ ____?____

PROBLEM SOLVING • APPLICATIONS

43. Mr. Trump picks up mail from 6 mailboxes. There are 24 letters in each mailbox. How many letters are there in all?

★44. There are 7 mailbags on Ms. Washington's truck. Each mailbag has 42 letters. Mr. Scott has 8 mailbags with 38 letters each. Who has more letters? How many letters are there in all?

Skills Maintenance

Write the numbers.

1. five thousand, three hundred eighty-nine

2. eight thousand, two hundred nine

3. six thousand, three

4. one thousand, one hundred seventeen

5. four thousand, nine hundred twenty

6. seven thousand, five hundred

7. two thousand, fifty-two

8. nine thousand, six hundred forty-eight

Multiplying Three-Digit Numbers

There are 321 crates of peaches in each truck. 4 trucks are carrying the peaches to the farmers' market. How many crates of peaches are there in all?

$4 \times 321 = ?$

Estimate the answer.

Think: Round 321 to 300. Multiply by 4.

$$
\begin{array}{r} 321 \\ \times\ \ 4 \end{array}
\longrightarrow
\begin{array}{r} 300 \\ \times\ \ 4 \\ \hline 1{,}200 \end{array}
$$

There are about 1,200 crates.

Use the estimate to see if your answer makes sense.
Multiply: 4×321.

Step 1
Multiply the ones.
$$\begin{array}{r} 321 \\ \times\ \ 4 \\ \hline 4 \end{array}$$

Step 2
Multiply the tens.
$$\begin{array}{r} 321 \\ \times\ \ 4 \\ \hline 84 \end{array}$$

Step 3
Multiply the hundreds. Regroup 12 hundreds as 1 thousand 2 hundreds.
$$\begin{array}{r} 321 \\ \times\ \ 4 \\ \hline 1{,}284 \end{array}$$

There are 1,284 crates of peaches in all.

More Examples

$$
\begin{array}{r} 1 \\ 607 \\ \times\ \ 2. \\ \hline 1{,}214 \end{array}
\qquad
\begin{array}{r} 1 \\ 214 \\ \times\ \ 4 \\ \hline 856 \end{array}
\qquad
\begin{array}{r} 3 \\ 641 \\ \times\ \ 8 \\ \hline 5{,}128 \end{array}
\qquad
\begin{array}{r} 1 \\ 232 \\ \times\ \ 4 \\ \hline 928 \end{array}
\qquad
\begin{array}{r} 1 \\ 721 \\ \times\ \ 9 \\ \hline 6{,}489 \end{array}
$$

Practice • Estimate the product. Then multiply. Compare.

1. $\begin{array}{r} 214 \\ \times\ \ 6 \\ \hline \end{array}$
2. $\begin{array}{r} 327 \\ \times\ \ 3 \\ \hline \end{array}$
3. $\begin{array}{r} 113 \\ \times\ \ 2 \\ \hline \end{array}$
4. $\begin{array}{r} 324 \\ \times\ \ 4 \\ \hline \end{array}$
5. $\begin{array}{r} 361 \\ \times\ \ 9 \\ \hline \end{array}$

| 6. 208
× 9 | 7. 531
× 6 | 8. 212
× 4 | 9. 513
× 6 | 10. 770
× 5 |

Mixed Practice • Multiply.

| 11. 914
× 3 | 12. 423
× 4 | 13. 209
× 5 | 14. 751
× 5 | 15. 281
× 6 | 16. 136
× 2 |

| 17. 682
× 4 | 18. 323
× 2 | 19. 974
× 2 | 20. 212
× 8 | 21. 240
× 9 | 22. 819
× 3 |

| 23. 950
× 9 | 24. 461
× 7 | 25. 207
× 5 | 26. 523
× 3 | 27. 113
× 7 | 28. 345
× 2 |

| 29. 913
× 5 | 30. 721
× 4 | 31. 531
× 5 | 32. 603
× 6 | 33. 411
× 6 | 34. 716
× 6 |

35. $4 \times 815 =$?   36. $5 \times 961 =$?   37. $8 \times 401 =$?

38. $6 \times 316 =$?   39. $9 \times 420 =$?   40. $3 \times 852 =$?

Find the missing digits.

★41.
```
   73
×  ■
 3■5
```

★42.
```
  ■7
×  9
 87■
```

★43.
```
   36
×  ■
 ■■6
```

★44.
```
  1■3
×   4
 ■9■
```

PROBLEM SOLVING • APPLICATIONS

45. Melons are shipped in 4 trucks. There are 518 melons in each truck. How many melons are there in all?

★46. Mr. Harris delivers melons to 3 stores. He delivers 163 melons to each store. How many melons does Mr. Harris deliver in all? If Mr. Harris delivers to 4 stores, how many melons does he deliver?

PROBLEM SOLVING · STRATEGIES

Multiplying Money

Multiply amounts of money as if you were multiplying whole numbers.

Ellie bought 4 beach balls. Each ball cost 79¢. How much did Ellie spend in all?

Multiply to solve.

$$79¢ \leftarrow \text{can be written as} \rightarrow \$.79$$
$$\underline{\times\ 4} \qquad\qquad\qquad\qquad\quad \underline{\times\ \ \ 4}$$
$$316¢ \leftarrow \text{is the same amount as} \rightarrow \$3.16$$

Ellie spent $3.16 in all.

Remember to write the dollar sign and cents point.

Rewrite each answer using a $ and a . .

1. Brad bought 3 kites. Each kite cost 54¢. How much did Brad spend?

   Brad spent 162¢.

To write cents as dollars and cents, think that 100¢ = $1.00.

2. Lucy wants 2 model airplanes that cost 98¢ each. How much money will Lucy need?

   Lucy will need 196¢.

3. Mr. Cox bought 5 sets of checkers. Each set cost 85¢. How much did he spend?

   Mr. Cox spent 425¢.

4. Mrs. Best has 4 children. She bought each of them a ball for 39¢ each. How much did the balls cost?

   The balls cost 156¢.

Solve. Write the answer using a $ and . .

5. Juan bought 3 space people for 99¢. How much did he spend all together?

Use addition to check the answer.

6. Shawn wants to buy 5 toys that cost 47¢ each. How much money will Shawn need?

7. Chi Wan bought 4 toy cars. Each car cost 76¢. How much did he spend in all?

8. Marty bought 6 pieces of model train track. Each piece cost 92¢. How much did Marty spend all together?

9. Kay bought 3 dollhouse rugs. Each rug cost 61¢. How much did Kay pay for the rugs?

10. Mrs. Porter bought 7 bean-bag toys for 88¢ each. How much did she spend?

★11. Curtis bought 8 darts for 73¢ each. He bought a dart box for $1.85. How much money did he spend in all?

★12. Inez and Sal want to buy 9 ball-and-jacks sets. Each set costs 65¢. If they give the checker $6.00, how much change should they get?

REVIEW

Multiply. (pages 250–259)

1. 40
× 3

2. 60
× 2

3. 20
× 9

4. 50
× 8

5. 30
× 1

6. 100
× 6

7. 500
× 3

8. 900
× 7

9. 300
× 4

10. 800
× 6

11. 23
× 3

12. 31
× 2

13. 11
× 8

14. 44
× 2

15. 79
× 1

16. 24
× 4

17. 13
× 7

18. 47
× 2

19. 16
× 6

20. 35
× 2

21. 55
× 3

22. 78
× 4

23. 47
× 6

24. 62
× 8

25. 39
× 7

26. 203
× 4

27. 261
× 8

28. 119
× 5

29. 183
× 3

30. 741
× 7

Solve.

31. Each box has 20 pieces of chalk. Mrs. Woods has 4 boxes. How many pieces of chalk does she have? (p. 250)

32. In each box are 24 crayons. There are 2 boxes on the table. How many crayons are on the table? (p. 252)

33. There are 48 pencils in each package. You buy 8 packages. How many pencils are there in all? (p. 256)

34. There are 350 pages in each notebook. You buy 6 notebooks. How many pages are there in all? (p. 258)

Ask Me a Riddle

Each answer stands for a letter.
Find the answers. Then solve the riddles.

72 ×7 —— A	41 ×5 —— B	92 ×8 —— C	51 ×2 —— D	13 ×5 —— E	6 ×3 —— F	14 ×2 —— G
69 ×3 —— H	44 ×5 —— I	54 ×8 —— J	42 ×7 —— K	51 ×6 —— L	67 ×5 —— M	39 ×3 —— N
26 ×6 —— O	55 ×5 —— P	67 ×3 —— Q	94 ×4 —— R	16 ×6 —— S	26 ×9 —— T	90 ×5 —— U
34 ×8 —— V	78 ×9 —— W	84 ×7 —— X	79 ×9 —— Y	43 ×8 —— Z		

1. What is a calf after it is 6 months old?
   96–65–272–65–117   335–156–117–234–207–96   156–306–102

2. What do you get when you put ducks in a box?
   504   205–156–588   156–18   201–450–504–736–294–65–376–96

3. When did the fly fly?
   702–207–65–117   234–207–65   96–275–220–102–65–376
   96–275–220–65–102   207–65–376

4. Why does a hummingbird hum?
   205–65–736–504–450–96–65   220–234   102–156–65–96
   117–156–234   294–117–156–702   234–207–65
   702–156–376–102–96

TEST

Multiply.

1. 70
    × 2

2. 50
    × 6

3. 30
    × 8

4. 40
    × 0

5. 90
    × 7

6. 200
    ×   4

7. 700
    ×   8

8. 600
    ×   3

9. 500
    ×   4

10. 900
    ×   3

11. 43
    × 2

12. 11
    × 7

13. 12
    × 3

14. 21
    × 4

15. 33
    × 3

16. 12
    × 8

17. 19
    × 5

18. 17
    × 4

19. 13
    × 5

20. 46
    × 2

21. 69
    × 8

22. 93
    × 6

23. 85
    × 4

24. 78
    × 9

25. 27
    × 7

26. 181
    ×   9

27. 460
    ×   5

28. 519
    ×   3

29. 705
    ×   4

30. 652
    ×   4

Solve.

31. There are 20 balloons in a package. You buy 3 packages. How many balloons are there in all?

32. Mr. Evans buys 18 boxes of costumes. There are 8 costumes in each box. How many costumes are there in all?

33. Alexis sells 88 packages of masks. There are 6 masks in each package. How many masks does she sell?

34. Mrs. Evans buys 6 bags of buttons. There are 150 buttons in each bag. How many buttons does she buy?

Multiplying Choices

Three kinds of meat:

  ham
  beef
  turkey

Two kinds of bread:

  white
  whole wheat

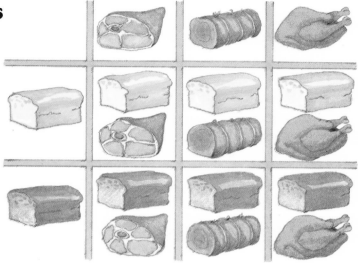

Use only one kind of each at a time. Do you see how many different ways you can make a sandwich?

$$\begin{array}{r} 3 \\ \times 2 \\ \hline 6 \end{array}$$
kinds of meat
kinds of bread
different ways

Solve. Remember to use only one kind of each at a time.

1. Two kinds of crackers. Three kinds of cheese. How many different ways can you have crackers and cheese?

2. Two kinds of yogurt. Four kinds of fruit. How many different ways can you have yogurt and fruit?

3. Three kinds of crackers. Four kinds of cheese. How many different ways can you have crackers and cheese?

4. Four different shirts. Three different pairs of slacks. How many different outfits can you make?

5. Three different shirts. Five different neckties. How many different ways can you wear the shirts and ties?

6. Five different sweaters. Two different skirts. How many different outfits can you make?

Make a table that is like the one above. Use one of the problems as your example.

COMPUTER

Nibbles and Bytes

Computers can only use the digits 0 and 1.
Remember the binary number for 100,000?
It is 11000011010100000, a 17-bit number.
You say that as "one one oh oh oh oh one one oh one
    oh one oh oh oh oh oh."
A program called an interpreter helps the programmer
    talk to computers. Programs are called software.
The interpreter works with groups of four bits, called
    nibbles. There are only 16 possible kinds of nibbles:

0000	0001	0010	0011	0100	0101	0110	0111	1000	1001	1010	1011	1100	1101	1110	1111

The first nibble, 0000, is all zeros. The name of the nibble is 0.
The second nibble is 0001. It has a nibble name of 1.
Study the next nibbles. Each nibble is one larger than the one
    before it. The next nibbles have names
    of 2, 3, 4, 5, 6, 7, 8, and 9.
Now we have the same problem as before. We need
    names that take only one space. Computer experts
    chose nibble names A, B, C, D, E, and F for the rest.

0000	0001	0010	0011	0100	0101	0110	0111	1000	1001	1010	1011	1100	1101	1110	1111
0	1	2	3	4	5	6	7	8	9	A	B	C	D	E	F

If we could write with only 10 digits and 6 letters,
    these names would be enough. But we need more.
The interpreter combines two nibbles to form a byte.
    That word is pronounced the same way as the word *bite.*

Copy and complete. Write the missing words.

1. Computers can use only the digits ____?____ and ____?____ .

2. A program called an __?__ helps a programmer talk to a computer.

3. The interpreter works with groups of __?__ bits, called __?__ .

4. List seven different nibble names. _____

5. The interpreter puts ____?____ nibbles together to form a __?__ .

266

One decimal digit can have 10 values: 0, 1, 2, 3, 4, 5,
6, 7, 8, and 9.
Two decimal digits can have 100 values, from 00
through 99. 100 = 10 × 10.
One nibble can have 16 values: 0, 1, 2, 3, 4, 5, 6, 7, 8,
9, A, B, C, D, E, F.
Two nibbles—one byte—can have 256 values, from 00
to FF. 256 = 16 × 16.
Each byte has a name, too. So there are 256 names for 256 bytes.
Like a person, each byte has a first name and a last name.

Byte AD has a first name of A and a last name of D.
Byte AD is nibble A followed by nibble D.
Nibble A has the value 1010. Nibble D has the value 1101.
Therefore, byte AD has the value 10101101.

Find the values for the bytes. Find bytes for the values.

6. C0 = ___?___
7. D2 = ___?___
8. 77 = ___?___

9. 10010101 = ___?___
10. 00101011 = ___?___
11. 11110000 = ___?___

The programmer writes in bytes.
The interpreter talks in bits to the computer.
The computer works only with bits.
It changes input bits to output bits.
The computer talks in bits to the interpreter.
The interpreter gives bytes to the programmer.

In a diagram the process looks like this. Fill in the blanks.
Make up your own input and output for problems 16 and 17.

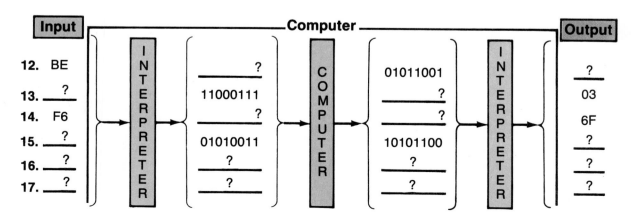

Input	Interpreter	Computer	Interpreter	Output
12. BE	_____?	01011001	_____?	?
13. ___?	11000111	_____?	03	
14. F6	_____?	_____?	6F	
15. ___?	01010011	10101100	?	
16. ___?	_____?	_____?	?	
17. ___?	_____?	_____?	?	

Choose the correct answers.

1. Write the number for three hundred ninety-six thousand, four.

- A. 39,604
- B. 396,004
- C. 396,400
- D. not here

2.
$$836 + 198$$

- A. 924
- B. 1,128
- C. 1,034
- D. not here

3. $601 - 276 = \underline{\ ?\ }$

- A. 477
- B. 485
- C. 325
- D. not here

4. What time is it?

- A. 9:50
- B. 5:10
- C. 9:05
- D. not here

5. $\underline{\ ?\ } \times 5 = 0$

- A. 5
- B. 1
- C. 0
- D. not here

6. $63 \div 7 = \underline{\ ?\ }$

- A. 8
- B. 9
- C. 6
- D. not here

7. $6\overline{)35}$

- A. 4 r 5
- B. 7 r 1
- C. 6
- D. not here

8. Find the perimeter.

4 cm

3 cm ▭ 3 cm

4 cm

- A. 7 cm
- B. 14 cm
- C. 12 cm
- D. not here

9.
$$86 \times 9$$

- A. 665
- B. 774
- C. 864
- D. not here

10. Mr. Porfirio had a box of 8 batteries. There are only 5 left. How many batteries has he sold?

- A. 13
- B. 3
- C. 40
- D. not here

11. Nils buys a flashlight for $2.59. He gives Mr. Porfirio $5.00. How much change does Nils get?

- A. $2.41
- B. $3.51
- C. $7.59
- D. not here

Dividing by One-Digit Numbers

CHAPTER 10

Dividing Tens and Hundreds

If you can divide ones, you can divide tens.

$$2\overline{)6} = 3$$

$$2\overline{)60} = 30$$

You can use a basic fact to help you divide tens.

$$2\overline{)4} = 2 \qquad 2\overline{)40} = 20$$

$$3\overline{)12} = 4 \qquad 3\overline{)120} = 40$$

You can use a basic fact to help you divide hundreds.

$$3\overline{)6} = 2 \qquad 3\overline{)60} = 20 \qquad 3\overline{)600} = 200$$

$$5\overline{)35} = 7 \qquad 5\overline{)350} = 70 \qquad 5\overline{)3,500} = 700$$

Practice • Divide.

1. $2\overline{)8}$ $2\overline{)80}$ $2\overline{)800}$ 2. $4\overline{)4}$ $4\overline{)40}$ $4\overline{)400}$

3. $3\overline{)9}$ $3\overline{)90}$ $3\overline{)900}$ 4. $6\overline{)6}$ $6\overline{)60}$ $6\overline{)600}$

5. $2\overline{)14}$ $2\overline{)140}$ $2\overline{)1,400}$ 6. $5\overline{)15}$ $5\overline{)150}$ $5\overline{)1,500}$

7. $3\overline{)21}$ $3\overline{)210}$ $3\overline{)2,100}$ 8. $4\overline{)20}$ $4\overline{)200}$ $4\overline{)2,000}$

270

More Practice ● Divide.

9. $4\overline{)8}$ $4\overline{)80}$ $4\overline{)800}$ 10. $5\overline{)5}$ $5\overline{)50}$ $5\overline{)500}$

11. $2\overline{)6}$ $2\overline{)60}$ $2\overline{)600}$ 12. $3\overline{)6}$ $3\overline{)60}$ $3\overline{)600}$

13. $4\overline{)12}$ $4\overline{)120}$ $4\overline{)1,200}$ 14. $2\overline{)10}$ $2\overline{)100}$ $2\overline{)1,000}$

15. $5\overline{)35}$ $5\overline{)350}$ $5\overline{)3,500}$ 16. $3\overline{)24}$ $3\overline{)240}$ $3\overline{)2,400}$

17. $6\overline{)18}$ $6\overline{)180}$ $6\overline{)1,800}$ 18. $4\overline{)28}$ $4\overline{)280}$ $4\overline{)2,800}$

19. $3\overline{)15}$ $3\overline{)150}$ $3\overline{)1,500}$ 20. $5\overline{)20}$ $5\overline{)200}$ $5\overline{)2,000}$

Find the missing factors.

	Factor		Factor		Product
★ 21.	2	×	?	=	60
★ 23.	3	×	?	=	90
★ 25.	5	×	?	=	250
★ 27.	6	×	?	=	420

	Factor		Factor		Product
★ 22.	7	×	?	=	70
★ 24.	4	×	?	=	80
★ 26.	4	×	?	=	160
★ 28.	8	×	?	=	400

PROBLEM SOLVING ● APPLICATIONS

29. Mrs. Babcock is a school nurse. She tests the hearing of 240 students. Each day she tests 8 students. How many days does she need to give all the tests?

★ 30. Mrs. Babcock has 300 cotton pads in one box and 60 in another. There are 6 pads in a packet. How many packets are there?

Dividing Two-Digit Numbers

There are 64 tickets.
Each person buys 2 tickets.
How many people buy tickets?

$64 \div 2 = ?$

Here is a way
to think about
the quotient.

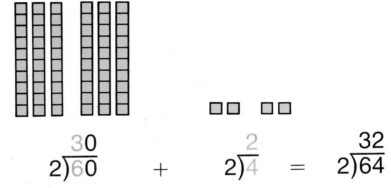

$$\begin{array}{r} 30 \\ 2\overline{)60} \end{array} \quad + \quad \begin{array}{r} 2 \\ 2\overline{)4} \end{array} \quad = \quad \begin{array}{r} 32 \\ 2\overline{)64} \end{array}$$

Here is how you show the work.

Step 1
Find the tens.
Think: 2)6.
Write 3 in the tens place.
Multiply. Subtract.

$$\begin{array}{r} 3 \\ 2\overline{)64} \\ -6 \\ \hline 0 \end{array}$$

Step 2
Find the ones.
Think: 2)4.
Write 2 in the ones place.
Multiply. Subtract.

$$\begin{array}{r} 32 \\ 2\overline{)64} \\ -6\downarrow \\ \hline 04 \\ -4 \\ \hline 0 \end{array}$$

32 people buy tickets.

Practice • Divide.

1. $3\overline{)63}$ 2. $4\overline{)84}$ 3. $2\overline{)24}$ 4. $5\overline{)55}$ 5. $3\overline{)69}$ 6. $6\overline{)66}$

7. $3\overline{)36}$ 8. $2\overline{)68}$ 9. $2\overline{)44}$ 10. $2\overline{)26}$ 11. $3\overline{)33}$ 12. $4\overline{)48}$

Mixed Practice • Divide.

13. $2\overline{)86}$ 14. $3\overline{)39}$ 15. $4\overline{)88}$ 16. $3\overline{)93}$ 17. $2\overline{)28}$ 18. $9\overline{)99}$

19. $2\overline{)66}$ 20. $7\overline{)77}$ 21. $2\overline{)82}$ 22. $2\overline{)48}$ 23. $3\overline{)60}$ 24. $4\overline{)80}$

25. $3\overline{)96}$ 26. $1\overline{)75}$ 27. $4\overline{)40}$ 28. $6\overline{)60}$ 29. $2\overline{)84}$ 30. $3\overline{)90}$

31. $50 \div 5 = $ ___?___   32. $99 \div 3 = $ ___?___   33. $64 \div 2 = $ ___?___

34. $44 \div 4 = $ ___?___   35. $80 \div 2 = $ ___?___   36. $42 \div 2 = $ ___?___

Find the missing digits.

★37. $6\overline{)\blacksquare0}$ (1$\blacksquare$)   ★38. $4\overline{)8\blacksquare}$ ($\blacksquare$1)   ★39. $\blacksquare\overline{)93}$ (3$\blacksquare$)   ★40. $5\overline{)5\blacksquare}$ ($\blacksquare$1)   ★41. $2\overline{)\blacksquare0\blacksquare}$ (300)

PROBLEM SOLVING • APPLICATIONS

42. Cleo Clown has 84 balloons. He puts 4 balloons into each bag. How many bags are there?

43. There are 36 rings. Each juggler has 3 rings. How many jugglers are there?

44. There are 24 gold tassels. Each pony has 2 gold tassels. How many ponies are there?

★45. There are 24 dogs in the first ring and 32 in the center ring. The dogs are in groups of 4. How many groups are there in all?

Dividing Two-Digit Numbers with Remainders

There are 85 apples for sale.
3 apples are in each bag.
How many bags of apples are there?
How many apples are left over?

$85 \div 3 = ?$

Step 1
Divide the tens.
Think: 3)8. Multiply.
Subtract.

```
    2
3)85
 -6
  2
```
This answer must be less than the divisor, 3.

Step 2
Regroup the 2 tens and 5 ones as 25 ones.

```
    2
3)85
 -6↓
  25
```

Step 3
Divide the ones.
Think: 3)25.
Multiply. Subtract.
Show the remainder.

```
   28 r 1
3)85
 -6↓
  25
 -24
   1
```

There are 28 bags of apples. 1 apple is left over.

Check your answer.

Step 1.
Multiply the quotient by the divisor.

Step 2
Add the remainder. ⟶

```
   28
 ×  3
   84
 +  1
   85
```
should equal the dividend.

Practice • Divide. Check your answer.

1. 4)58   2. 3)45   3. 5)56   4. 2)71   5. 6)78   6. 4)75

7. 2)43   8. 5)72   9. 4)60   10. 6)83   11. 3)57   12. 6)94

Mixed Practice • Divide. Check your answer.

13. $2\overline{)37}$ 14. $4\overline{)86}$ 15. $6\overline{)72}$ 16. $3\overline{)49}$ 17. $5\overline{)85}$ 18. $2\overline{)63}$

19. $4\overline{)51}$ 20. $3\overline{)75}$ 21. $2\overline{)67}$ 22. $6\overline{)68}$ 23. $7\overline{)88}$ 24. $4\overline{)76}$

25. $4\overline{)92}$ 26. $5\overline{)58}$ 27. $3\overline{)93}$ 28. $4\overline{)70}$ 29. $2\overline{)56}$ 30. $9\overline{)99}$

31. $3\overline{)37}$ 32. $4\overline{)64}$ 33. $5\overline{)60}$ 34. $2\overline{)84}$ 35. $6\overline{)79}$ 36. $8\overline{)92}$

37. $50 \div 5 = $ ___?___   38. $36 \div 3 = $ ___?___   39. $49 \div 7 = $ ___?___

40. $84 \div 7 = $ ___?___   ★ 41. $65 \div 3 = $ ___?___   ★ 42. $55 \div 4 = $ ___?___

PROBLEM SOLVING • APPLICATIONS

43. There are 75 pears on the shelf. Then 5 pears are put into each basket. How many baskets are there?

44. There are 59 ears of corn. Now 4 are put into each bag. How many bags are there? How many ears of corn are left over?

★ 45. There are 37 red apples and 23 yellow apples. There are 5 apples in each bag. How many bags are there?

Midchapter Review

Divide.

1. $5\overline{)50}$ 2. $3\overline{)900}$ 3. $4\overline{)160}$ 4. $2\overline{)46}$ 5. $3\overline{)93}$

6. $8\overline{)88}$ 7. $4\overline{)52}$ 8. $2\overline{)43}$ 9. $3\overline{)79}$ 10. $6\overline{)74}$

Dividing Three-Digit Numbers

Michael has 735 stamps.
He has 2 stamp books.
He puts the same number
of stamps in each book.
How many stamps does he put
in each book?
How many stamps are left over?

$735 \div 2 = ?$

Step 1
Divide the hundreds.
Think: $2\overline{)7}$.
Multiply. Subtract.

```
    3
2)735
 -6
   1
```

Step 2
Regroup. Divide the tens.
Think: $2\overline{)13}$.
Multiply. Subtract.

```
   36
2)735
 -6↓
  13
 -12
   1
```

Step 3
Regroup. Divide the ones.
Think: $2\overline{)15}$.
Multiply. Subtract.
Show the remainder.

```
  367 r 1
2)735
 -6↓
  13
 -12↓
   15
  -14
    1
```

Michael puts 367 stamps in each book. 1 stamp is left over.

Practice • Divide.

1. $4\overline{)548}$ 2. $3\overline{)791}$ 3. $5\overline{)610}$ 4. $2\overline{)656}$ 5. $4\overline{)647}$

6. $2\overline{)725}$ 7. $5\overline{)586}$ 8. $6\overline{)732}$ 9. $4\overline{)865}$ 10. $3\overline{)474}$

Mixed Practice • Divide.

11. $3\overline{)642}$ 12. $3\overline{)814}$ 13. $4\overline{)576}$ 14. $5\overline{)813}$ 15. $4\overline{)617}$

16. $2\overline{)331}$ 17. $2\overline{)231}$ 18. $6\overline{)750}$ 19. $3\overline{)573}$ 20. $3\overline{)985}$

21. $6\overline{)803}$ **22.** $5\overline{)575}$ **23.** $4\overline{)726}$ **24.** $2\overline{)493}$ **25.** $3\overline{)822}$

26. $5\overline{)730}$ **27.** $3\overline{)658}$ **28.** $6\overline{)954}$ **29.** $4\overline{)872}$ **30.** $2\overline{)511}$

31. $863 \div 4 = $ ___?___   **32.** $524 \div 2 = $ ___?___   **33.** $810 \div 6 = $ ___?___

34. $674 \div 3 = $ ___?___   **35.** $667 \div 5 = $ ___?___   **36.** $565 \div 4 = $ ___?___

Find the answers.

★**37.** $872 \div 4 \div 2 = ?$ ★**38.** $954 \div 6 \div 3 = ?$

PROBLEM SOLVING • APPLICATIONS

39. Vanya has 614 postcards. Vanya puts them in 5 books. Each book has the same number of postcards. How many postcards are in each book? How many postcards are left over?

40. Eric has 530 buttons to put in 3 jars. Each jar has the same number of buttons. How many buttons are in each jar? How many buttons are left over?

★**41.** Copy the number flag. Write 4, 5, 6, 7, 8, and 9 in the stars so that the sum for each side of the flag is 17. Use each number only one time.

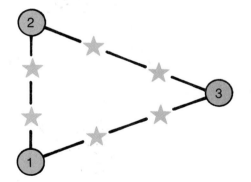

Skills Maintenance

1. $\begin{array}{r} 6 \\ \times 3 \\ \hline \end{array}$ **2.** $\begin{array}{r} 9 \\ \times 5 \\ \hline \end{array}$ **3.** $\begin{array}{r} 3 \\ \times 4 \\ \hline \end{array}$ **4.** $\begin{array}{r} 4 \\ \times 7 \\ \hline \end{array}$ **5.** $\begin{array}{r} 9 \\ \times 8 \\ \hline \end{array}$ **6.** $\begin{array}{r} 6 \\ \times 5 \\ \hline \end{array}$

7. $\begin{array}{r} 4 \\ \times 4 \\ \hline \end{array}$ **8.** $\begin{array}{r} 8 \\ \times 3 \\ \hline \end{array}$ **9.** $\begin{array}{r} 7 \\ \times 7 \\ \hline \end{array}$ **10.** $\begin{array}{r} 8 \\ \times 4 \\ \hline \end{array}$ **11.** $\begin{array}{r} 7 \\ \times 8 \\ \hline \end{array}$ **12.** $\begin{array}{r} 9 \\ \times 7 \\ \hline \end{array}$

PROBLEM SOLVING · STRATEGIES

Too Much Information

Sometimes more facts are given than
are needed to solve a problem.

George is writing a report about the
Parktown Library. He wrote down
the facts in his notebook. Which facts
does he need to answer the question?

QUESTION: How many people
in Parktown have a library card?

Only two facts are needed to
answer the question.
211 adults have a library card.
114 children have a library card.
He added to solve the problem.

325 people in Parktown have library cards.

Facts

1. The Parktown Library has 274 books about animals.
2. The library is at 550 Elm Street.
3. 211 adults have a library card.
4. The library is open 6 days a week from 9 A.M to 9 P.M.
5. 114 children have a library card.
6. A person can check out 6 books at a time.

$$\begin{array}{r} 211 \\ +114 \\ \hline 325 \end{array}$$

Use George's notebook. Give the fact numbers you need to solve
each problem.

1. How many hours a day is
   the library open?
   Fact number(s) _____

Read each fact carefully.

2. The Parktown Library has
   216 books about plants.
   How many more books does
   it have about animals?
   Fact number(s) _____

3. Max borrows as many books
   as he can on 4 different
   days. He still has all the
   books. How many books
   does Max have?
   Fact number(s) _____

4. Alice put the same number
   of animal books on each of 6
   shelves. How many books fit
   on each shelf? How many
   books were left over?
   Fact number(s) _____

Solve. Use only the facts you need.

5. Patty writes 8 pages of notes. She writes about 95 words on each page. She talks to 12 people. About how many words does she write in all?

Decide which facts are needed to solve the problem.

---

6. Bonita talks to 24 people on the telephone. She reads 6 books. Then she talks to 39 people in person. How many people does Bonita talk to in all?

7. Jacob made 8 trips to the library. He checked out 64 books. He read 18 of the books. How many of the books hasn't he read yet?

8. Julie wrote 6 reports this year. Her last report had 275 words. Bart helped Julie rewrite the report. He left in 196 words. How many words did he take out?

9. Francine wrote 2 stories for the school paper. One story had 3 pictures. Each story had 310 words. How many words did Francine write in all?

10. Sue read 12 books. Each book had 9 pictures. The pictures in 3 of the books were in color. How many pictures did Sue see in all?

★ 11. Frank finds 96 books in the library about rocks. There are the same number of books about rocks on each of 8 shelves. How many books are on each shelf?

★ 12. Abdul took 28 pictures. He used the same number of pictures in each report. He wrote 7 reports. How many pictures were in each report?

REVIEW

Divide. (pages 270–277)

1. $2\overline{)80}$ 2. $5\overline{)100}$ 3. $8\overline{)3,200}$ 4. $7\overline{)4,900}$

5. $2\overline{)66}$ 6. $4\overline{)84}$ 7. $3\overline{)96}$ 8. $2\overline{)82}$

9. $5\overline{)59}$ 10. $6\overline{)67}$ 11. $3\overline{)94}$ 12. $4\overline{)49}$

13. $2\overline{)37}$ 14. $4\overline{)72}$ 15. $5\overline{)61}$ 16. $7\overline{)92}$

17. $8\overline{)95}$ 18. $6\overline{)80}$ 19. $3\overline{)72}$ 20. $5\overline{)84}$

21. $5\overline{)595}$ 22. $3\overline{)352}$ 23. $2\overline{)279}$ 24. $4\overline{)633}$

25. $7\overline{)847}$ 26. $6\overline{)880}$ 27. $2\overline{)934}$ 28. $3\overline{)718}$

Solve.

29. Pack V has 96 Cub Scouts. There are 8 scouts in each den. How many dens are there? (p. 272)

30. There are 84 scouts in Pack IV. They all march in a parade. They march 6 in a row. How many rows are there? (p. 272)

31. Scout Pack VI has 87 pictures. The pictures are put in 5 books. Each book has the same number of pictures. How many pictures are in each book? How many pictures are left over? (p. 274)

32. The scout leader has 389 badges. He puts 3 in each packet. How many packets are there? How many badges are left over? (p. 276)

Ordered Pairs

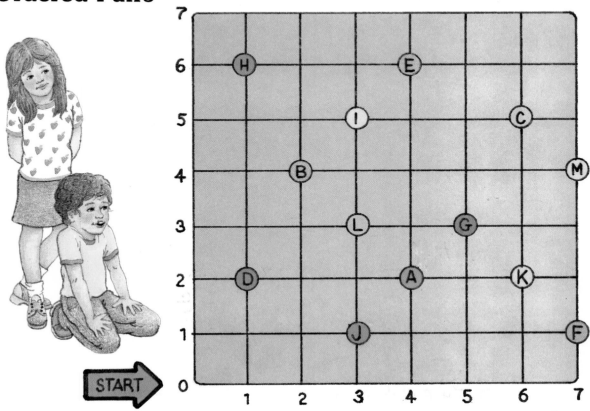

Do you see the A?
To tell someone how to find it,
you could say "Start at 0. Go over 4. Then go up 2."
You could write the ordered pair as (4, 2).

What ordered pair tells the location of the point?

1. B (? , ?)   2. C (? , ?)   3. D (? , ?)

4. E (? , ?)   5. F (? , ?)   6. G (? , ?)

7. H (? , ?)   8. I (? , ?)   9. J (? , ?)

10. K (? , ?)   11. L (? , ?)   12. M (? , ?)

281

TEST

Divide.

1. $4\overline{)40}$ 2. $4\overline{)320}$ 3. $6\overline{)3,600}$ 4. $5\overline{)2,500}$

5. $2\overline{)22}$ 6. $4\overline{)84}$ 7. $3\overline{)69}$ 8. $2\overline{)68}$

9. $3\overline{)48}$ 10. $2\overline{)57}$ 11. $4\overline{)85}$ 12. $8\overline{)96}$

13. $7\overline{)79}$ 14. $3\overline{)84}$ 15. $4\overline{)91}$ 16. $5\overline{)90}$

17. $6\overline{)68}$ 18. $5\overline{)57}$ 19. $2\overline{)87}$ 20. $4\overline{)63}$

21. $4\overline{)498}$ 22. $3\overline{)568}$ 23. $5\overline{)575}$ 24. $2\overline{)743}$

25. $3\overline{)942}$ 26. $4\overline{)567}$ 27. $3\overline{)524}$ 28. $6\overline{)714}$

Solve.

29. There are 70 students at a museum. There are 5 students in each group. How many groups are there?

30. Now 56 art students are working in groups. There are 4 students in each group. How many groups are there?

31. There are 55 coins in a collection. They are put in 3 books. Each book holds the same number of coins. How many coins are there in each book? How many coins are left over?

32. There are 894 tickets. There are 8 tickets in each booklet. How many booklets are there? How many tickets are left over?

ENRICHMENT

Using Logic

Each of these sentences is true.

 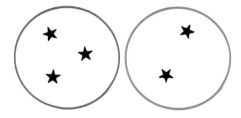

All of the stars inside the red ring are inside the blue ring.

None of the stars inside the red ring are inside the blue ring.

Some of the stars inside the red ring are inside the blue ring.

Write True or False for the sentence.

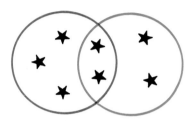

1. None of the letters inside the green ring are inside the brown ring.

2. Some of the letters inside the green ring are inside the brown ring.

3. All of the letters inside the green ring are inside the brown ring.

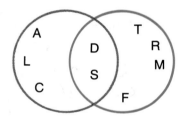

4. None of the digits inside the red ring are inside the green ring.

5. All of the digits inside the red ring are inside the green ring.

6. All of the dots inside the blue ring are inside the red ring.

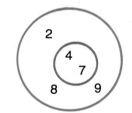

7. Some of the dots inside the blue ring are inside the red ring.

8. None of the dots inside the green ring are inside the blue ring.

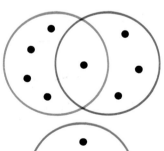

9. Some of the dots inside the red ring are inside the green ring.

283

COMPUTER

Computer Characters

In the last chapter you learned about a program called the interpreter. The programmer does not have to say "oh oh one oh oh oh one one" to a computer.

A programmer says "23" to the interpreter. The interpreter then says "oh oh one oh oh oh one one" to the computer.

Suppose a programmer wants to tell the computer "PRINT 24 × 38." The programmer looks at a list of matches:

P = 50   R = 52   I = 49   N = 4E   T = 54
2 = 02   4 = 04   X = 58   3 = 03   8 = 08
space = 20

The programmer would say "50 52 49 4E 54 20 02 04 20 58 20 03 08."

Every capital letter has its own byte. Every lowercase letter has its own byte. For example, "print" would be "70 72 69 6E 74."

There is a standard code that assigns bytes to every character.

A computer character can be:
- a single decimal digit, such as 5 or 8.
- a single capital letter, such as N or Q.
- a single lowercase letter, such as b or e.
- other symbols such as $, ", (,), &, *, ?, and the period.
- commands such as +, −, ×, and ÷.

Remember there are 256 possible bytes.

	There are	10	decimal digits,
	and	26	capital letters,
	and	26	lowercase letters,
	and	30	other symbols,
	and	10	commands.

In all there are 102 computer characters.

Copy and complete.

1. How do you say "TIP IT IN"? _____.

2. What does "74 69 6E" say? _____.

3. A computer character can be a __?__ , a __?__ , a __?__ , or a __?__ .

4. How would you tell the computer "PRINT 28 × 43"? _____

5. There are _____ possible bytes. _____ are computer characters.

The interpreter changes each computer character into
    bits. Then the computer works with the bits. Then
    the interpreter changes the bits into characters.
    Remember the table of nibbles and nibble names.

0000	0001	0010	0011	0100	0101	0110	0111	1000	1001	1010	1011	1100	1101	1110	1111
0	1	2	3	4	5	6	7	8	9	A	B	C	D	E	F

Suppose you had a very simple computer program. It
    changes lowercase letters into capital letters.

Follow the example. Fill in the blanks.

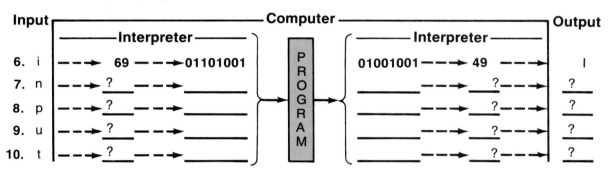

Now the pieces begin to fit together.
A person, the programmer, can type characters onto
    an input keyboard.
A program, the interpreter, changes characters into input bits.
A computer, the hardware, processes the bits. It
    changes input into output by means of a program.
The interpreter changes the output bits into characters.
The program can then print them or display them on a CRT.
The programmer can then look at the output and use the answers.

Copy and complete.

11. A programmer uses ___?___ as input and output.

12. A computer processes ___?___ to change ___?___ into ___?___ .

13. PRINT can be understood by a ___?___ .

14. 8E 40 7F 00 23 can be understood by an ___?___ .

15. 11000101010100010111010100110101 can be understood
    by a ___?___ .

285

Choose the correct answers.

1. $7 + 2 + 6 =$ ___?___

- A. 20
- B. 15
- C. 19
- D. not here

2. Compare.

3,145 3,154

- A. >
- B. <
- C. =
- D. not here

3.
$$\begin{array}{r} \$19.81 \\ +\ \ 3.56 \\ \hline \end{array}$$

- A. $16.25
- B. $23.37
- C. $32.27
- D. not here

4.
$$\begin{array}{r} 504 \\ -\ 86 \\ \hline \end{array}$$

- A. 590
- B. 518
- C. 428
- D. not here

5.
$$\begin{array}{r} \$9.00 \\ -\ 2.98 \\ \hline \end{array}$$

- A. $6.02
- B. $7.02
- C. $6.12
- D. not here

6. $9 \times$ ___?___ $= 72$

- A. 0
- B. 6
- C. 8
- D. not here

7. $4\overline{)32}$

- A. 8
- B. 5
- C. 6
- D. not here

8. What is the area?

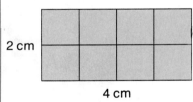

2 cm

4 cm

- A. 8 cm
- B. 6 square cm
- C. 8 square cm
- D. not here

9.
$$\begin{array}{r} 214 \\ \times\ \ 6 \\ \hline \end{array}$$

- A. 1,078
- B. 1,656
- C. 1,284
- D. not here

10. Jack earns 98 points on one test and 76 points on another test. How many points does he earn in all?

- A. 215
- B. 153
- C. 174
- D. not here

11. The Blair family takes a trip. They start at 8:30 A.M. They drive for 3 hours before stopping. At what time do they make their first stop?

- A. 11:30 A.M.
- B. 11:30 P.M.
- C. 10:30 A.M.
- D. not here

Fractions and Decimals

Fractions

Bob cuts a board into 3 equal parts.
He paints one part blue.
What part of the board is blue?

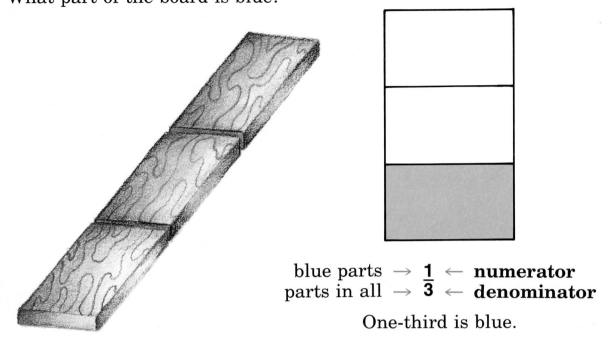

blue parts $\rightarrow$ **1** $\leftarrow$ **numerator**
parts in all $\rightarrow$ **3** $\leftarrow$ **denominator**

One-third is blue.

You can use fractions
to tell about equal parts.

More Examples

  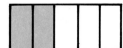 

$\frac{1}{2}$ one-half $\frac{3}{4}$ three-fourths $\frac{2}{5}$ two-fifths $\frac{7}{8}$ seven-eighths

Practice • Write the fraction that tells what part is blue.

1. 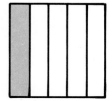   2. 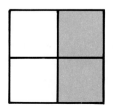   3. 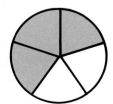   4.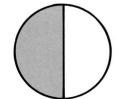

More Practice ● Write the fraction that tells what part is blue.

5.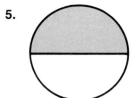

6.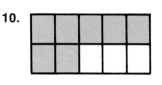

7.

8.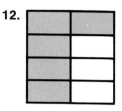

9.

10.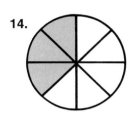

11.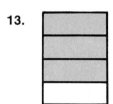

12.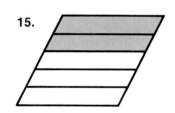

13.

14.

15.

16.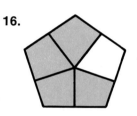

PROBLEM SOLVING ● APPLICATIONS

Write the fraction that tells what part is

17. red.

18. blue.

19. yellow.

20. purple.

★ 21. blue and red.

★ 22. blue and purple.

★ 23. not red.

★ 24. not yellow.

Parts of Groups

Mr. Parker is making a corsage. 2 flowers are red.
There are 5 flowers in all.
What part of the group of flowers is red?

You can use a fraction to tell about part of a group.

Think:
2 out of 5 are red.

$\dfrac{2}{5}$ ← red flowers
← flowers in all

So $\dfrac{2}{5}$ are red.

Practice • Write the fraction that tells what part is red.

1.

2.

3.

4.

More Practice • Write the fraction that tells what part is red.

5.

6.

7.

8.

9.

10.

PROBLEM SOLVING • APPLICATIONS

Write the fractions.

11.	What part is blue?	?	?	?
12.	What part is yellow?	?	?	?
13.	What part is pink?	?	?	?
★ **14.**	What part is large and blue?	?	?	?
★ **15.**	What part is large and pink?	?	?	?

Skills Maintenance

1. $\begin{array}{r} 403 \\ -195 \end{array}$	2. $\begin{array}{r} 705 \\ -449 \end{array}$	3. $\begin{array}{r} 800 \\ -253 \end{array}$	4. $\begin{array}{r} 604 \\ -378 \end{array}$	5. $\begin{array}{r} 400 \\ -236 \end{array}$
6. $\begin{array}{r} 907 \\ -288 \end{array}$	7. $\begin{array}{r} 300 \\ -58 \end{array}$	8. $\begin{array}{r} 501 \\ -487 \end{array}$	9. $\begin{array}{r} 806 \\ -517 \end{array}$	10. $\begin{array}{r} 600 \\ -164 \end{array}$

Finding Part of a Group

There are 12 eggs.
Scott cooks $\frac{1}{2}$ of them.
How many eggs does he cook?

$\frac{1}{2}$ of 12 = ?

Think:

Separate the 12 eggs into 2 groups
with the same number in each group. $\longrightarrow$ $12 \div 2 = 6$

There are 6 eggs in each group. $\longrightarrow$ $\frac{1}{2}$ of 12 = 6

Scott cooks 6 eggs.

Practice ● Complete.

1.

$\frac{1}{4}$ of 8 = ___?___

2.

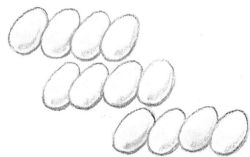

$\frac{1}{3}$ of 12 = ___?___

3.

$\frac{1}{2}$ of 6 = ___?___

4.

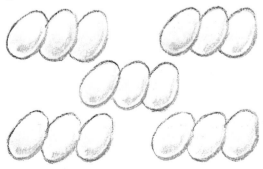

$\frac{1}{5}$ of 15 = ___?___

292

Mixed Practice • Complete.

5.

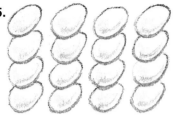

$\frac{1}{4}$ of 16 = ____?____

6.

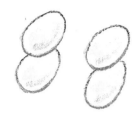

$\frac{1}{2}$ of 4 = ____?____

7.

$\frac{1}{3}$ of 6 = ____?____

8.

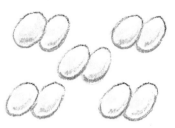

$\frac{1}{5}$ of 10 = ____?____

9.

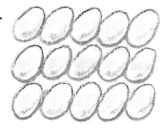

$\frac{1}{3}$ of 15 = ____?____

10.

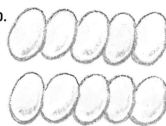

$\frac{1}{2}$ of 10 = ____?____

11. $\frac{1}{2}$ of 8 = ____?____

12. $\frac{1}{8}$ of 16 = ____?____

13. $\frac{1}{5}$ of 25 = ____?____

14. $\frac{1}{4}$ of 4 = ____?____

15. $\frac{1}{4}$ of 20 = ____?____

16. $\frac{1}{4}$ of 12 = ____?____

17. $\frac{1}{8}$ of 24 = ____?____

18. $\frac{1}{3}$ of 9 = ____?____

19. $\frac{1}{4}$ of 24 = ____?____

Is it true? Write YES or NO.

★ 20. $\frac{1}{5}$ of 20 = 4

★ 21. $\frac{1}{2}$ of 18 = 8

★ 22. $\frac{1}{2}$ of 14 = 7

PROBLEM SOLVING • APPLICATIONS

23. Lyle needs 16 bread pans. He has $\frac{1}{2}$ of them. How many bread pans does he have?

24. There are 8 pints of cream. Jiro uses $\frac{1}{4}$ of them. How many pints does Jiro use?

★ 25. There are 18 eggs. Mike uses $\frac{1}{3}$ of them. How many eggs does Mike use? How many eggs are left?

★ 26. Jan needs 28 paper muffin cups. She has $\frac{1}{4}$ of them. How many muffin cup does Jan have? How many more does she need?

Equivalent Fractions

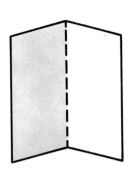

Fold a piece of paper to show halves. Color $\frac{1}{2}$ blue.

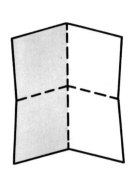

Fold the paper again. The paper shows fourths. $\frac{2}{4}$ is blue.

$$\frac{1}{2} = \frac{2}{4}$$

$\frac{1}{2}$ and $\frac{2}{4}$ are names for the same number. $\frac{1}{2}$ and $\frac{2}{4}$ are **equivalent fractions.**

Practice ● Complete.

1.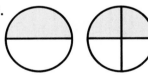

$\frac{1}{4} = \frac{?}{8}$

2.

$\frac{1}{2} = \frac{?}{4}$

3.

$\frac{2}{3} = \frac{?}{6}$

4.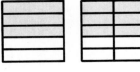

$\frac{3}{5} = \frac{?}{10}$

5.

$\frac{2}{4} = \frac{?}{8}$

6.

$\frac{1}{2} = \frac{?}{6}$

294

More Practice ● Complete.

7.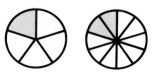

$$\frac{1}{5} = \frac{?}{10}$$

8.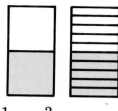

$$\frac{1}{2} = \frac{?}{10}$$

9.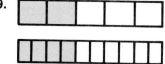

$$\frac{2}{5} = \frac{?}{10}$$

10.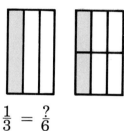

$$\frac{1}{3} = \frac{?}{6}$$

11.

$$\frac{1}{2} = \frac{?}{8}$$

12.

$$\frac{3}{4} = \frac{?}{8}$$

★ 13.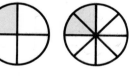

$$\frac{1}{4} = ?$$

★ 14.

$$\frac{4}{5} = ?$$

★ 15.

$$\frac{2}{3} = ?$$

PROBLEM SOLVING ● APPLICATIONS

Write TRUE or FALSE. Use the chart to help you.

16. One-half is equivalent to two-eighths.

17. Three-fourths is equivalent to six-eighths.

18. Three-eighths is equivalent to two-fourths.

★ 19. Eight-eighths is equivalent to two-halves.

★ 20. Seven-eighths is equivalent to four-fourths.

$\frac{1}{2}$				$\frac{1}{2}$			
$\frac{1}{4}$		$\frac{1}{4}$		$\frac{1}{4}$		$\frac{1}{4}$	
$\frac{1}{8}$	$\frac{1}{8}$	$\frac{1}{8}$	$\frac{1}{8}$	$\frac{1}{8}$	$\frac{1}{8}$	$\frac{1}{8}$	$\frac{1}{8}$

Comparing Fractions

When the denominators
are the same, compare the
numerators.

Which is less, $\frac{1}{4}$ or $\frac{3}{4}$?

Which is greater, $\frac{2}{8}$ or $\frac{5}{8}$?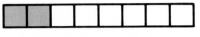

$\frac{1}{4}$ is less than $\frac{3}{4}$.

$$\frac{1}{4} < \frac{3}{4}$$

$\frac{5}{8}$ is greater than $\frac{2}{8}$.

$$\frac{5}{8} > \frac{2}{8}$$

When the denominators are not the same, you can draw a picture
to find an equivalent fraction.

Which is less, $\frac{2}{4}$ or $\frac{3}{8}$?

Which is greater, $\frac{1}{3}$ or $\frac{3}{6}$?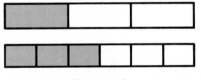

$$\frac{3}{8} < \frac{2}{4}$$

$$\frac{3}{6} > \frac{1}{3}$$

Practice • Write $>$ or $<$.

1.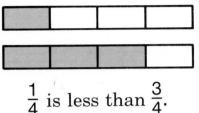

$$\frac{2}{4} \bigcirc \frac{1}{4}$$

2.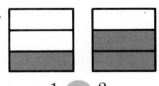

$$\frac{1}{3} \bigcirc \frac{2}{3}$$

3.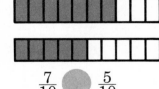

$$\frac{7}{10} \bigcirc \frac{5}{10}$$

4.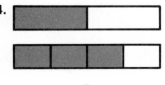

$$\frac{1}{2} \bigcirc \frac{3}{4}$$

5.

$$\frac{2}{3} \bigcirc \frac{2}{6}$$

6.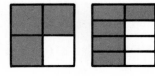

$$\frac{3}{4} \bigcirc \frac{5}{8}$$

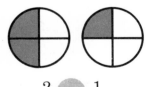
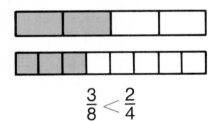

Mixed Practice ● Write > or <.

7.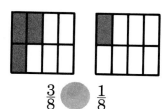

$$\frac{3}{8} \bigcirc \frac{1}{8}$$

8.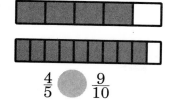

$$\frac{4}{5} \bigcirc \frac{9}{10}$$

9.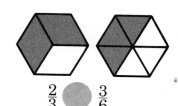

$$\frac{2}{3} \bigcirc \frac{3}{6}$$

10.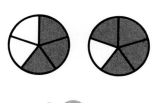

$$\frac{3}{5} \bigcirc \frac{4}{5}$$

11.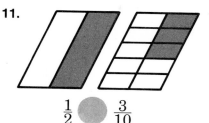

$$\frac{1}{2} \bigcirc \frac{3}{10}$$

12.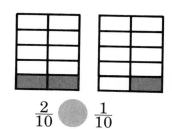

$$\frac{2}{10} \bigcirc \frac{1}{10}$$

13. $\frac{5}{6} \bigcirc \frac{4}{6}$

14. $\frac{4}{8} \bigcirc \frac{6}{8}$

15. $\frac{1}{10} \bigcirc \frac{9}{10}$

★ 16. $\frac{1}{2} \bigcirc \frac{1}{3}$

★ 17. $\frac{1}{3} \bigcirc \frac{1}{6}$

★ 18. $\frac{1}{4} \bigcirc \frac{1}{2}$

PROBLEM SOLVING ● APPLICATIONS

19. Tabia ate $\frac{2}{3}$ of a bar of cheese. Eleana ate $\frac{5}{8}$ of a bar of cheese. Who ate more cheese?

★ 20. Ella drank $\frac{2}{3}$ of a cup of milk. Ruth Ann drank $\frac{4}{6}$ of a cup of milk. Who drank the most milk?

Midchapter Review

Write the fraction that tells what part is blue.

1.

2.

3.

4.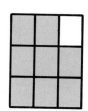

Complete.

5. $\frac{1}{3}$ of 15 = ____?____

6. $\frac{1}{2}$ of 24 = ____?____

7. $\frac{1}{4}$ of 16 = ____?____

Write > or <.

8. $\frac{2}{3} \bigcirc \frac{1}{3}$

9. $\frac{3}{5} \bigcirc \frac{4}{5}$

10. $\frac{9}{10} \bigcirc \frac{7}{10}$

PROBLEM SOLVING • STRATEGIES

Make Up an Easier Problem First

Sometimes you can make up
an easier problem first to help you
solve the given problem.

Jane had to solve this problem:

Rico and Jared cut the grass.
Rico cut $\frac{3}{4}$ of the grass. Jared
cut $\frac{1}{4}$ of the grass. Which boy
cut more of the grass?

Jane thought of an easier problem:

Rico cut 3 parts. Jared cut 1 part. Which boy cut more parts?

Jane used the easier problem to solve the harder problem.

Since 3 > 1, then $\frac{3}{4} > \frac{1}{4}$

Rico cut more of the grass.

Make up an easier problem for each.

1. Ginger cut $\frac{1}{3}$ of the grass on
   Monday. She cut $\frac{2}{3}$ of the
   grass on Tuesday. On which
   day did she cut more grass?

   **Try to solve the problem with
   easy numbers.**

2. Sally sold $\frac{5}{6}$ of a pitcher of
   lemonade on Thursday. She
   sold $\frac{1}{3}$ of a pitcher on Friday.
   On which day did she sell
   more?

3. Larry raked $\frac{7}{8}$ of a basket of
   leaves before lunch. He
   raked $\frac{3}{4}$ of a basket after
   lunch. When did he rake
   more leaves?

4. Brian washed windows to
   make money. He made $2.50
   the first week. He made
   $2.75 the second week. How
   much money did Brian
   make in all?

Solve.

5. Carla and Henry make the same amount of money delivering papers. Carla saves $\frac{2}{5}$ of her money. Henry saves $\frac{3}{10}$ of his money. Who saves more money?

Read the question carefully. What operation should you use?

---

6. Some students collect cans to sell. They collect 218 cans the first week and 407 cans the next week. How many cans do they collect in all?

7. Roger sells painted seashells. He makes $2.15 the first day and $3.62 the second day. How much more does he make the second day?

8. Nancy earned $4.60 feeding her neighbor's dog. She wants to buy a book that costs $7.00. How much more money does she need?

9. Oko sells 215 newspapers each week for 3 weeks. How many newspapers does Oko sell all together?

10. Maurice trims 6 trees. He trims the same number of branches off each tree. He trims 162 branches in all. How many branches does he trim from each tree?

★ 11. Lauren raked $\frac{1}{3}$ of the yard on Monday morning. She raked $\frac{1}{6}$ of the yard on Monday afternoon. On Tuesday morning she raked $\frac{1}{4}$ of the yard. When did she rake most of the yard?

★ 12. Earl and Betty sell dried flowers for 4 days. They sell the same amount each day. They make $8.60. How much do they make each day? Did they make more than $3.00 each day?

Mixed Numbers

Karen likes to eat graham crackers.
How many graham crackers
does Karen have?

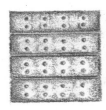 

1 cracker and $\frac{1}{3}$ cracker

1 and $\frac{1}{3}$

$1\frac{1}{3}$ ⟵ mixed number

Karen has $1\frac{1}{3}$ crackers.

How many crackers are there?

2 crackers and $\frac{3}{4}$ crackers

2 and $\frac{3}{4}$

$2\frac{3}{4}$

There are $2\frac{3}{4}$ crackers.

Practice • Write a mixed number that tells how much is blue.

1.

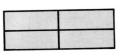
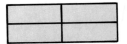
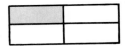

2.

3.

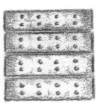

300

More Practice • Write a mixed number that tells how much is blue.

4.
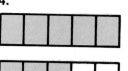

5.

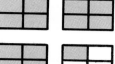

6.
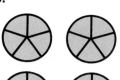

7.
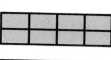
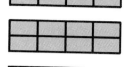

8.

9.

10.
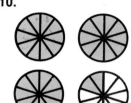

11.

PROBLEM SOLVING • APPLICATIONS

12. Karen eats 2 crackers at lunch. She eats $\frac{1}{2}$ of a cracker for an afternoon snack. How many crackers does she eat in all?

★ **13.** David eats 4 crackers. Then he eats $\frac{2}{3}$ of another cracker. He also eats 3 slices of whole wheat bread. How many crackers does he eat in all?

Skills Maintenance

1. $\begin{array}{r} 7 \\ \times 6 \\ \hline \end{array}$	**2.** $\begin{array}{r} 8 \\ \times 8 \\ \hline \end{array}$	**3.** $\begin{array}{r} 9 \\ \times 6 \\ \hline \end{array}$	**4.** $\begin{array}{r} 8 \\ \times 7 \\ \hline \end{array}$	**5.** $\begin{array}{r} 6 \\ \times 6 \\ \hline \end{array}$	**6.** $\begin{array}{r} 6 \\ \times 8 \\ \hline \end{array}$
7. $\begin{array}{r} 9 \\ \times 7 \\ \hline \end{array}$	**8.** $\begin{array}{r} 9 \\ \times 9 \\ \hline \end{array}$	**9.** $\begin{array}{r} 8 \\ \times 6 \\ \hline \end{array}$	**10.** $\begin{array}{r} 9 \\ \times 8 \\ \hline \end{array}$	**11.** $\begin{array}{r} 7 \\ \times 7 \\ \hline \end{array}$	**12.** $\begin{array}{r} 5 \\ \times 6 \\ \hline \end{array}$

Tenths

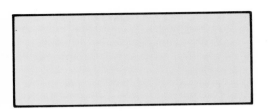

Start with a piece of paper.

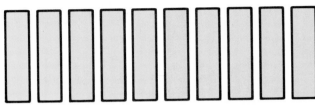

Cut it into 10 parts that are the same size.

Each part is one-tenth of the whole.

$$\frac{1}{10} = 0.1$$

fraction   decimal

You can write **decimals** to name tenths.

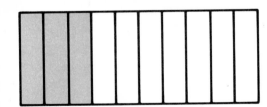

What part is blue?

$$\frac{3}{10} = 0.3$$

Read both this way: three-tenths

You can use a place-value chart to show decimals.

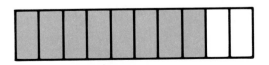

ones	tenths
0	8

decimal point

Read. $\longrightarrow$ eight-tenths
Write. $\longrightarrow$ 0.8

Practice • Write the decimal that tells what part is blue.

1.

2.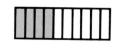

3.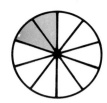

Write the decimals.

4.
ones	tenths
0	5

5.
ones	tenths
0	2

6.
ones	tenths
0	9

7. four-tenths

8. seven-tenths

9. eight-tenths

Mixed Practice • Write the decimal that tells what part is blue.

10.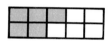

11.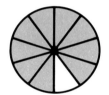

12.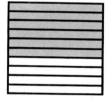

Write the decimals.

13.
ones	tenths
0	1

14.
ones	tenths
0	6

15.
ones	tenths
0	4

16. $\frac{5}{10}$

17. $\frac{7}{10}$

18. $\frac{2}{10}$

19. nine-tenths

20. five-tenths

21. one-tenth

Write in words.

★ 22. 0.5

★ 23. 0.1

★ 24. 0.9

PROBLEM SOLVING • **APPLICATIONS**

Complete the patterns.

25. $0.5, 0.6,$ ___?___ , ___?___ , ___?___

★ 26. $1.4, 1.7, 2.0,$ ___?___ , ___?___ , ___?___

Decimals Greater Than One

You can write decimals to name
numbers greater than one.

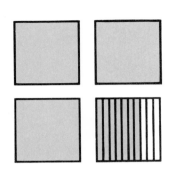

How much is blue?

$3\frac{7}{10}$ 3.7

↑ mixed numeral   ↑ decimal

Read both this way:
three and seven-tenths.

You can use a place-value chart to show decimals.

Read. ⟶ five and two-tenths
Write. ⟶ 5.2

ones	tenths
5	2

Practice • Write the decimal that tells how much is blue.

1.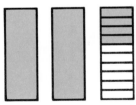

2.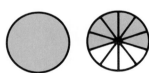

3.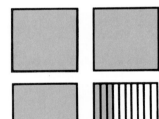

Write the decimals.

4.
ones	tenths
9	2

5.
ones	tenths
2	8

6.
ones	tenths
6	1

7. $5\frac{2}{10}$ 8. $8\frac{9}{10}$ 9. $7\frac{5}{10}$ 10. $3\frac{1}{10}$ 11. $9\frac{4}{10}$ 12. $4\frac{7}{10}$

13. four and six-tenths

14. eight and three-tenths

Mixed Practice • Write the decimal that tells how much is blue.

15.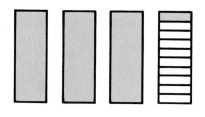

16.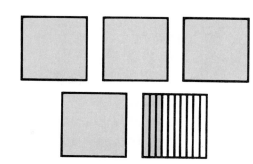

Write the decimals.

17.
ones	tenths
4	3

18.
ones	tenths
7	7

19.
ones	tenths
3	5

20.
ones	tenths
8	6

21.
ones	tenths
1	4

22.
ones	tenths
5	9

23. $3\frac{4}{10}$ 24. $6\frac{2}{10}$ 25. $8\frac{5}{10}$ 26. $2\frac{9}{10}$ 27. $1\frac{6}{10}$ 28. $5\frac{7}{10}$

29. $4\frac{8}{10}$ 30. $1\frac{1}{10}$ 31. $2\frac{3}{10}$ 32. $6\frac{7}{10}$ 33. $7\frac{9}{10}$ 34. $9\frac{4}{10}$

35. three and nine-tenths   36. one and five-tenths

37. seven and one-tenth   38. two and eight-tenths

★ 39. sixteen and two-tenths   ★ 40. twenty and six-tenths

★ 41. fifty-one and three-tenths   ★ 42. thirty-seven and seven-tenths

PROBLEM SOLVING • APPLICATIONS

Complete the patterns.

43. 4.3, 4.4, 4.5, ___?___, ___?___, ___?___, ___?___

44. 6.2, ___?___, 6.6, ___?___, ___?___, 7.2

★ 45. 30.2, 31.3, 32.4, ___?___, ___?___, ___?___, ___?___

Comparing Decimals

Laura and Barry have gardens.
The gardens are the same size.
Laura plants peas in 0.7 of her garden.
Barry plants peas in 0.4 of his garden.
Who plants the greatest amount of peas?
Use the drawings to find out.

0.7 is greater than 0.4.   0.4 is less than 0.7.
$$0.7 > 0.4$$ $$0.4 < 0.7$$

Laura plants the greatest amount of peas.

Compare the decimals. Use > or <.

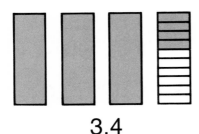   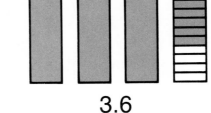

3.4   3.6

Think:
Same number of ones.
Compare the tenths. $4 < 6$
So $3.4 < 3.6$.

Practice • Write > or <.

1.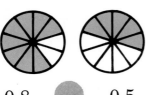
0.8   0.5

2.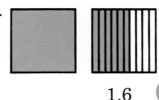
1.6   1.8

3. 0.4   0.7   4. 3.2   4.1   5. 2.8   2.7

Mixed Practice • Write > or <.

6.

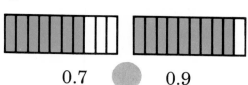

0.7 ⬤ 0.9

7.

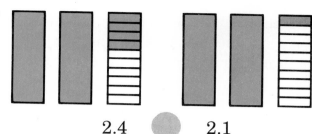

2.4 ⬤ 2.1

8. 0.6 ⬤ 0.8   **9.** 0.5 ⬤ 0.2   **10.** 0.7 ⬤ 0.6

11. 0.2 ⬤ 0.4   **12.** 4.2 ⬤ 4.3   **13.** 8.9 ⬤ 8.4

14. 7.5 ⬤ 7.4   **15.** 2.5 ⬤ 1.8   **16.** 5.3 ⬤ 5.6

Name 1 more tenth.

★**17.** 0.4   ★**18.** 2.7   ★**19.** 1.9

PROBLEM SOLVING • APPLICATIONS

20. Suki and Rob were running a race. Suki ran the race in 9.6 seconds. Rob ran the race in 9.8 seconds. Who won the race?

★**21.** Lester, Rosa, and Lono were in a race. Lono finished in 11.5 seconds. Lester finished in 10.9 seconds, and Rosa finished in 11.2 seconds. Who finished first? Second? Third?

Skills Maintenance

Divide.

1. $2\overline{)8}$ **2.** $5\overline{)10}$ **3.** $3\overline{)27}$ **4.** $2\overline{)16}$ **5.** $4\overline{)24}$ **6.** $2\overline{)14}$

7. $4\overline{)12}$ **8.** $3\overline{)21}$ **9.** $4\overline{)32}$ **10.** $5\overline{)25}$ **11.** $5\overline{)35}$ **12.** $5\overline{)40}$

Adding and Subtracting Decimals

Sam rides his bicycle
2.8 kilometers to a friend's home.
Then he rides 4.5 kilometers to
the park.
How far does Sam ride?

$2.8 + 4.5 = \quad ?$

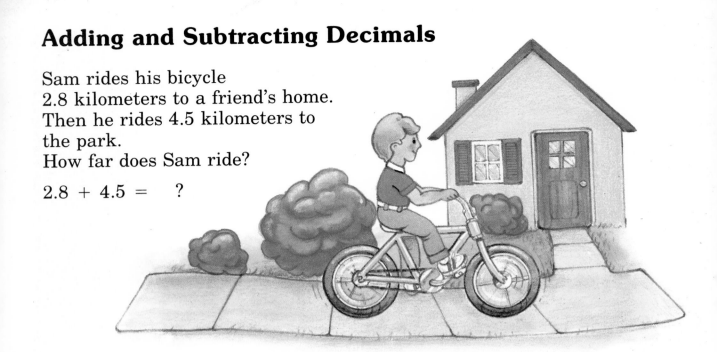

You can add decimals as if you were adding whole numbers.

Step 1
Line up the decimal
points.

$$\begin{array}{r} 2.8 \\ +4.5 \\ \hline \end{array}$$

Step 2
Add the tenths.
Regroup 13 tenths
as 1 one 3 tenths.

$$\begin{array}{r} 1 \\ 2.8 \\ +4.5 \\ \hline 3 \end{array}$$

Step 3
Add the ones. Write
the decimal point
in the answer.

$$\begin{array}{r} 1 \\ 2.8 \\ +4.5 \\ \hline 7.3 \end{array}$$

Sam rides 7.3 kilometers.

You can subtract decimals as if you were subtracting whole numbers.

Subtract: $6.2 - 4.9$.

Step 1
Line up the decimal
points.

$$\begin{array}{r} 6.2 \\ -4.9 \\ \hline \end{array}$$

Step 2
Regroup 6 ones 2
tenths as 5 ones 12
tenths. Subtract the
tenths.

$$\begin{array}{r} 5\ 12 \\ 6.2 \\ -4.9 \\ \hline 3 \end{array}$$

Step 3
Subtract the ones.
Write the decimal
point in the answer.

$$\begin{array}{r} 5\ 12 \\ 6.2 \\ -4.9 \\ \hline 1.3 \end{array}$$

Practice ● Add.

1. 4.7
    +1.8

2. 6.8
    +1.8

3. 3.7
    +4.6

4. 4.5
    +5.2

5. 2.2
    +4.4

6. 5.6
    +2.6

Subtract.

7. 3.5
    −1.3

8. 2.3
    −1.8

9. 4.6
    −1.8

10. 3.4
    −2.6

11. 5.2
    −4.7

12. 8.6
    −1.9

Mixed Practice ● Add.

13. 2.9
    +3.7

14. 7.8
    +1.5

15. 5.6
    +3.9

16. 3.9
    +3.4

17. 2.5
    +6.7

18. 7.2
    +1.8

19. 5.8
    +3.6

20. 7.5
    +1.1

21. 3.8
    +4.9

22. 2.5
    +6.5

23. 2.6
    +3.7

24. 1.5
    +8.3

Subtract.

25. 8.6
    −1.9

26. 9.5
    −3.7

27. 4.5
    −2.2

28. 9.6
    −5.6

29. 6.7
    −4.8

30. 3.6
    −2.7

31. 2.5
    −1.8

32. 8.2
    −2.4

33. 8.5
    −4.9

★ 34. 3.0
    −2.8

★ 35. 4.0
    −1.7

★ 36. 3.0
    −1.6

PROBLEM SOLVING ● APPLICATIONS

37. Jane walks 2.3 kilometers on Monday. She walks 3.9 kilometers on Tuesday. How far does Jane walk on Monday and Tuesday?

★ 38. Josi rides her bicycle 5.2 kilometers. Bruce rides his bicycle 4.8 kilometers. Who rides farther? How much farther?

PROBLEM SOLVING • STRATEGIES

Missing Information

Sometimes a problem does not give you enough information to find the answer. What information is missing in this problem?

Karen visited the sea lion pool.
The pool was 0.8 full.
How much water was in the pool?

You do not have enough information to solve this problem. You need to know the total amount of water that the pool can hold.

Do you have enough information to solve the problem?
Write YES or NO.

1. Gail saw 14 sea turtles in a tank. She saw 9 sea turtles in another tank. How many sea turtles did she see in all?

Read carefully to find all the needed information.

---

2. Mr. Campos fed 5 gray sea lions. Then he fed the brown sea lions. How many sea lions did he feed in all?

3. Greg counted 23 sea gulls on the fence. How many sea gulls are not on the fence?

4. Kori sees 0.3 of the sea horses in a tank. Terry sees 7 sea horses. Who sees more sea horses, Kori or Terry?

5. Yesterday 258 people came to the park. Today 381 people came. How many more people came today?

What information do you need to find the answer?

6. A seal does 11 tricks. It eats some fish and does more tricks. How many tricks does it do in all?

Decide what the question is asking.

---

7. First 78 people watch whales. Some of the people leave. How many people are watching the whales now?

9. Ms. Arno moves 0.7 of the snails to a new tank. Mr. Soares moves some of the snails. Who moves more snails, Ms. Arno or Mr. Soares?

10. On Monday 114 people buy tickets for the morning show. How many more people buy tickets for the afternoon show?

11. Each shark tank holds the same number of sharks. There are 7 tanks. How many sharks are there in all?

8. The seal trainer feeds 3 fish to each seal. How many fish does he feed the seals in all?

12. The Sea Park has 216 fish. Each tank has the same number of fish. How many tanks are there?

REVIEW

Write the fraction that tells what part is blue. (pages 288–291)

1.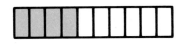

2.

3.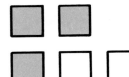

Complete. (pages 292–293)

4. $\frac{1}{2}$ of 18 = ___?___

5. $\frac{1}{3}$ of 6 = ___?___

6. $\frac{1}{6}$ of 24 = ___?___

Write > or <. (pages 296–297)

7. $\frac{1}{3}$ ⬤ $\frac{2}{3}$

8. $\frac{5}{8}$ ⬤ $\frac{3}{8}$

9. $\frac{7}{9}$ ⬤ $\frac{4}{9}$

Write the decimal that tells what part is blue. (pages 302–305)

10.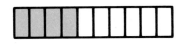

11.

12.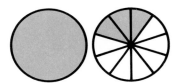

Write the decimals. (pages 302–305)

13. $\frac{7}{10}$

14. $8\frac{1}{10}$

15. $6\frac{4}{10}$

16. four-tenths   **17.** one and nine-tenths   **18.** six and three-tenths

Write > or <. (pages 306–307)

19. 0.9 ⬤ 0.6

20. 3.5 ⬤ 3.8

21. 0.8 ⬤ 1.1

Solve.

22. Amy buys 2.5 meters of blue fabric. She buys 1.4 meters of red fabric. How many meters of fabric does Amy have all together? (p. 308)

23. Mrs. Diaz has 4.2 meters of fabric. She uses 2.8 meters for a dress. How much fabric does she have left? (p. 308)

PROJECT

Probability

Put 1 blue marble and 1 red marble in a dish. Without looking, take one out. Record its color. Put the marble back in the dish.

What would happen in 20 times?

A. Red will show more often.
B. Blue will show more often.
C. Both will show about the same.

Guess. Then try it. Were you right?

Put 2 blue marbles and 1 red marble in a dish. Without looking, take one out, record its color, and put it back.

What would happen in 20 times?

A. Red will show more often.
B. Blue will show more often.
C. Both will show about the same.

Guess. Then try it. Were you right?

In 20 tries will you take out a red one more often, a blue one more often, a green one more often, or all about the same? Guess. Then try it.

1.

2.

3.

Write the fraction that tells what part is blue.

1.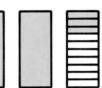

2.

3.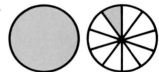

Complete.

4. $\frac{1}{4}$ of 16 = ___?___

5. $\frac{1}{3}$ of 18 = ___?___

6. $\frac{1}{8}$ of 24 = ___?___

Write > or <.

7. $\frac{1}{4}$ $\frac{3}{4}$

8. $\frac{5}{6}$ ⬤ $\frac{4}{6}$

9. $\frac{3}{5}$ ⬤ $\frac{2}{5}$

Write the decimal that tells what part is blue.

10.

11.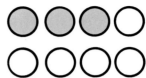

12.

Write the decimals.

13. $\frac{8}{10}$

14. $3\frac{3}{10}$

15. $7\frac{5}{10}$

16. six-tenths

17. two and seven-tenths

18. nine and four-tenths

Write > or <.

19. 0.6 6.2

20. 0.8 ⬤ 0.9

21. 6.4 4.6

Solve.

22. Mr. Browning drives 1.6 kilometers to the bakery. Then he drives 4.8 kilometers to the doctor. How many kilometers does he drive in all?

23. Bruce rides his bicycle 4.6 kilometers on Sunday. He rides 3.8 kilometers on Monday. How much farther did he ride on Sunday?

Adding Fractions on the Number Line

This line is marked to show 4 equal parts between 0 and 1. What fractions are shown between 0 and 1?

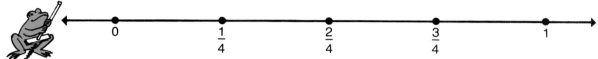

This line shows 8 parts of the same length. What fractions are shown between 0 and 1?

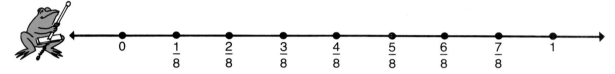

The frog hops $\frac{1}{3}$ space. It hops $\frac{2}{3}$ more. Where does it land?

$$\frac{1}{3} + \frac{2}{3} = 1$$

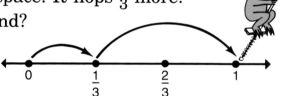

The frog hops $\frac{3}{4}$ space. It hops $\frac{4}{4}$ more. Where does it land?

$$\frac{3}{4} + \frac{4}{4} = 1\frac{3}{4}$$

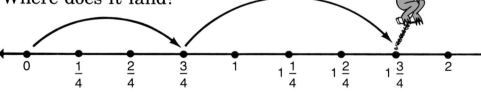

The frog hops $\frac{3}{8}$ space. It hops $\frac{7}{8}$ more. Where does it land?

$$\frac{3}{8} + \frac{7}{8} = 1\frac{2}{8}$$

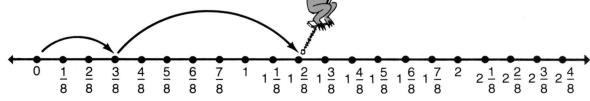

315

Where does the frog land?

|0| |$\frac{1}{2}$| |1| |$1\frac{1}{2}$| |2| |$2\frac{1}{2}$|

1. $\frac{1}{2} + \frac{1}{2} = $ ___?___

2. $\frac{1}{2} + \frac{2}{2} = $ ___?___

3. $\frac{2}{2} + \frac{2}{2} = $ ___?___

4. $\frac{2}{2} + \frac{1}{2} = $ ___?___

5. $\frac{2}{2} + \frac{3}{2} = $ ___?___

6. $\frac{1}{2} + \frac{3}{2} = $ ___?___

|0| |$\frac{1}{4}$| |$\frac{2}{4}$| |$\frac{3}{4}$| |1| |$1\frac{1}{4}$| |$1\frac{2}{4}$| |$1\frac{3}{4}$| |2| |$2\frac{1}{4}$| |$2\frac{2}{4}$|

7. $\frac{1}{4} + \frac{2}{4} = $ ___?___

8. $\frac{3}{4} + \frac{2}{4} = $ ___?___

9. $\frac{3}{4} + \frac{1}{4} = $ ___?___

10. $\frac{2}{4} + \frac{2}{4} = $ ___?___

11. $\frac{3}{4} + \frac{3}{4} = $ ___?___

12. $\frac{4}{4} + \frac{2}{4} = $ ___?___

|0| |$\frac{1}{8}$| |$\frac{2}{8}$| |$\frac{3}{8}$| |$\frac{4}{8}$| |$\frac{5}{8}$| |$\frac{6}{8}$| |$\frac{7}{8}$| |1| |$1\frac{1}{8}$| |$1\frac{2}{8}$| |$1\frac{3}{8}$| |$1\frac{4}{8}$| |$1\frac{5}{8}$| |$1\frac{6}{8}$| |$1\frac{7}{8}$| |2| |$2\frac{1}{8}$| |$2\frac{2}{8}$| |$2\frac{3}{8}$| |$2\frac{4}{8}$|

13. $\frac{2}{8} + \frac{3}{8} = $ ___?___

14. $\frac{3}{8} + \frac{2}{8} = $ ___?___

15. $\frac{7}{8} + \frac{1}{8} = $ ___?___

16. $\frac{4}{8} + \frac{4}{8} = $ ___?___

17. $\frac{7}{8} + \frac{3}{8} = $ ___?___

18. $\frac{5}{8} + \frac{9}{8} = $ ___?___

316

CALCULATOR

Decimals on a Calculator

The calculator handles decimals very well.
When you write a problem with decimals, you must line up the
    decimal points.
The calculator remembers where decimal points were input.
Turn the calculator on. Find the decimal-point button. $\boxed{\cdot}$

Enter 47. The screen shows ⬡ 47. .

Enter 4.7. The screen shows ⬡ 4.7 .

Calculate 4.7 − 2.3 by pushing ④ $\boxed{\cdot}$ ⑦ ⊖ ② $\boxed{\cdot}$ ③ ⊜.

Did your screen look like this? ⬡ 2.4

If the answer ends in zero, be sure to write the zero. 8.3 − 4.3 = 4.0

Calculate.

1. 3.2 − 1.9 = _?_   2. 8.1 + 1.8 = _?_
3. 6.8 − 5.4 = _?_   4. 5.8 + 2.4 = _?_

Copy problems 5 through 10 on a sheet of paper. Calculate.
Write the answers in the blank spaces. Then work the new problem.

5.	4.3	6.	9.6	7.	2.7	8.	8.0
	+ 3.6		− 5.1		− 1.5		− 6.7

9. _?_ − _?_ = _?_   10. _?_ + _?_ = _?_
   (Answer (Answer   (Answer (Answer
   from 5) from 6)   from 7) from 8)

11. 4.7 − _?_ = 2.4   12. _?_ + 8.3 = 9.4   13. 7.4 − 3.6 = _?_

14. _?_ − 6.2 = 1.4   15. 7.8 + 2.1 = _?_   16. 4.2 − _?_ = 2.3

17. _?_ − 1.0 = 7.7   18. 3.0 + 6.6 = _?_   19. _?_ + 2.0 = 8.6

Remember to turn the calculator off.

Choose the correct answers.

1. Name 1,000 less.

5,967

- **A.** 5,867
- **B.** 4,867
- **C.** 4,967
- **D.** not here

2.

$$
\begin{array}{r}
686 \\
14 \\
+739 \\
\hline
\end{array}
$$

- **A.** 1,322
- **B.** 1,439
- **C.** 1,399
- **D.** not here

3. What time will it be in 25 minutes?

- **A.** 10:55
- **B.** 10:45
- **C.** 11:55
- **D.** not here

4. Write the amount.

2 dollars
2 quarters
3 dimes
1 nickel
1 penny

- **A.** $2.76
- **B.** $20.98
- **C.** $2.86
- **D.** not here

5. Measure the length to the nearest centimeter.

- **A.** 2.5 cm
- **B.** 1.5 cm
- **C.** 3 cm
- **D.** not here

6. $819 \times 6 = $ ___?___

- **A.** 4,914
- **B.** 3,814
- **C.** 4,954
- **D.** not here

7. $84 \div 4 = $ ___?___

- **A.** 41
- **B.** 21
- **C.** 44
- **D.** not here

8. $3\overline{)869}$

- **A.** 289 r 2
- **B.** 323
- **C.** 279 r 1
- **D.** not here

9. What fraction of the marbles are blue?

- **A.** $\frac{1}{6}$
- **B.** $\frac{5}{6}$
- **C.** $\frac{4}{5}$
- **D.** not here

10. Mr. Jennings buys pet food for his dog, Pepper. He spends $6.79. He gives the clerk $10.00. How much change does Mr. Jennings get?

- **A.** $4.31
- **B.** $16.79
- **C.** $3.21
- **D.** not here

11. Ali has 17 dog bones. She puts 4 bones in each bag. How many bags does she fill? How many dog bones are left over?

- **A.** 5
- **B.** 21
- **C.** 4 r 1
- **D.** not here

Geometry

CHAPTER 12

**Solid Geometric Figures—
Cube, Cylinder, Cone, Sphere, and Rectangular Prism
● Faces, Edges, and Corners
● Plane Figures—Rectangle, Square, Triangle, and Circle
● Line Segments and Endpoints
● Congruent Figures ● Line of Symmetry
● Problem Solving: Reading a Map ● Angles**

Solid Geometric Figures

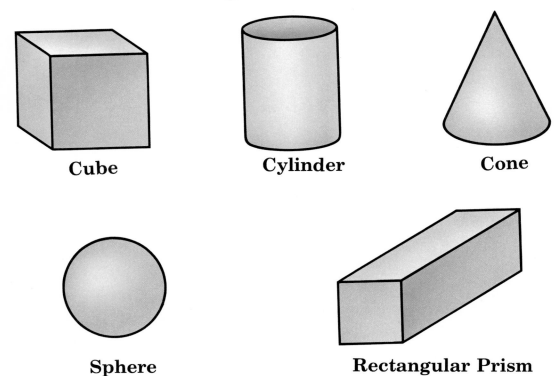

Cube

Cylinder

Cone

Sphere

Rectangular Prism

Can you find objects in your classroom that are shaped like a cube, a cylinder, a cone, a sphere, or a rectangular prism?

Practice • Name the figures.

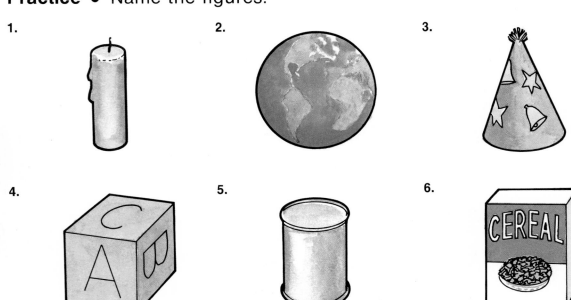

1.

2.

3.

4.

5.

6.

Mixed Practice • Name the figures.

7.

8.

9.

10.

11.

12.

13.

14.

15.

Tell how many.

★ 16.

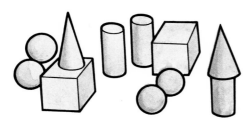

_____? cubes _____? cones

_____? cylinders _____? spheres

★ 17.

_____? rectangular prisms

_____? cylinders _____? cones

_____? spheres

PROBLEM SOLVING • APPLICATIONS

★ 18. Find pictures of objects that are shaped like a cube, a cylinder, a cone, a sphere, and a rectangular prism. Copy the chart. List the names of the objects under the correct headings.

Cube	Cylinder	Cone	Sphere	Rectangular Prism

Faces, Edges, and Corners

A cylinder has 1 **curved surface** and 2 **flat surfaces.** A cylinder can roll on the curved surface. It can stand on the flat surfaces.

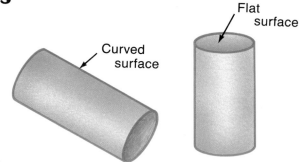

Curved surface

Flat surface

A cube has 6 flat surfaces. A flat surface is called a **face.** Two faces meet at an **edge.** The edges meet at a **corner.**

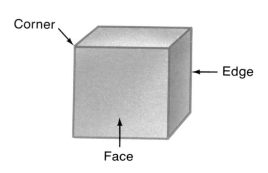

Corner

Edge

Face

Practice ● Tell how many.

1.

_?_ curved surfaces
_?_ flat surfaces

2.

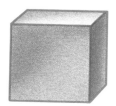

_?_ curved surfaces
_?_ flat surfaces

3.

_?_ faces
_?_ edges
_?_ corners

4.

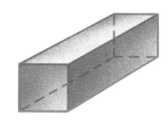

_?_ faces
_?_ edges
_?_ corners

Mixed Practice ● Tell how many.

5.

_____ ? curved surfaces

_____ ? flat surfaces

6.

_____ ? curved surfaces

_____ ? flat surfaces

7.

_____ ? curved surfaces

_____ ? flat surfaces

8.

_____ ? faces

_____ ? edges

_____ ? corners

9.

_____ ? faces

_____ ? edges

_____ ? corners

10.

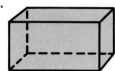

_____ ? faces

_____ ? edges

_____ ? corners

★ **11.**

_____ ? faces

_____ ? edges

_____ ? corners

★ **12.**

_____ ? faces

_____ ? edges

_____ ? corners

★ **13.**

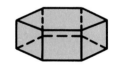

_____ ? faces

_____ ? edges

_____ ? corners

PROBLEM SOLVING ● APPLICATIONS

★ **14.** Trace the pattern. Cut it out. Fold along the dotted lines. Tape the edges together. What shape did you make?

★ **15.** What has 6 faces, 12 edges, and 8 corners? Draw your answer.

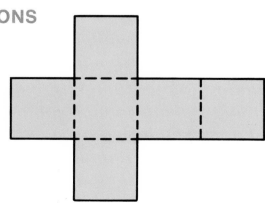

Plane Figures

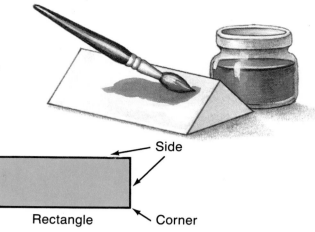

Cover one face of a rectangular
prism with poster paint.
Trace around the shape.
Make a print on paper.

The figure is a **rectangle**.
A rectangle has 4 **sides**
and 4 **corners**.

Side

Rectangle · Corner

More Examples

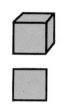

Square
4 equal sides
4 corners

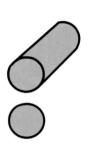

Triangle
3 sides
3 corners

Circle
no sides
no corners

Practice • Name the shapes.

1.
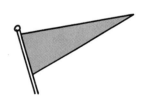

2.

3.

Tell how many.

4.

___?___ sides

___?___ corners

5.
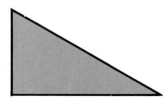

___?___ sides

___?___ corners

6.

___?___ sides

___?___ corners

Mixed Practice ● Name the shapes.

7.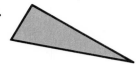

8.

9.

10.

11.

12.

13.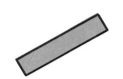

14.

15.

Tell how many.

★ 16.

_____?_____ sides

_____?_____ corners

★ 17.

_____?_____ sides

_____?_____ corners

★ 18.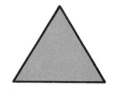

_____?_____ sides

_____?_____ corners

Here are other plane figures. Tell how many sides and corners.

★ 19.

Pentagon

_____?_____ sides

_____?_____ corners

★ 20.

Hexagon

_____?_____ sides

_____?_____ corners

★ 21.

Octagon

_____?_____ sides

_____?_____ corners

PROBLEM SOLVING ● **APPLICATIONS**

★ 22. John drew a pentagon and a hexagon. He counted all the sides. How many did he count in all?

★ 23. Toshio drew 4 octagons. He counted all the sides and corners. How many sides and corners are there?

325

Line Segments and Endpoints

Each edge of this rectangular prism is a **line segment.**

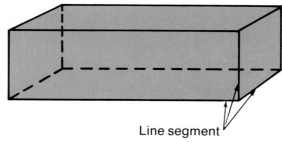

Line segment

Each side of this triangle is a line segment.

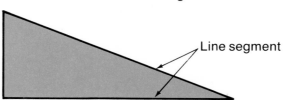

Line segment

A line segment is straight. It has two **endpoints.**

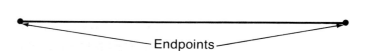

Endpoints

Practice • Is it a line segment? Write YES or NO.

1.

2.

3.

4.

5.

6.

7.

8.

Mixed Practice • Is it a line segment? Write YES or NO.

9.

10.

11.

12.

How many line segments are in each shape?

13.
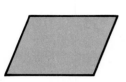

14.
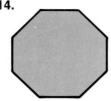

15.
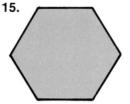

16.
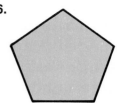

How many line segments can you draw using

17. 2 endpoints?

18. 3 endpoints?

19. 4 endpoints?

PROBLEM SOLVING • APPLICATIONS

Where is the dot? Write INSIDE or OUTSIDE.

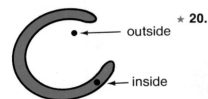

← outside

← inside

★ **20.**

★ **21.**

Midchapter Review

Name each shape. Tell how many.

1.

_____ ? _____ faces
_____ ? _____ edges
_____ ? _____ corners

2.
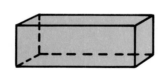

_____ ? _____ faces
_____ ? _____ edges
_____ ? _____ corners

3.
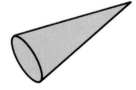

_____ ? _____ curved surfaces
_____ ? _____ flat surfaces

4.

_____ ? _____ sides
_____ ? _____ corners

5.
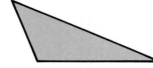

_____ ? _____ sides
_____ ? _____ corners

6.

_____ ? _____ sides
_____ ? _____ corners

Congruent Figures

Congruent figures are the
same size and shape.
Are these triangles congruent?
Here is how to find out.

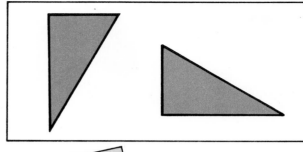

Trace one triangle.

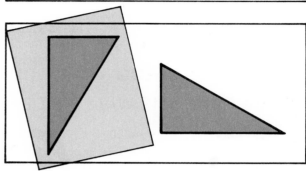

Place the tracing on top of
the other triangle. If they
match exactly, then they
are congruent.
These triangles are the same
size and shape. They are
congruent.

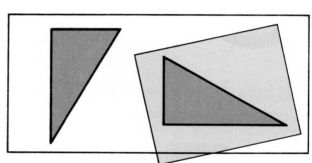

Practice • Are the figures congruent? Write YES or NO.

1.
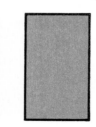

2.
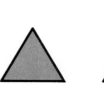

3.
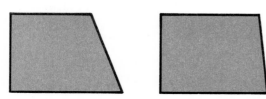

4.
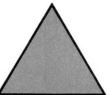
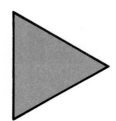
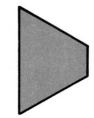

Mixed Practice ● Tell which figure is congruent to the first.

5.   a.   b.   c.

6. 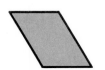   a.   b.   c.

7.   a.   b.   c.

8.   a.   b. 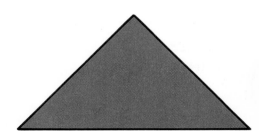   c.

PROBLEM SOLVING ● APPLICATIONS

★ 9. Trace the small triangle four times.
Cut out the triangles.
Fit them together to make
the large triangle.

Skills Maintenance

Multiply.

1. 45 × 3	2. 83 × 2	3. 32 × 5	4. 64 × 4	5. 75 × 5	6. 23 × 7
7. 87 × 4	8. 73 × 3	9. 96 × 2	10. 30 × 5	11. 28 × 4	12. 69 × 3

Line of Symmetry

Fold a sheet of paper. Cut out a shape. Unfold the cutout.

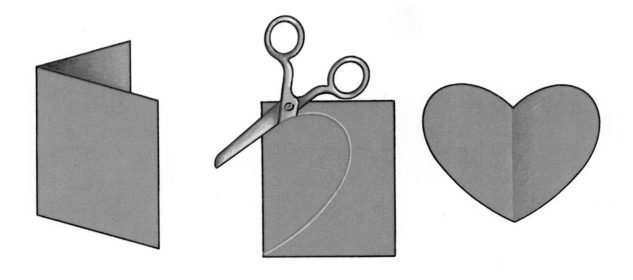

Fold your cutout again.

Both parts match. One part will fit over the other part. The line along the fold is a **line of symmetry.**

Practice • Is the blue line a line of symmetry? Write YES or NO.

1.

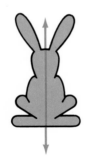

2.

3.

Mixed Practice ● Is the blue line a line of symmetry? Write YES or NO.

4.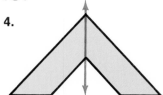

5.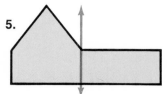

6.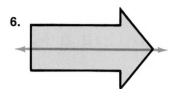

7.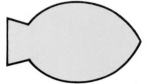

8.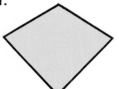

9.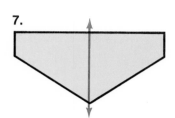

Does the figure have a line of symmetry? Write YES or NO. Trace the figure. Cut it out and fold to check.

10.

11.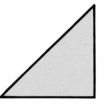

12.

13.

14.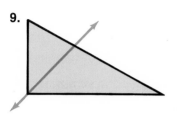

15.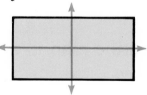

Some figures have more than one line of symmetry.

PROBLEM SOLVING ● APPLICATIONS

Trace the figures. Draw as many lines of symmetry as you can.

★ **16.**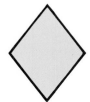

★ **17.**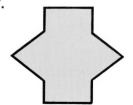

★ **18.**

PROBLEM SOLVING · STRATEGIES

Reading a Map

We use maps $\left\{\begin{array}{l}\text{to find how to get to a place.} \\ \text{to find how far away a place is.}\end{array}\right.$

The Jackson family decided to visit the Big Hills Zoo.
They went through the gate and stopped at Lion Country.
Then they walked to the Elephant House using the shortest way.

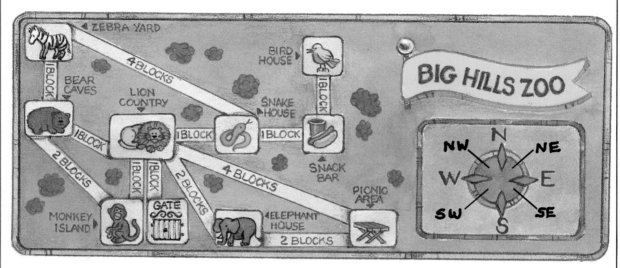

In which direction did they travel to go to Lion Country?

They traveled north from the gate to Lion Country.

How far did they walk from the gate to the Elephant House?

They walked 1 block to Lion Country and then walked 2 blocks
to the Elephant House. In all they walked 3 blocks.

Use the map to answer the questions.

1. How far is it from the Snack
   Bar to the Zebra Yard?

2. In which direction would
   you travel to go from the
   Picnic Area to Lion Country?

**When you are figuring the
distance, take the shortest
way.**

Solve. Use the map to answer the questions.

3. Jack walked from the Zebra Yard to the Snake House. How many blocks did he walk?

4. Is the Snack Bar east or west of the Bear Caves?

5. Sheryl walked from the Elephant House to Lion Country. She walked from Lion Country to the Bird House. How many blocks did she walk in all?

6. In which direction would you go from the Snack Bar to get to the Bird House?

7. Bill went through the gate and walked 1 block north. He then walked 4 blocks southeast. Where is he now?

8. How far is it from the Bird House to Monkey Island using the shortest way?

9. If Sonya can walk 1 block in 5 minutes, how many blocks can she walk in 30 minutes?

10. Using the shortest way, how far is it from the Elephant House to the Zebra Yard?

11. In which direction would you go from the Bear Caves to get to the Zebra Yard?

Use the arrows on the map to locate directions.

★ 12. Jack walked from the Bird House to the Snake House, from the Snake House to Lion Country, and from Lion Country to the Picnic Area. How many blocks did he walk?

★ 13. Bella walked 4 blocks southeast from Lion Country. Then she walked 2 blocks west. Where is she now?

333

Name the figures. (pages 320–321)

1.

2.

3.

Tell how many. (pages 322–325)

4.

_?_ curved surfaces
_?_ flat surfaces

5.

_?_ faces
_?_ edges
_?_ corners

6.

_?_ sides
_?_ corners

Is it a line segment? Write YES or NO. (pages 326–327)

7.

8.

9.
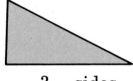

Are the figures congruent? Write YES or NO. (pages 328–329)

10.

11.

12.

Is the blue line a line of symmetry? Write YES or NO. (pages 330–331)

13.

14.
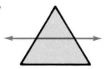

15.
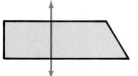

PROJECT

Paint Designs

You can use paint to make a blot design. Follow these steps.

Step 1

Fold a piece of paper in half.

Step 2

Drop some paint on the fold.

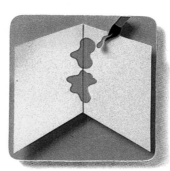

Step 3

Press the halves together.

Each half is the same size and shape. The fold line is a line of symmetry. Make some more paint-blot designs. Does each design have a line of symmetry?

Name the figures.

1.

2.

3.

Tell how many.

4.

_____?_____ curved surfaces

_____?_____ flat surfaces

5.

_____?_____ faces

_____?_____ edges

_____?_____ corners

6.

_____?_____ sides

_____?_____ corners

Is it a line segment? Write YES or NO.

7.

8.

9.

Are the figures congruent? Write YES or NO.

10.

11.

12.

Is the blue line a line of symmetry? Write YES or NO.

13.

14.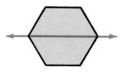

15.

Angles

Two sides of a figure meet to
form an **angle.**
One angle is shown in blue on
each figure.

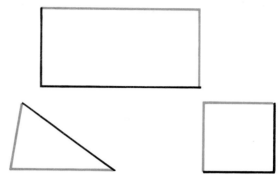

The corners of this page are square corners, or **right angles.**
Can you find other right angles? Make a right-angle
tester to check them.

Fold a piece of
paper.

Fold it again.
Make the folded
edges match.

Use your right-angle
tester to find other
right angles.

Is it a right angle? Write YES or NO.

1.

2.

3.

Tell how many right angles.

4.

5.

6.

7.

8.

9.

Computers Every Day

Every day people are helped by computers. At many supermarkets, a computer "reads" price codes on food packages. The computer adds the prices and the tax. It shows the total on a screen. Look for the computer bar code on a cereal box or a can of soup.

Banks use computers to keep records. You can ask the computer how much money is in your account. It will show you the amount on a screen. Nurses and doctors use computers to keep medical records. Businesses use computers to print paychecks. Computers can also keep count of sales.

There are other computer uses too. Computers help engineers design ships and bridges. They are used by scientists in rocket takeoffs and landings. Some libraries use a computer to find books.

In any career you choose, you will probably work with computers in some way. You may even choose a career in the important field of computers itself. People are needed to design and build computers and to clean and take care of them. Other people write programs and operate computers. The world of computers offers many career choices.

1. What kinds of computers have you seen? Tell some of the ways in which people use computers.

2. Choose a career that interests you. Write a paragraph about how you might use computers. You may also want to find out about a computer career and write a paragraph about it.

Choose the correct answers.

1. Compare.

2,163 2,136

- **A.** >
- **B.** <
- **C.** =
- **D.** not here

2.

$$\begin{array}{r} 356 \\ 189 \\ 76 \\ +\ 24 \\ \hline \end{array}$$

- **A.** 535
- **B.** 624
- **C.** 645
- **D.** not here

3.

$$\begin{array}{r} \$16.48 \\ -\quad 7.59 \\ \hline \end{array}$$

- **A.** $9.09
- **B.** $8.89
- **C.** $7.99
- **D.** not here

4. It is 7:30. What time will it be in 45 minutes?

- **A.** 6:45
- **B.** 8:45
- **C.** 8:15
- **D.** not here

5. Choose the correct measure.

- **A.** 25 liters
- **B.** 25 milliliters
- **C.** 250 liters
- **D.** not here

6. $264 \times 8 = $ _____ ?

- **A.** 2,112
- **B.** 2,082
- **C.** 2,012
- **D.** not here

7.

$$\begin{array}{r} 842 \\ \times\quad 8 \\ \hline \end{array}$$

- **A.** 5,926
- **B.** 4,678
- **C.** 6,736
- **D.** not here

8. $48 \div 4 = $ _____ ?

- **A.** 21
- **B.** 12
- **C.** 11 r 2
- **D.** not here

9. $5\overline{)689}$

- **A.** 126 r 4
- **B.** 135 r 2
- **C.** 137 r 3
- **D.** not here

10. $\frac{1}{6}$ of 24 = _____ ?

- **A.** 4
- **B.** 6
- **C.** 3
- **D.** not here

11. Write the decimal for $\frac{5}{10}$.

- **A.** 5.0
- **B.** 0.5
- **C.** 10.5
- **D.** not here

12. Name the figure.

- **A.** cylinder
- **B.** cone
- **C.** cube
- **D.** not here

Choose the correct answers.

13. Mrs. Casey has 1,689 records in her shop. She orders 750 more. How many records will she have?

A. 939   **B.** 2,145
C. 2,439   **D.** not here

14. Carlatta buys a shirt for $7.49. She gives the clerk $10.00. How much change should the clerk give Carlatta?

A. $2.50   **B.** $3.51
C. $2.51   **D.** not here

15. We use 6 trucks to ship lamps. There are 245 lamps in each truck. How many lamps are there in all?

A. 41   **B.** 239
C. 1,430   **D.** not here

16. Mrs. Quinn has 652 batteries to put in boxes. She can put 4 batteries in each box. How many boxes can she fill?

A. 113   **B.** 2,608
C. 163   **D.** not here

17. Pierre has 24 eggs. He uses $\frac{1}{4}$ of them in a cake. How many eggs does Pierre use?

A. 48   **B.** 12
C. 6   **D.** not here

18. Roger runs 4.5 kilometers. Heather runs 3.9 kilometers. How much farther does Roger run?

A. 1.6 km   **B.** 8.4 km
C. 0.6 km   **D.** not here

19. Brian pours himself a glass of milk. About how much milk is that?

A. 2 liters   **B.** 220 ml
C. 22 liters   **D.** not here

20. It is 6:25. Lisa began playing the piano 40 minutes ago. What time did she begin?

A. 5:45   **B.** 4:55
C. 7:05   **D.** not here

Extra Practice

chapter
1

Set 1 (pages 2–9)

Add.

1. $4 + 0 = $ _____
   $0 + 4 = $ _____

2. $3 + 6 = $ _____
   $6 + 3 = $ _____

3. $9 + 1 = $ _____
   $1 + 9 = $ _____

4. $\begin{array}{r} 3 \\ +2 \\ \hline \end{array}$

5. $\begin{array}{r} 4 \\ +4 \\ \hline \end{array}$

6. $\begin{array}{r} 1 \\ +6 \\ \hline \end{array}$

7. $\begin{array}{r} 9 \\ +0 \\ \hline \end{array}$

8. $\begin{array}{r} 4 \\ +8 \\ \hline \end{array}$

9. $\begin{array}{r} 7 \\ +7 \\ \hline \end{array}$

10. $\begin{array}{r} 8 \\ +2 \\ \hline \end{array}$

11. $\begin{array}{r} 5 \\ +6 \\ \hline \end{array}$

12. $\begin{array}{r} 9 \\ +8 \\ \hline \end{array}$

13. $\begin{array}{r} 9 \\ +7 \\ \hline \end{array}$

14. $\begin{array}{r} 8 \\ +7 \\ \hline \end{array}$

15. $\begin{array}{r} 9 \\ +9 \\ \hline \end{array}$

16. $(2 + 1) + 5 = $ _____
    $2 + (1 + 5) = $ _____

17. $(3 + 2) + 7 = $ _____
    $3 + (2 + 7) = $ _____

18. $(5 + 4) + 6 = $ _____
    $5 + (4 + 6) = $ _____

19. $(9 + 1) + 8 = $ _____
    $9 + (1 + 8) = $ _____

Set 2 (pages 12–21)

Subtract.

1. $7 - 3 = $ _____
2. $2 - 2 = $ _____
3. $9 - 4 = $ _____
4. $11 - 9 = $ _____
5. $16 - 8 = $ _____
6. $15 - 7 = $ _____

7. $\begin{array}{r} 8 \\ -6 \\ \hline \end{array}$

8. $\begin{array}{r} 4 \\ -0 \\ \hline \end{array}$

9. $\begin{array}{r} 3 \\ -3 \\ \hline \end{array}$

10. $\begin{array}{r} 10 \\ -1 \\ \hline \end{array}$

11. $\begin{array}{r} 17 \\ -8 \\ \hline \end{array}$

12. $\begin{array}{r} 11 \\ -3 \\ \hline \end{array}$

Find the missing addends.

13. $3 + $ _____ $= 9$
14. _____ $+ 1 = 8$
15. $8 + $ _____ $= 10$
16. _____ $+ 9 = 18$
17. $8 + $ _____ $= 16$
18. $5 + $ _____ $= 13$

Problem Solving for Chapter 1 (pages 10–11, 22–23)

1. There are 8 guppies and 4 angelfish in Wilma's fish tank. How many fish are in the tank in all?

2. Bob worked 3 hours on Monday and 7 hours on Wednesday. How many more hours did he work on Wednesday?

Extra Practice

Set 3   (pages 32–39)

Write the numbers.

1. 2 tens 9 ones
2. 8 tens 8 ones
3. seventy-four
4. 1 hundreds 3 tens 0 ones
5. 9 hundreds 0 tens 5 ones
6. six hundred sixty

Write > or <.

7. 57 75
8. 298 304
9. 921 823
10. 568 586

Round to the nearest ten.

11. 72
12. 27
13. 44
14. 85

Round to the nearest hundred.

15. 680
16. 939
17. 3,208
18. 1,150

Set 4   (pages 40–47)

Write the numbers.

1. 5 thousands 0 hundreds 4 tens 7 ones
2. 2 thousands 9 hundreds 0 tens 3 ones
3. fifty-six thousand, six hundred forty-three
4. eighty thousand, twelve
5. nine hundred seventy thousand, sixty

Write in words.

6. 3,011
7. 50,007
8. 28,020
9. 100,010

Problem Solving for Chapter 2   (pages 48–49)

1. There are 8 red roses and 6 pink roses in a vase. How many roses are in the vase in all?

2. Maria buys 12 apples. She eats 3 apples and her brother Julio eats 4 apples. How many apples are left?

Extra Practice

Set 5 (pages 58–65)

Add.

1. $24 + 5 =$ _____   2. $62 + 12 =$ _____   3. $18 + 51 =$ _____

4. $39 + 40 =$ _____   5. $53 + 35 =$ _____   6. $26 + 71 =$ _____

7. $\begin{array}{r} 46 \\ +82 \\ \hline \end{array}$ 8. $\begin{array}{r} 50 \\ +65 \\ \hline \end{array}$ 9. $\begin{array}{r} 76 \\ +73 \\ \hline \end{array}$ 10. $\begin{array}{r} 67 \\ +54 \\ \hline \end{array}$ 11. $\begin{array}{r} 88 \\ +99 \\ \hline \end{array}$ 12. $\begin{array}{r} 91 \\ +19 \\ \hline \end{array}$

Estimate the sum. Then add. Compare.

13. $\begin{array}{r} 489 \\ +304 \\ \hline \end{array}$ 14. $\begin{array}{r} 428 \\ +462 \\ \hline \end{array}$ 15. $\begin{array}{r} 679 \\ +117 \\ \hline \end{array}$ 16. $\begin{array}{r} 288 \\ +609 \\ \hline \end{array}$

Set 6 (pages 68–77)

Add.

1. $577 + 143 =$ _____   2. $271 + 945 =$ _____

3. $\begin{array}{r} 27 \\ 12 \\ +\ 3 \\ \hline \end{array}$ 4. $\begin{array}{r} 45 \\ 38 \\ +11 \\ \hline \end{array}$ 5. $\begin{array}{r} 347 \\ 303 \\ +694 \\ \hline \end{array}$ 6. $\begin{array}{r} 760 \\ 529 \\ +411 \\ \hline \end{array}$ 7. $\begin{array}{r} \$2.42 \\ 5.88 \\ +\ .39 \\ \hline \end{array}$

8. $\begin{array}{r} \$6.39 \\ +\ 2.90 \\ \hline \end{array}$ 9. $\begin{array}{r} 4,925 \\ +1,658 \\ \hline \end{array}$ 10. $\begin{array}{r} 3,881 \\ +5,372 \\ \hline \end{array}$ 11. $\begin{array}{r} 7,738 \\ +4,694 \\ \hline \end{array}$ 12. $\begin{array}{r} \$9.75 \\ +\ 8.96 \\ \hline \end{array}$

Problem Solving for Chapter 3   (pages 66-67)

Estimate.

1. Nicky has 27 books. His friend Felicia has 42 books. About how many books do they have in all?

2. Tina spent 36 minutes on homework and 15 minutes practicing piano. About how much time was that in all?

Extra Practice

Set 7 (pages 86–91, 94–95)

Subtract.

1.
   77
   − 23

2.
   64
   − 31

3.
   89
   − 62

4.
   48
   − 5

5.
   96
   − 36

6.
   55
   − 50

7.
   32
   − 17

8.
   85
   − 28

9.
   71
   − 4

10.
   64
   − 49

11.
   43
   − 35

12.
   90
   − 13

13.
   532
   − 41

14.
   356
   − 185

15.
   728
   − 478

16.
   904
   − 213

17.
   680
   − 390

18.
   623
   − 417

Set 8 (pages 96–101, 104–105)

Subtract.

1.
   534
   − 149

2.
   862
   − 477

3.
   303
   − 115

4.
   941
   − 346

5.
   810
   − 233

6.
   $4.73
   − 2.85

7.
   $7.06
   − 6.89

8.
   $5.00
   − 1.53

9.
   $9.00
   − 4.44

10.
   $4.00
   − 3.07

11.
   3,542
   − 1,753

12.
   8,361
   − 4,485

13.
   5,704
   − 2,878

14.
   9,048
   − 3,299

15.
   1,826
   − 859

16.
   4,000
   − 1,111

17.
   7,552
   − 2,557

18.
   $66.00
   − 19.25

19.
   $20.80
   − 4.86

20.
   $30.04
   − 10.55

Problem Solving for Chapter 4 (pages 92–93, 102–103)

1. There are 650 pages in a book. Yesterday Elvira read 137 pages. How many more pages must Elvira read?

Estimate the answer. Round to the nearest ten.

2. An airplane has 348 seats. There are 159 people on the flight. About how many seats are empty?

Extra Practice

Set 9 (pages 114–119)

How many minutes from

1.	**2.**	**3.**
to 11:20?	to 4:40?	to 1:00?

What time will it be

4.	**5.**	**6.**
one hour later?	one hour later?	in 40 minutes?

What time was it

7.	**8.**	**9.**	**10.**
one hour earlier?	one hour earlier?	one-half hour earlier?	three hours earlier?

Set 10 (pages 122-127)

Use $ and . to write the amount.

List the money you would give to a salesperson.

1. 2 quarters
   3 dimes
   1 penny

2. 1 dollar
   5 quarters
   4 nickels
   2 pennies

3. $.57
   quarter, quarter
   dime, dime
   nickel, penny
   penny, penny

4. $1.42
   dollar, half-dollar
   quarter, dime
   nickel, nickel
   penny, penny

Name the least number of coins to show the amount.

5. $.24   6. $.37   7. $.51   8. $.78   9. $.86   10. $.99

Problem Solving for Chapter 5   (pages 120–121, 128–129)

1. The train to Clark leaves Bay at 9:17. The trip takes one and one-half hours. When does the train arrive at Clark?

2. Ms. Montoya buys groceries for $11.23. Her change is 2 pennies, 3 quarters, and 8 dollars. What did she give the checker?

Extra Practice

Set 11 (pages 138–149)

Multiply.

1. $3 \times 4 = $?   2. $8 \times 1 = $?   3. $2 \times 7 = $?

4. $6 \times 5 = $?   5. $0 \times 9 = $?   6. $7 \times 3 = $?

7. $\begin{array}{r} 9 \\ \times 1 \\ \hline \end{array}$ 8. $\begin{array}{r} 4 \\ \times 6 \\ \hline \end{array}$ 9. $\begin{array}{r} 0 \\ \times 1 \\ \hline \end{array}$ 10. $\begin{array}{r} 3 \\ \times 3 \\ \hline \end{array}$ 11. $\begin{array}{r} 7 \\ \times 4 \\ \hline \end{array}$ 12. $\begin{array}{r} 1 \\ \times 5 \\ \hline \end{array}$

13. $\begin{array}{r} 2 \\ \times 2 \\ \hline \end{array}$ 14. $\begin{array}{r} 5 \\ \times 3 \\ \hline \end{array}$ 15. $\begin{array}{r} 9 \\ \times 4 \\ \hline \end{array}$ 16. $\begin{array}{r} 1 \\ \times 1 \\ \hline \end{array}$ 17. $\begin{array}{r} 8 \\ \times 0 \\ \hline \end{array}$ 18. $\begin{array}{r} 5 \\ \times 6 \\ \hline \end{array}$

Set 12 (pages 150–151, 154–163) Multiply.

1. $6 \times 7 = $?   2. $5 \times 8 = $?   3. $9 \times 6 = $?
   $7 \times 6 = $? $8 \times 5 = $? $6 \times 9 = $?

4. $7 \times 5 = $?   5. $8 \times 7 = $?   6. $9 \times 8 = $?
   $5 \times 7 = $? $7 \times 8 = $? $8 \times 9 = $?

7. $\begin{array}{r} 7 \\ \times 9 \\ \hline \end{array}$ 8. $\begin{array}{r} 8 \\ \times 8 \\ \hline \end{array}$ 9. $\begin{array}{r} 6 \\ \times 8 \\ \hline \end{array}$ 10. $\begin{array}{r} 9 \\ \times 5 \\ \hline \end{array}$ 11. $\begin{array}{r} 7 \\ \times 7 \\ \hline \end{array}$ 12. $\begin{array}{r} 9 \\ \times 9 \\ \hline \end{array}$

13. $\begin{array}{r} 5 \\ \times 8 \\ \hline \end{array}$ 14. $\begin{array}{r} 6 \\ \times 6 \\ \hline \end{array}$ 15. $\begin{array}{r} 5 \\ \times 6 \\ \hline \end{array}$ 16. $\begin{array}{r} 4 \\ \times 7 \\ \hline \end{array}$ 17. $\begin{array}{r} 3 \\ \times 9 \\ \hline \end{array}$ 18. $\begin{array}{r} 9 \\ \times 8 \\ \hline \end{array}$

19. $(3 \times 2) \times 4 = $?   20. $3 \times (2 \times 4) = $?

Find the missing factors.

21. $5 \times $? $= 30$ 22. ? $\times$? $= 81$

Problem Solving for Chapter 6 (pages 152–153, 164–165)

1. Sven can type 7 pages each hour. How many pages can he type in 4 hours?

2. A silver bracelet costs $7.00. A gold ring costs eight times as much. How much more does the gold ring cost?

Extra Practice

Set 13   (pages 174–183, 186–187)

Find each quotient.

1. $21 \div 3 = \underline{\quad ? \quad}$ 2. $3 \div 3 = \underline{\quad ? \quad}$
3. $32 \div 4 = \underline{\quad ? \quad}$ 4. $6 \div 3 = \underline{\quad ? \quad}$

5. $3\overline{)27}$ 6. $5\overline{)5}$ 7. $4\overline{)24}$

8. $4\overline{)36}$ 9. $5\overline{)45}$ 10. $3\overline{)24}$

Set 14   (pages 188–197, 200–201)

Find each quotient.

1. $81 \div 9 = \underline{\quad ? \quad}$ 2. $48 \div 6 = \underline{\quad ? \quad}$
3. $72 \div 8 = \underline{\quad ? \quad}$ 4. $28 \div 7 = \underline{\quad ? \quad}$

5. $8\overline{)48}$ 6. $8\overline{)56}$ 7. $7\overline{)42}$

8. $6\overline{)54}$ 9. $8\overline{)40}$ 10. $6\overline{)36}$

Find each quotient and remainder.

11. $29 \div 6 = \underline{\quad ? \quad}$ 12. $17 \div 3 = \underline{\quad ? \quad}$
13. $68 \div 9 = \underline{\quad ? \quad}$ 14. $44 \div 5 = \underline{\quad ? \quad}$

15. $4\overline{)33}$ 16. $9\overline{)40}$ 17. $7\overline{)41}$

18. $6\overline{)57}$ 19. $7\overline{)61}$ 20. $8\overline{)79}$

Problem Solving for Chapter 7   (pages 184–185, 198–199)

1. There are 28 children at Giovanni's party. Each table can seat 4 children. How many tables are there?

2. Greta picks 23 lemons in the morning and 31 lemons in the afternoon. She puts 6 lemons into each bag. How many bags does she fill in all?

Extra Practice

Set 15 (pages 210–219, 222–225)

Copy and complete.

1. 2 m = ___?___ cm

2. 9 m = ___?___ cm

3. ___?___ km = 7,000 m

4. 4 km = ___?___ m

Find the perimeter in centimeters.

5.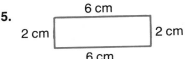

6.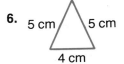

7.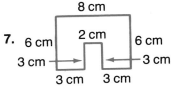

Find the area. Each square is equal to 1 square centimeter.

8.

9.

10.

Find the volume. Each cube is equal to 1 cubic centimeter.

11.

12.

13.

Set 16 (pages 228–239) How many

1. inches in 4 feet?

2. inches in 4 yards?

3. cups in 2 pints?

4. pints in 3 quarts?

5. quarts in 4 gallons?

6. ounces in 6 pounds 4 ounces?

Find the perimeter. Find the area. Each square equals 1 square inch.

7.

8.

9.

Problem Solving for Chapter 8 (pages 220-221, 240-241)

1. A checkerboard measures 8 centimeters on each side. What is its perimeter? What is its area?

2. On a map, 1 inch equals 4 miles. The lake and the park are 20 miles apart. How many inches separate them on the map?

Extra Practice

Set 17 (pages 250–255)

Multiply.

1. $\begin{array}{r} 40 \\ \times\ 6 \\ \hline \end{array}$	2. $\begin{array}{r} 70 \\ \times\ 5 \\ \hline \end{array}$	3. $\begin{array}{r} 50 \\ \times\ 3 \\ \hline \end{array}$	4. $\begin{array}{r} 90 \\ \times\ 4 \\ \hline \end{array}$	5. $\begin{array}{r} 30 \\ \times\ 7 \\ \hline \end{array}$
6. $\begin{array}{r} 11 \\ \times\ 7 \\ \hline \end{array}$	7. $\begin{array}{r} 83 \\ \times\ 0 \\ \hline \end{array}$	8. $\begin{array}{r} 27 \\ \times\ 3 \\ \hline \end{array}$	9. $\begin{array}{r} 15 \\ \times\ 4 \\ \hline \end{array}$	10. $\begin{array}{r} 12 \\ \times\ 8 \\ \hline \end{array}$
11. $\begin{array}{r} 38 \\ \times\ 2 \\ \hline \end{array}$	12. $\begin{array}{r} 16 \\ \times\ 5 \\ \hline \end{array}$	13. $\begin{array}{r} 18 \\ \times\ 4 \\ \hline \end{array}$	14. $\begin{array}{r} 14 \\ \times\ 7 \\ \hline \end{array}$	15. $\begin{array}{r} 15 \\ \times\ 6 \\ \hline \end{array}$

Set 18 (pages 256–259)

Multiply.

1. $\begin{array}{r} 760 \\ \times\ \ 4 \\ \hline \end{array}$	2. $\begin{array}{r} 507 \\ \times\ \ 6 \\ \hline \end{array}$	3. $\begin{array}{r} 608 \\ \times\ \ 8 \\ \hline \end{array}$	4. $\begin{array}{r} 131 \\ \times\ \ 9 \\ \hline \end{array}$	5. $\begin{array}{r} 872 \\ \times\ \ 3 \\ \hline \end{array}$
6. $\begin{array}{r} 221 \\ \times\ \ 8 \\ \hline \end{array}$	7. $\begin{array}{r} 540 \\ \times\ \ 7 \\ \hline \end{array}$	8. $\begin{array}{r} 415 \\ \times\ \ 6 \\ \hline \end{array}$	9. $\begin{array}{r} 791 \\ \times\ \ 9 \\ \hline \end{array}$	10. $\begin{array}{r} 909 \\ \times\ \ 8 \\ \hline \end{array}$

Find the missing digits.

11. $\begin{array}{r} \blacksquare 7 \\ \times\ 8 \\ \hline 37\blacksquare \end{array}$	12. $\begin{array}{r} 29 \\ \times\ \ \blacksquare \\ \hline 1\blacksquare 5 \end{array}$	13. $\begin{array}{r} 4\blacksquare \\ \times\ 7 \\ \hline 3\blacksquare 2 \end{array}$	14. $\begin{array}{r} 2\blacksquare 5 \\ \times\ \ 3 \\ \hline \blacksquare 0\blacksquare \end{array}$	15. $\begin{array}{r} 1\blacksquare\blacksquare \\ \times\ \ \ 9 \\ \hline 9\blacksquare 3 \end{array}$

Problem Solving for Chapter 9 (pages 260-261)

1. A half-gallon of apple cider costs $.92. A grocer orders 9 half-gallons. How much does his order cost in all?

2. Morris buys 7 airmail stamps. Each stamp costs $.31. How much does Morris pay for the stamps?

3. A loaf of bread costs 59¢. Mrs. Escobar buys 8 loaves. If she gives the checker $5.00, how much change does she get back?

Extra Practice

Set 19 (pages 270–275)

Divide.

1. $6\overline{)90}$ 2. $2\overline{)61}$ 3. $7\overline{)96}$ 4. $5\overline{)70}$ 5. $3\overline{)80}$

6. $9\overline{)93}$ 7. $6\overline{)78}$ 8. $5\overline{)65}$ 9. $7\overline{)89}$ 10. $8\overline{)99}$

11. $67 \div 3 = \underline{\ ?\ }$ 12. $2{,}400 \div 4 = \underline{\ ?\ }$

Find the missing digits.

13. $\begin{array}{r} 1\blacksquare \\ 7\overline{)\blacksquare 4} \end{array}$ 14. $\begin{array}{r} \blacksquare 6 \\ 3\overline{)7\blacksquare} \end{array}$ 15. $\begin{array}{r} 4\blacksquare \\ \blacksquare\overline{)82} \end{array}$ 16. $\begin{array}{r} 24 \\ \blacksquare\overline{)9\blacksquare} \end{array}$ 17. $\begin{array}{r} 5\blacksquare \\ 5\overline{)\blacksquare 50} \end{array}$

Set 20 (pages 276–277)

Divide.

1. $4\overline{)860}$ 2. $3\overline{)776}$ 3. $6\overline{)693}$ 4. $8\overline{)898}$ 5. $2\overline{)554}$

6. $5\overline{)721}$ 7. $6\overline{)942}$ 8. $2\overline{)378}$ 9. $7\overline{)975}$ 10. $4\overline{)596}$

11. $687 \div 3 = \underline{\ ?\ }$ 12. $940 \div 8 = \underline{\ ?\ }$

Find the missing digits.

13. $\begin{array}{r} \blacksquare 23 \\ 8\overline{)98\blacksquare} \end{array}$ 14. $\begin{array}{r} 20\blacksquare \\ 3\overline{)\blacksquare 21} \end{array}$ 15. $\begin{array}{r} \blacksquare 49 \\ 4\overline{)5\blacksquare 6} \end{array}$ 16. $\begin{array}{r} 12\blacksquare \\ 7\overline{)8\blacksquare 5} \end{array}$ 17. $\begin{array}{r} 473 \\ \blacksquare\overline{)\blacksquare\blacksquare 6} \end{array}$

Problem Solving for Chapter 10 (pages 278–279)

1. A hardware store stocks 5 crates of light bulbs. Each crate contains 18 boxes of bulbs. There is one bulb in each box. Each bulb costs $.79. How many bulbs are in the store?

2. Ed walks 27 blocks. He rests for 24 minutes and then walks another 39 blocks. How many blocks does he walk in all?

Extra Practice

Set 21   (pages 288–297)

Complete.

1. $\frac{1}{6}$ of 12 = ___?___

2. $\frac{1}{7}$ of 21 = ___?___

3. $\frac{1}{9}$ of 9 = ___?___

Write > or <.

4. $\frac{2}{7}$ ⬤ $\frac{4}{7}$

5. $\frac{8}{10}$ ⬤ $\frac{9}{10}$

6. $\frac{1}{3}$ ⬤ $\frac{1}{4}$

7. $\frac{1}{2}$ ⬤ $\frac{2}{3}$

Set 22   (pages 300–309)

Write the decimals.

1. $\frac{9}{10}$

2. $\frac{2}{10}$

3. $3\frac{7}{10}$

4. $1\frac{1}{10}$

Write each as a decimal and as a mixed number.

5. two and eight-tenths

6. four and three-tenths

7. nine and five-tenths

8. fifteen and nine-tenths

Write > or <.

9. 0.3 ⬤ 0.5

10. 1.6 ⬤ 1.4

11. 3.1 ⬤ 2.1

12. 7.8 ⬤ 8.7

Add or subtract.

13. $\begin{array}{r} 6.2 \\ +1.3 \\ \hline \end{array}$

14. $\begin{array}{r} 2.7 \\ +4.6 \\ \hline \end{array}$

15. $\begin{array}{r} 8.1 \\ -2.7 \\ \hline \end{array}$

16. $\begin{array}{r} 9.0 \\ -5.1 \\ \hline \end{array}$

17. $\begin{array}{r} 5.6 \\ +3.4 \\ \hline \end{array}$

Problem Solving for Chapter 11   (pages 298–299, 310–311)

1. Arturo spends $\frac{1}{2}$ of his salary on food and clothing, $\frac{1}{3}$ on rent, and $\frac{1}{6}$ on entertainment. On what does Arturo spend the least amount of money?

2. A jogger wants to run a total of 8 kilometers. She runs 4.3 kilometers before taking a rest. How many more kilometers must she still run?

Extra Practice

Set 23 (pages 320-327)

Name the figures.

1. 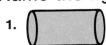 2. 3. 4. 5.

Tell how many.

6.  7. 8.

    ?   sides   ?   curved   ?   faces

    ?   corners   surfaces   ?   edges

                       ?   flat surfaces   ?   corners

How many line segments are in each shape?

9. 10. 11.

Set 24 (pages 328-331)

Are the figures congruent? Write YES or NO.

1. 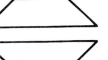 2.  3.

Is the blue line a line of symmetry? Write YES or NO.

4. 5. 6.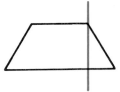

Problem Solving for Chapter 12 (pages 332-333)

1. The directions on a treasure map say "Start at the oak tree. Walk 12 meters north, 6 meters east, 12 meters south, and 2 meters west." How far from the oak tree is the treasure buried?

2. Mrs. Wheeler's car can travel 40 kilometers in 30 minutes. How many kilometers can Mrs. Wheeler's car travel in 2 hours?

TABLE OF MEASURES

Metric

Length

10 millimeters (mm) = 1 centimeter (cm)
100 centimeters = 1 meter (m)
1,000 meters = 1 kilometer (km)

Area

100 square millimeters = 1 square centimeter
10,000 square centimeters = 1 square meter

Volume

1,000 cubic millimeters = 1 cubic centimeter
1,000,000 cubic centimeters = 1 cubic meter

Capacity

1,000 milliliters (mL) = 1 liter (L)

Mass/Weight

1,000 grams (g) = 1 kilogram (kg)

United States Customary

Length

12 inches (in.) = 1 foot (ft)
$\left.\begin{array}{l}\text{36 inches} \\ \text{3 feet}\end{array}\right\}$ = 1 yard (yd)
5,280 feet = 1 mile (mi)

Area

144 square inches = 1 square foot
9 square feet = 1 square yard

Volume

1,728 cubic inches = 1 cubic foot
27 cubic feet = 1 cubic yard

Capacity

2 cups = 1 pint (pt)
2 pints = 1 quart (qt)
4 quarts = 1 gallon (gal)

Mass/Weight

16 ounces (oz) = 1 pound (lb)

Time

60 seconds (s) = 1 minute (min)
60 minutes = 1 hour (h)
24 hours = 1 day (d)
7 days = 1 week (wk)
$\left.\begin{array}{l}\text{12 months} \\ \text{52 weeks}\end{array}\right\}$ = 1 year (yr)
100 years = 1 century (cen)

TABLE OF SYMBOLS

+	plus
−	minus
×	times
÷	divided by
=	equals or is equal to
≠	is not equal to
>	is greater than
<	is less than
...	pattern continues without end
( )	parentheses: do the operation inside the ( ) first.
2 r1	two remainder one
3.2	decimal point: three and two-tenths
$\frac{2}{3}$	fraction: two-thirds
∟	right angle
°C	degree Celsius
°F	degree Fahrenheit
10¢	money: ten cents
$2.50	money: two dollars and fifty cents
3:45	time: three forty-five

GLOSSARY

Addend   A number that is added. (p. 2)
Example: 5 + 8 = 13
The addends are 5 and 8.

Addition (+)   An operation on two numbers to find how many in all or how much in total. (p. 2)
Example: 6 + 9 = 15
6 and 9 are addends. 15 is the sum.

Angle   A shape formed by two lines that meet. (p. 337)
Example:

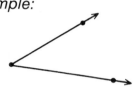

Area   The number of square units needed to cover a surface. (p. 216)
Example: The area of this rectangle is 6 square units.

Area = length × width

Circle   A closed curve with all points an equal distance from a center point. (p. 324)
Example:

Cone   A solid with one face that is a circle. (p. 320)
Example:

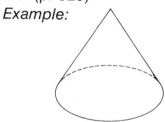

Congruent   Having the same size and shape. (p. 328)
Example:

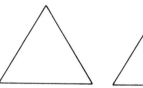

Cube   A solid with six square faces. (p. 320)
Example:

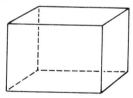

Customary measurement system
A measurement system that uses inches, feet, yards, and miles as units of length; cups, pints, quarts, and gallons as units of liquid capacity; ounces, pounds, and tons as units of weight; and degrees Fahrenheit as units of temperature. (p. 228)

Cylinder A solid with two faces that are circles. (p. 320)
Example:

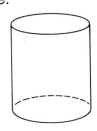

Decimal A number that uses place value and a decimal point to show tenths, hundredths, and so on. (p. 302)
Example: 3.6 Read three and six-tenths.

Degree Celsius (°C) A standard unit for measuring temperature in the metric system. (p. 226)
Example: Water freezes at 0°C and boils at 100°C.

Degree Fahrenheit (°F) A standard unit for measuring temperature in the customary measurement system. (p. 243)
Example: Water freezes at 32°F and boils at 212°F.

Denominator The number below the bar in a fraction. (p. 288)
Example: $\frac{1}{2}$ The denominator is 2.

Difference The answer to a subtraction problem. (p. 12)
Example: $10 - 7 = 3$
The difference is 3.

Digit Any one of the ten symbols 0, 1, 2, 3, 4, 5, 6, 7, 8, or 9. (p. 2)

Dividend The number that is divided in a division problem. (p. 174)
Example: $5\overline{)35}$ or $35 \div 5$
The dividend is 35.

Division ($\overline{)}$ or ÷) An operation on two numbers that results in a quotient and a remainder. (p. 174)
Example: $4\overline{)29}$ 7 r1
The divisor is 4 and the dividend is 29. The quotient is 7 and the remainder is 1.

Divisor The number by which the dividend is divided. (p. 174)
Example: $3\overline{)18}$ or $18 \div 3$
The divisor is 3.

Edge The line segment where two faces of a solid meet. (p. 322)
Example:

edge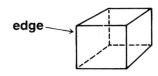

Endpoint A point at the end of a line segment. (p. 326)
Example: A______B
A and B are endpoints.

Equals (=) Has the same value. (p. 2)
Example: $7 + 8 = 15$ Read seven plus eight equals (or is equal to) fifteen.

Equation A number sentence with an equals sign. (p. 2)
Examples: $5 + 7 = 12$
$15 - 8 = 7$

Equivalent fractions Fractions that name the same number. (p. 294)
Examples: $\frac{1}{2}$, $\frac{2}{4}$, and $\frac{3}{6}$ are equivalent fractions.

Estimate To guess a reasonable answer. One way to estimate is to round the numbers before doing the problem. (p. 66)

Even number A whole number with 0, 2, 4, 6, or 8 in the ones place. (p. 51)
Examples: 4, 18, 30, and 572 are even numbers.

Face A flat surface of a solid. (p. 322)
Example:

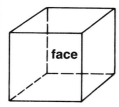

Factor A number that is multiplied. (p. 138)
Example: $4 \times 7 = 28$
The factors are 4 and 7.

Fraction A number that names part of a whole or group. (p. 288)
Example: $\frac{1}{2}$ 1 is the numerator.
2 is the denominator.

Grouping property of addition The way in which addends are grouped does not change the sum. (p. 8)
Example:
$(3 + 2) + 4 = 3 + (2 + 4)$

Grouping property of multiplication The way in which factors are grouped does not change the product. (p. 155)
Example:
$(2 \times 3) \times 4 = 2 \times (3 \times 4)$

Hexagon A polygon with six sides. (p. 325)
Example:

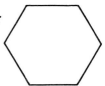

Length The measurement of an object from end to end. (p. 210)

Line A straight path extending in both directions with no endpoints. (p. 330)

Line of symmetry A line that divides a shape into two congruent parts. The fold line is called a line of symmetry. (p. 330)
Example:

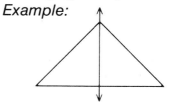

Line segment Part of a line with two endpoints. (p. 326)

Metric system A measurement system that uses centimeters, meters, and kilometers as units of length; milliliters and liters as units of capacity; grams and kilograms as units of mass; and degrees Celsius as units of temperature. (p. 210)

Minus (−)   A symbol that shows subtraction. (p. 12)
Example: 15 − 6 = 9   Read fifteen minus six equals nine.

Mixed number   The sum of a whole number and a fraction. (p. 300)
Example: $3\frac{1}{2} = 3 + \frac{1}{2}$

Multiplication (×)   An operation on two numbers, called factors, which results in a product. (p. 138)
Example: 8 × 9 = 72   8 and 9 are factors and 72 is the product.

Numerator   The number above the bar in a fraction. (p. 288)
Example: $\frac{2}{3}$ The numerator is 2.

Octagon   A polygon with eight sides. (p. 325)
Example:

Odd number   A whole number that is not a multiple of 2. An odd number ends in 1, 3, 5, 7, or 9. (p. 51)
Examples: 7, 19, 53, and 235 are odd numbers.

Order property of addition   The order in which addends are added does not change the sum. (p. 4)
Example: 6 + 4 = 4 + 6

Order property of multiplication   The order in which factors are multiplied does not change the product. (p. 150)
Example: 5 × 7 = 7 × 5

Ordinal number   A whole number telling a position such as first, second, third, and so on. (p. 46)

Parentheses ( )   A grouping symbol. Parentheses tell which part or parts of a problem to do first. (p. 8)
Example: (8 + 7) − 9
Do (8 + 7) first.

Pentagon   A polygon with five sides. (p. 325)
Example:

Perimeter   The distance around a shape. The perimeter of a shape is the sum of the lengths of the sides. (p. 214)
Example:

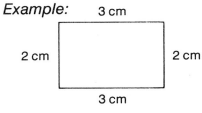

Perimeter = 3 + 2 + 3 + 2 = 10 cm

Pictograph   A way to show comparisons. A key always appears at the bottom of a pictograph showing how many each object represents. (p. 167)

Place value   The value given to the place in which a digit appears in a number. (p. 32)
Example: 5,347
The place value of 3 is hundreds.
The place value of 7 is ones.

Plus (+) A symbol that shows addition. (p. 2)
Example: 5 + 8 = 13 Read five plus eight equals thirteen.

Polygon A closed plane figure formed by three or more line segments joined at the endpoints. (p. 324)

Product The answer to a multiplication problem. (p. 138)
Example: 3 × 12 = 36
The product is 36.

Pyramid A solid figure. One face is a triangle, rectangle, or other shape with angles. The other faces are triangles. (p. 323)
Example:

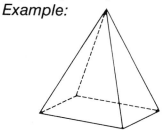

Quotient The answer to a division problem. (p. 174)
Example: 15 ÷ 3 = 5
The quotient is 5.

Rectangle A shape with four sides and four right angles. (p. 324)
Example:

Rectangular prism A solid with six faces that are rectangles. (p. 320)
Example:

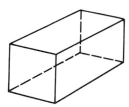

Remainder The number left over in a division problem. The remainder must be less than the divisor. (p. 200)
Example: $5\overline{)19}$ with $3\text{ r}4$
The remainder is 4.

Right angle An angle with the same shape as the corner of a square. (p. 337)
Example:

Roman numerals Symbols used by the Romans to name numbers. Roman numeration does not use place value. (p. 53)
Examples:

I	V	X	L	C	D	M
1	5	10	50	100	500	1,000

Rounding Expressing a number to the nearest thousandth, hundredth, tenth, one, ten, hundred, thousand. (p. 38)
Example: 37.85 rounded to the nearest tenth is 37.9.

Sphere   A solid with all points the same distance from a center point. (p. 320)

Example:

Square   A shape with four equal sides and four right angles. (p. 324)

Example:

Subtraction (−)   An operation on two numbers to find how many are left or how much greater one number is than the other. (p. 12)

Example: $15 - 6 = 9$
9 is the difference.

Sum   The answer to an addition problem. (p. 2)

Example: $12 + 7 = 19$
The sum is 19.

Times (×)   A symbol that shows multiplication. (p. 138)

Example: $5 \times 9 = 45$ Read five times nine equals forty-five.

Triangle   A polygon with three sides. (p. 324)

Example:

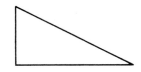

Volume   The number of cubic units needed to fill a solid. (p. 218)

Example: The volume of this cube is 8 cubic units.

Volume = length × width × height

Zero property for addition   When 0 is added to any addend, the sum equals the addend. (p. 2)

Examples: $9 + 0 = 9$
$0 + 12 = 12$

Zero property for multiplication   If 0 is a factor, the product is always 0. (p. 148)

Examples: $13 \times 0 = 0$
$0 \times 7 = 0$

5
6
D 7
E 8
F 9
G 0
H 1
I 2
J 3